Rudolf Virchow

DOCTOR ∘ STATESMAN ∘ ANTHROPOLOGIST

RUDOLF VIRCHOW IN THE LATE 1850's

Photo: Courtesy of the New York Academy of Medicine.

Rudolf Virchow

DOCTOR   STATESMAN
ANTHROPOLOGIST

by ERWIN H. ACKERKNECHT

MADISON

The UNIVERSITY OF WISCONSIN PRESS

1953

Preface

ONE HUNDRED YEARS ago a thirty-year-old pathology professor in the small Bavarian University of Wuerzburg ventured for the first time the idea that the basic units of life are the self-reproducing cells of living bodies and that pathology has to study primarily cell changes. This idea, named later "cellular pathology," has dominated biology and pathology up to this very day; and when the creator of cellular pathology died fifty years ago, the whole medical world bowed at his grave. It honored him in addition as a great pioneer of public health, a gifted epidemiologist, and a reformer of the professional set-up.

Yet the world would have heard of the death of this unusual man even if his contribution to medicine had been less extensive and less basic. In 1861 he was elected into the Prussian parliament where he remained till his death in 1902. He soon became one of the leaders of the opposition against Bismarck, who then started Germany on the way of "blood and iron," and he remained one of the symbols of a democratic Germany till death quieted the indefatigable fighter.

Even without Virchow's medical and political accomplishments the world would have noticed his death. In the late 1860's he had taken up the study of anthropology. His gigantic racial survey of German school children, his archeological work in Germany and the Near East, his organizational work had become milestones in the history of the young science.

v

To make a detailed study of the life and work of this man, whose greatness transcends the fields he worked in or the nation he belonged to, seemed eminently desirable. It becomes almost imperative in view of the fact that during the last twenty years the facts of his life and work have become more and more submerged by a mostly negative "myth." This myth is partly the result of simple unfamiliarity with the original data. Partly it is due to the efforts of the late Nazi and the present Russian governments. Both have honored Virchow by feeling that even so long after his death he is still a "dangerous influence." They have reacted, as usual, by "alterating the past." Their falsifications are so crude that no polemic seems needed. Presentation of the facts is a sufficient refutation. That the late Ludwig Aschoff published his camouflaged but courageous defense of Virchow and his ideas in 1940 in Hitler's Germany should remain remembered.

This book is primarily an analysis of Virchow's work, not a description of his life. This is partly due to external circumstances. The extensive personal archives of Virchow, insofar as they have survived World War II, are at present in Soviet Germany and therefore out of reach. Even if they had been available, I would have preferred to deal rather with the man's work than with irrelevant details of his life which it has become so fashionable to discuss in our decadent epoch. It is my belief that only in concentrating on the work we can avoid a distortion of the historical perspective. It is true that men make history and that "great men" do exist. Some are mere accidents of history only called to play a great role. But some are intrinsically great—and Virchow belongs to this category—and would have been great no matter when and where they lived. Yet even the greatest of great men not only form their time and environment but are formed by it; they are heirs as well as legators; they are, in spite of their uniqueness which is primarily anchored in their characters, in many ways typical members of their generations, of groups, of movements. A study of their work reveals this much more clearly than a study of their relationships to their mothers-in-law or their preferences in neckties. I hope that my study will show Virchow both in his uniqueness and as a rather typical representative of that generation of liberal scientists which brought about the victory of the sciences in German medicine in the second half of the nineteenth century.

The life history that introduces the book is intended to orient the reader chronologically. In an analysis of the work it is impossible to synchronize Virchow's simultaneous activities without falling into utter confusion. On the contrary, in order to be intelligible they have to be artificially separated and examined in three great divisions: medicine, politics, anthropology. A certain chronological order is nevertheless obtained through the fact that Virchow's life evolved in three periods, in the first of which he was primarily active in medicine, in the second in politics, and in the third and last in anthropology.

It seemed impossible to write about some of Virchow's medical work without being rather technical. Omitting the technicalities would have deprived the book of much of its value. Readers without a medical background should skip such passages (contained in the second, third, fourth, and fifth medical chapters) instead of giving up. I do not think that after the fifth medical chapter the educated layman will encounter any more difficulties.

I have taken very much to heart, perhaps too much for the taste of many of my readers, a remark of the master himself: "Brevity is the best guarantee for being read" (in *Archiv fuer pathologische Anatomie und Physiologie und fuer klinische Medizin*, L [1870], 9). I have therefore not written a history of pathology or German liberalism or anthropology, but rather have strictly limited myself to the accomplishments and opinions of Virchow and his contemporaries.

Limitations of space made it necessary to confine the Bibliography strictly to such items quoted in the text. In the case of Virchow himself, even this seemed not restrictive enough. The Bibliography contains only the titles of the books and monographs of Virchow which are quoted. To insert the titles of the hundreds of articles of Virchow quoted from periodicals would have thrown the book out of balance and would have been superfluous in view of the existence of J. Schwalbe's *Virchow*

Bibliographie. All the passages from periodicals are completely identified in the reference notes at the end of the volume. Those who want the title of the article are referred to the original or Schwalbe's book. Some books and periodicals had to be cited so frequently that much space could be saved by using abbreviations for them. These abbreviations are explained in the Key to Abbreviations and the Bibliography.

The book contains a great number of names of medical, political, and anthropological contemporaries of Virchow which are not likely to be familiar to those who know the history of only one of the three fields in which Virchow worked—that is, to a great many of the prospective readers of this book. It was impossible to give any biographical data on these men in a text kept down to essentials. Under these circumstances it seemed desirable to add a glossary of such names which I hope will add to the usefulness of the book.

The reader will perhaps be more indulgent with my enterprise when he realizes that this is the first full-length study of Virchow in any language. The small books of Becher, Posner, and Aschoff are admittedly only sketches. Virchow's very versatility, so attractive in our age of specialization, made him, on the other hand, a difficult subject for the historian of either medicine or anthropology or politics. His extreme productivity (the Schwalbe *Bibliographie* which does not list his political production contains more than two thousand items) was another deterrent. If I have reluctantly tackled this difficult task, I have drawn some encouragement from the fact that I have been trained in medicine as well as in anthropology and history. I can also claim an acquaintance with and an interest in my subject which has lasted about twenty-five years and which goes back to the time when I wrote my doctoral dissertation in the Leipzig Institute of the History of Medicine under the stimulating influence of H. E. Sigerist and his collaborators Ernst Hirschfeld and Owsei Temkin. Last, but perhaps not least, I was born and raised in the same region of Germany as Virchow. The names that appear in the story of his youth, his vacations, and excavations and that mean nothing to the average reader are quite dear to me, reminding me of a happy childhood and of a series of tragic events and stupidities which have continually victimized Virchow's home province.

In concluding this book it is a pleasant task to thank those who have helped me in the course of my work. I am indebted above all to Drs. John W. Harman, H. H. Gerth (both of Madison, Wisconsin), and E. W. Count (Clinton, New York), who have sacrificed much of their valuable time in reading the medical, historical, and anthropological parts of the manuscript respectively and have given me freely of their expert advice and criticism. They are, of course, not to be held responsible for my opinions and blunders. I have enjoyed the generous hospitality of Dr. and Mrs. Thor Jager (Wichita, Kansas) while working in Dr. Jager's unique collection. Dr. Walter Pagel has helped me with suggestions, and materials from his late father's collection. I am also indebted for advice given during the preparation of this manuscript to Drs. Walter Artelt, H. Buess, Paul Cranefield, the late Judson Gilbert, Edith Heischkel-Artelt, Robert H. Lowie, Alfred Plaut, H. H. Reese, George Rosen, and Owsei Temkin. The University of Wisconsin Medical School and especially its dean, Dr. W. S. Middleton, and its librarian, Miss Helen Crawford, have always been most helpful to me—morally and materially—in the pursuit of my researches.

ERWIN H. ACKERKNECHT

Madison, Wisconsin
June, 1952

Contents

Preface   v
List of Illustrations   xiii
Key to Abbreviations   xv

RUDOLF VIRCHOW
Life History   3

THE DOCTOR
General Ideas   43
Pathological Physiology   59
On the Road to *Cellular Pathology*   70
Synthesis   86
Tumors   98
Parasites and Bacteria   105
Anticlimax   118
Epidemiology and Public Health   123
Medical Reform   137
Medical History   146

THE STATESMAN
Revolutionary Beginnings   159
The Constitutional Conflict   167
In the New Reich   181

THE ANTHROPOLOGIST
Dynamics of Skull Growth   195
The Origin of Man   199
Races, Especially in Germany   207
Germanic and Slavonic Antiquities   219
Archeology in the Near East   224
The Organizer of German Anthropology   229

EPICRISIS

Epicrisis   239
Notes   245
Biographical Glossary   267
Bibliography   283
Index   293

List of Illustrations

Virchow in the Late 1850's   *Frontispiece*

Virchow on February 2, 1849   *facing page* 144

Virchow as a Septuagenarian   208

Key to Abbreviations

THE FOLLOWING abbreviations are used in referring to periodicals and books frequently cited. Book references are preceded by the authors' or editors' names and complete publication information can be found in the Bibliography. Periodicals are also listed alphabetically by title in the Bibliography, where place and inclusive dates of publication are given.

A	*Archiv fuer pathologische Anatomie und Physiologie und fuer klinische Medizin* (known since 1903 as *Virchows Archiv . . .*)
BG	*Verhandlungen der Berliner Gesellschaft fuer Anthropologie, Ethnologie und Urgeschichte*
BKW	*Berliner klinische Wochenschrift*
BM	Ackerknecht: *Beitraege zur Geschichte der Medizinalreform von 1848*
Briefe	Virchow: *Briefe an seine Eltern, 1839 bis 1864*
CP	Virchow: *Die Cellularpathologie*
DN	Sudhoff (ed.): *Rudolf Virchow und die deutschen Naturforscherversammlungen*
GA	Virchow: *Gesammelte Abhandlungen zur wissenschaftlichen Medizin*
H	Virchow: *Handbuch der speziellen Pathologie und Therapie*
KG	Virchow: *Die krankhaften Geschwuelste*
K-H	Klein-Hattingen: *Geschichte des deutschen Liberalismus*
Korrbl	*Korrespondenzblatt der deutschen Gesellschaft fuer Anthropologie, Ethnologie und Urgeschichte*
OM	Virchow: *Gesammelte Abhandlungen aus dem Gebiet der oeffentlichen Medizin und der Seuchenlehre*
WV	*Verhandlungen der physikalisch-medizinischen Gesellschaft zu Wuerzburg*
ZE	*Zeitschrift fuer Ethnologie*

xv

Rudolf Virchow

Life History

O<small>N OCTOBER</small> 13, 1821, in the small Pomeranian city of Schivelbein, a son was born to Carl Christian Siegfried Virchow (1785–1865) and his wife Johanna Maria née Hesse (1785–1857). He was given the name of Rudolf Ludwig Carl and was destined to live eighty-one years, till September 5, 1902. His father, an intelligent but somewhat queer man, combined farming with a small city job (treasurer) and many unsuccessful business ventures. Of the mother nothing is known but an inclination to worrying and complaining.

Rudolf Virchow was to remain the only child of this, in the notions of the time, elderly couple without showing any disadvantageous consequences thereof. Although a paternal uncle gained some fame as an inventor of military equipment and a maternal one as an architect, it must be truthfully stated that through several generations the majority of the Virchows and their in-laws were engaged in the honorable but plain trade of butchery. Nothing in the social background of the child was to suggest that he once would become for his contemporaries the symbol of medicine, like Paracelsus or Boerhaave had been before and Freud would be later. Nothing suggested that at his death Germany would complain of having lost four great men in one: her leading pathologist, her leading anthropologist, her leading sanitarian, and her leading liberal.

Virchow never forgot his modest rural background. While

3

working on the foundations of modern medicine, he would still worry about his father's potato crop.

Schivelbein was located in eastern Pomerania, always one of the most backward and *Junker*-ridden regions of Germany, till it was ruthlessly stricken from the map after the Yalta and Potsdam decisions in 1945, and its inhabitants, rich and poor, driven out. There was a great deal of submissiveness in these eastern rural regions of Germany. Virchow reacted to this environment in a different and characteristic fashion. While remaining devoted to his *Heimat* all his life,* he was to fight its political set-up. He became a radical. In the 1860's the son of the Pomeranian farmer became the outstanding political opponent of the Pomeranian *Junker* Von Bismarck. Several of his closer political friends and leading radicals in the 1848 revolution were fellow Pomeranians: Arnold Ruge, Lothar Bucher, and Salomon Neumann.†

Virchow's childhood and early youth fell into the dull years of reaction, when the youthful enthusiasm of the war of liberation had been buried in prison and exile, when Metternich ruled Europe, and Frederick William III Prussia.‡ The child

* In his 1906 Virchow biography, Julius Pagel reports that he enjoyed the protection of Virchow ever since the latter in an examination discovered that Pagel was a fellow Pomeranian.

† Other well-known Pomeranian radicals of the period were Robert Prutz and Paul Boerner. This traditional radical reaction of a few brilliant individuals in Pomerania had survived into the twentieth century with such men as Franz Mehring, Kurt Tucholsky, and George Gross. Many unfamiliar but important names, particularly those of Virchow's contemporaries, are identified in the Biographical Glossary.

‡ A better idea of chronology may be gained if one recalls Virchow's national and international contemporaries. Born in 1821, he was the same age as H. Helmholtz, F. Th. Waitz, H. Schliemann, G. de Mortillet, Ch. Baudelaire, G. Flaubert, H. Taine, and Mary Baker Eddy. He was slightly younger than Claude Bernard, M. Pettenkofer, Ludwig Traube, I. Semmelweis, J. P. Joule, Karl Marx, Lewis H. Morgan, and Jacob Burckhardt (all born in 1818); Queen Victoria, Cyrus Field, Walt Whitman, Herman Melville, Gottfried Keller, Theodor Fontane, J. Ruskin, Frerichs, and G. Courbet (all born in 1819); H. Spencer and J. Tyndall (1820). He was slightly older than Louis Pasteur, G. Mendel, Kussmaul, Francis Galton, and J. Moleschott (all born in 1822); Joseph Leidy and E. Renan (born in 1823); P. Broca, Lord Kelvin, and G. R. Kirchhoff (born in 1824).

Virchow liked to look at natural history books and showed
early linguistic talents. Grade school and private tuition prepared him for the gymnasium in Koeslin, for which he de-
parted from home in 1835 at the age of fourteen. His scholastic
record was always brilliant, but his behavior so nonconformist
that in this respect he ranked last in his class. This probably
only increased his popularity with his classmates, who called
him their "king." Virchow finished the gymnasium in 1839 not
without experiencing great difficulties with a Greek professor
of the *Unrat* variety. His graduation composition [1] bears the
fateful title: "Ein Leben voller Muehe und Arbeit ist keine
Last, sondern eine Wohltat" ("A Life Full of Work and Toil
Is Not a Burden, but a Benediction"). The theme reminds one
of Osler's 1903 Toronto address, "The Master Word Is Work."

Young Virchow's goal was a gigantic one: "An all-around
knowledge of nature, from the deity down to the stone." [2]
There did exist an opportunity for a poor boy in Prussia to
approach such a goal: to be accepted in the Friedrich-Wilhelms Institut or *pépinière* in Berlin. This institute, founded in
1795 by Goercke, provided free medical education for a certain number of gifted boys in view of later employment as
army doctors. The institute might have been in many ways a
reactionary institution (Virchow asked in vain for its abolition
in 1848 [3]), yet its methods of selection from the inexhaustible
reservoir of talent still provided by the lower strata of society
seem to have been fairly adequate. It produced, besides Virchow, such luminaries of nineteenth-century German medicine
as Schultz-Schultzenstein, Meyen, Helmholtz, Reichert, Leyden, Nothnagel, Loeffler, Gaffky, Behring, Marchand, Martius,
and Hueppe. The administration had the good sense to release
scientifically promising individuals from their military obligations.

The army medical officer who examined Virchow in Koeslin
in 1839 stated: "This young man is gifted for everything but
for becoming diseased." [4] Thus in October, 1839, Virchow entered the *pépinière*. He started the study of medicine when
medical science had reached an all-time low in Germany.
While a new scientific medicine had brilliantly arisen in France

and Great Britain and even Austria in the first decades of the
century, in reactionary Germany medicine had lost itself in the
jungles of romantic speculation or the deserts of naked empiricism. It was Virchow's great good luck that Berlin University
at this moment could boast at least of having on its staff the
outstanding German medical scientist of the time, Johannes
Mueller, and the outstanding German clinician, J. L. Schoenlein. Virchow has left short biographies of both men, who made
a profound impression on him. Schoenlein had started as a
romanticist, but later assimilated French methods of clinical
examination. Virchow's interest in epidemiology and the history of diseases might be traced back to Schoenlein and
another early Berlin teacher, J. Hecker.

Johannes Mueller, famous physiologist, comparative anatomist, embryologist, and pathologist, was one of the most
magnetic teachers of all times. Virchow himself remembered
sitting at his feet together with Bruecke, Du Bois–Reymond,
B. Reinhardt, and Riess (president of the workers' association in 1848).[5] A list of Mueller's outstanding pupils comprises anatomists like Th. Schwann, Valentin, Miescher,
Henle, Reichert, Gerlach, Koelliker, Aug. Mueller, Remak,
LaVallette, His, Sr., Haeckel, Lieberkuehn, Max Schultze,
Bardeleben, and Kupfer; physiologists like Bruecke, Du Bois–
Reymond, E. Pflueger, F. H. Stannius, and Helmholtz; pathologists like Reinhardt, Virchow, and H. Meckel von Hemsbach.[6]
Johannes Mueller, emancipating himself from the romanticism
of his youth, had developed the one element of its heritage,
biology, which contained great potentialities and which had
been underestimated in other countries. In applying to this
field exact methods and thus cultivating the laboratory sciences
in medicine, he prepared for the supremacy of German medicine in the second half of the nineteenth century when the
limits of the purely clinical-autopsic approach had been
reached in France and England. There is no doubt that Virchow's lines of interest and sound scientific methods were
largely determined by Mueller. As early as 1841 Virchow had
asked his father to set aside rabbits for him for experimental
purposes.

While the student Virchow was thus industriously acquiring medical knowledge, critical political remarks of increasing sharpness appeared more frequently in his letters after 1840 and showed him developing early another important aspect of his personality. The letters mirror the political unrest that had seized Prussia in 1840, after the death of the old king, and that was to explode eight years later in a full-blown revolution. Virchow's critical political attitude found expression in his first publications, which were not medical but historical in nature and which contained numerous disparaging remarks on feudal institutions. Virchow seems to have published anonymous notes on the history of his home town after 1842. His first extensive article on the same subject, "Zur Geschichte des Carthauses in Schivelbein," appeared in 1844.[7] Although his letters to his father show no signs of mental suffering in the military academy, a most eloquent description of those of Schiller in a similar institution (the Karlsschule) in Virchow's 1861 book on Goethe suggests that Virchow did not particularly enjoy the barracks-like environment. Long vacation trips on foot through the island of Ruegen (1841), Bohemia, and Thuringia (1842) extended the student's horizon.

In 1843 Virchow obtained his M.D. degree from the hands of Johannes Mueller, then dean of the medical faculty. His Latin thesis, "De rheumate praesertim corneae" ("On Rheumatic Disease, Particularly of the Cornea"), clearly foreshadows his later work in pathological physiology and his theories on inflammation. It is characteristic that, of the eight Latin aphorisms appended to the thesis for public discussion according to the custom of the time, two are only vaguely related to medicine. The one, *Nisi qui liberalibus rebus favent, veram medicinae indolem non cognoscunt* (Only the liberal-minded can gain insight into the nature of medicine), expresses his political leanings; the other, *Pomeraniae petrificata glacie primordiali disjecta* (The stones of Pomerania are products of glaciation), his interest in prehistory and his home province.[8]

In the same year Virchow was appointed "company surgeon" in the Charité Hospital, a position similar to a rotating internship. Virchow liked this exhausting practical work and was apparently extremely popular with the patients, who gave him the friendly nickname *der kleine Doctor* (the little doctor).[9] It must be remembered that the short, thin, blond, dark-eyed young man from eastern Pomerania, who within a few years would rise to national prominence in several fields, was physically solid, yet anything but imposing.

In 1843 Virchow seems to have started chemical work with Linde and microscopical work with Robert Froriep, the prosector of the Charité. His military superiors tried to obtain a permanent and official position for him in the Charité, as what we would call today a clinical pathologist, but failed on account of the resistance of Schoenlein who wanted such a job for his brilliant pupil Robert Remak. Only in 1846 was Virchow's situation at the Charité regularized by his becoming the successor of his teacher Froriep. The contact with Froriep, the coeditor of an abstract journal specializing in foreign material, is probably responsible for Virchow's early acquaintance with French and British medical publications.

His material insecurity did not deter Virchow from experimenting and planning, together with his newly won friend Benno Reinhardt. As early as 1844 he reported plans for a "big book." The plans for this book, which he obviously never wrote, were still with him in 1863.[10] In 1845 his first publications on fibrin and "white blood" appeared in Froriep's *Neue Notizen*,[11] thus opening up the two essential accomplishments of his early period: his work on embolism and on leukemia. These publications were continued in 1846 in Henle and Pfeufer's *Zeitschrift fuer rationelle Medizin* and in the short-lived *Beitraege zur experimentellen Pathologie und Physiologie* of his friend Traube.[12] Virchow thus started the incessant stream of medical publications that will be reported and analyzed in later chapters. From this period also seems to date his friendship with the German histopathologist Hermann Lebert, who had settled in Paris. A priceless helper of this period was E. F. Gurlt, the professor of veterinary medicine, who provided space and material for the young experimenters Virchow, Traube, Reinhardt, and A. Mendelsohn.

Appointed orator at the celebration of the birthday of the

founder of the Friedrich-Wilhelms Institute (May 3, 1845), Virchow gave a paper "Ueber das Beduerfnis und die Richtigkeit einer Medizin vom mechanischen Standpunkt" ("On the Need and Correctness of a Medicine Based on a Mechanistic Approach").[13] The youthful speaker without any hesitation admonished his audience, consisting mostly of romantic vitalists or of empiricists, to base further research on a triad of clinical observation (including physical and chemical examination), animal experiment, and necropsy (including microscopy). Life, according to Virchow, is nothing but a sum of phenomena submitted to the ordinary physical and chemical (that is, mechanical) laws. To look for the reasons of these laws is "transcendental pertness." The possibility of spontaneous generation is disproved. Life is essentially cell activity, and the cell the basic unit to be studied. (The influence of Schwann, another Mueller pupil, in the last two theses is unmistakable.)

After thus expounding his general program, Virchow illustrated its usefulness by submitting results of his researches and experiments on fibrin and blood sedimentation in inflammation and on fat metabolism in alcoholism, not without attacking valiantly the then dominant humoral pathology.

Similar medical ideas had been proclaimed a few years previous by Wunderlich, Griesinger, Henle, Pfeufer, and others in more liberal southern Germany. A few of the younger Berlin doctors felt similarly. But nobody had ever before publicly challenged the medical past in such an outspoken manner in the northern citadel of reaction.

In spite of the aggressiveness of his address, Virchow was charged to deliver a second one on August 2, 1845, to an even larger and more representative audience at a meeting commemorating the fiftieth anniversary of the Friedrich-Wilhelms Institute. Only the special parts of this address are preserved (Virchow's first discussion of embolism following thrombophlebitis; see *GA*, pp. 478 ff.). To judge from the reactions of the audience as reported by Virchow himself, this address must have been at least as aggressive as its predecessor. One *Geheimrat* said: "Did you hear it? We don't know anything any longer." [14] Others defended Virchow. The refusal of Wunderlich and Griesinger to publish these addresses in their *Archiv fuer physiologische Heilkunde* decided Virchow to create an organ of his own and probably contributed to the animosity that colored later polemics between these men whose basic approaches were so similar.

Some quotations from letters to his father show what gave Virchow the strength to act in a way that seemed certainly most foolhardy for a struggling young army doctor and scientist.

I like to accept [the offer of the second speech]. Unfortunately the occasion to give a piece of one's mind to *Geheimraeten,* secretaries of state and generals arises so rarely, and I hope to make myself understood. I don't deceive myself; with real knowledge and a determined language one can today impress everybody, even in the highest ranks, because everything is hollow and rotten up to the top. . . . Although I have not yet published a line, people know, not only in Berlin, but in Halle, even in Prague, and Vienna, that there is now a man in the Charité who takes the cause seriously. . . . It is a true work of Danaïdes, this medicine. Nothing has been examined properly. Everywhere one has to start from scratch again, and there is so much that sometimes one really despairs. If I had not the results in front of me that now everybody in the Charité regards me as an authority in scientific matters, and that everybody believes my statements, really I would have given up already. I, who have worked for such a short time, and who do not know innumerable things, I to be an authority? It is ridiculous. How little should those know who ask me, knowing myself so little.[15]

This somewhat overwhelming complete confidence in himself sustained Virchow throughout his life. Though he erred often and knew it, he remained apparently undisturbed and thus kept his grip on people. The strange thing is that the twenty-four-year-old "company surgeon" must at this fateful moment of his career have succeeded in strongly impressing even his adversaries, to the point where they at least respected him instead of ridiculing or breaking him. There have been quite a few young men in history making what sounded almost like megalomaniac claims, but very few who have encountered so much meekness, especially from high-ranking bureaucrats and army officers.

In 1846 Virchow, who was just taking his state board examination, made an even bolder step in demolishing critically the humoral theories of C. Rokitansky of Vienna, then the leading pathological anatomist in Europe.[16] Rokitansky wanted to crown his exemplary labors in gross pathological anatomy by a synthesis. Accepting the then prevalent idea that cells were formed from amorphous material (blastema), he came to the conclusion that the basic pathological changes were therefore in the blood, which produced the exudate, which in turn produced pathological cells. He thus dissolved all pathology into a series of "blood diseases," dyscrasias. It was not difficult for Virchow to demonstrate the speculative nature of this amazing relapse into humoral pathology. Rokitansky paid a compliment as great to himself as to his critic in omitting the incriminated passages in further editions of his handbook.

Virchow always showed a marked ability to work through and to co-operate in organizations. Opportunities for such work offered themselves in 1846 through the *Verein fuer wissenschaftliche Medizin* (Society for Scientific Medicine) and the *Gesellschaft fuer Geburtshilfe* (Obstetrical Society) of Berlin. Both newly founded (in 1844) societies were mostly composed of progressive young medical men. The guiding spirit of the Obstetrical Society was the young *Geheimrat* Carl Mayer, a close personal and political friend of Virchow, who four years later was to become his father-in-law. Through Mayer, Virchow came in contact with leading radical writers like Arnold Ruge and Berthold Auerbach, and a group of leading liberal medical practitioners like H. G. Wegscheider, F. Koerte, P. Langerhans, members or founders of medical dynasties in Berlin and important aids in Virchow's subsequent political and medical career.

Mayer's wife (née Martins), who was as much a personal friend of Virchow as was her husband, was the daughter, niece, sister-in-law, and mother-in-law of liberal bureaucrats [17] who survived, even after the purge of the Stein-Hardenberg reformers, in the more technical branches of Prussian government. Mrs. Mayer's brothers were mechanics who turned manufacturers.

Doctors, artists, liberal bureaucrats, liberal and radical politicians gathered thus at the Mayer house.[18] This was typical of the political as well as the cultural leanings of medical people of the period. It was at the same time representative of the liberal traditions of a large sector of the Berlin intelligentsia, who found their expression also in the free participation of numerous people of Jewish descent in these circles.

In the same year of 1846 Virchow began to give courses in pathological anatomy. His audience was composed of some veritable *Geheimraete,* some older physicians, and a group of enthusiastic young doctors. With some of the latter, like Von Frantzius, later secretary of the German Anthropological Society, or C. Pagenstecher, the son of the *Paulskirche* leader, Virchow developed lasting friendships. The Dane, P. L. Panum, and the unfortunate instrument of Lassalle, Dr. Arnold Mendelsohn, a most promising experimentalist, also belonged for a while to this circle. A. Hein and Duemmler found an untimely and long-lamented end in the cholera epidemic of 1848.[19] Reinhardt, Traube, and Leubuscher were other early comrades in arms. Devotion and faithfulness to his friends was another characteristic trait of Virchow.

In spite of his openly rebellious political and medical opinions, Virchow still enjoyed the protection of high military and civilian bureaucrats. His main protector was now the *Geheimrat* J. H. Schmidt, who had just published a pseudoradical pamphlet on medical reform. Schmidt sent Virchow on a study trip to Prague and Vienna in the summer of 1846. The report Virchow submitted after his return [20] centers around the necessity of developing a pathological physiology based on experiment and suggests all the organizational features that he later realized in developing his Berlin Institute.

In 1847 Virchow and Reinhardt published the first volume of the *Archiv fuer pathologische Anatomie und Physiologie und fuer klinische Medizin (Archives for Pathological Anatomy and Physiology and Clinical Medicine)* through the well-known publishing firm of Georg Reimer, who was also politically close to them. It seemed an uncertain adventure of two little-known young men. Reinhardt died in 1852 from tuberculosis, but

Virchow was to carry through this publication to Volume 169 (1902). The name alone indicates a program that will be discussed in detail in the following chapters. Already the first numbers of the *Archives* had, besides members of Virchow's own circle like Leubuscher and Neumann, collaborators of the stature of Panum, Bardeleben, Lebert, and Julius Vogel. Through the quality of its contributions, the *Archives* became one of the greatest formative factors in the history of modern medicine.

In 1847, at the age of twenty-six, Virchow became *Privat-dozent*—that is, he entered definitely the academic hierarchy. His inaugural lecture, again delivered with Johannes Mueller in the chair, dealt with pathological ossification; [21] his *Probe-vorlesung* (test lecture), with muscle inflammation.[22]

In the same year of 1847 another pupil of J. Mueller and Schoenlein, Robert Remak, became *Privatdozent*. This was somewhat belated, as Remak was born in 1815. Remak happened to be of the Jewish faith and refused to be baptized (like Paul Ehrlich, Louis Lewin, and many other outstanding German scientists of Jewish extraction later). Only a special decree of the king would make him eventually the first Jewish *Privatdozent* in Prussia. Remak had been Schoenlein's candidate for the job that Virchow eventually obtained. Remak was a most brilliant man, in many ways similar to Virchow, and, as we will see later, preceded him in several of his basic discoveries. Continual academic sabotage forced Remak to give up scientific research for neurological practice where again he excelled; but he died suddenly in 1865. The fate of Remak reminds one of the fact that behind many a great man there stand the frustrated and tragic shadows of other men who might have played the role of the great man, if, to begin with, the great man had never lived, and if so many other accidents had not occurred. One wonders whether Virchow might have ever occupied the towering position of his later years if such extremely promising pathologists as Kaltenbrunner (1803–33), F. Guensburg (1820–59), H. Meckel von Hemsbach (1821–56), B. Reinhardt (1819–52), Aug. Foerster (1822–65), Von

Baerensprung (1822–64), and O. Beckmann (1832–62) had not died in their early thirties or forties.

In the summer of 1847 Virchow traveled through the Rhine Valley to Belgium and Holland. In Holland he befriended F. C. Donders with whom he shared many scientific and social ideas. For his parents he summed up his trip as follows: "I know now almost all German universities and most of the German medical big shots, and, what is no less important, they know me. Our *Archives* have thus gained in distribution and influence, and I will be able to consciously pursue my goal of becoming the representative of a certain trend in medicine." [23]

During this trip Virchow participated in Aachen in the twenty-fifth meeting of the famous Versammlung deutscher Naturforscher und Aerzte (an institution comparable to our AAAS) with two papers, one on parenchymatous inflammation [24] and one on malignant tumors. He thus started a connection which was to last for more than fifty years, and his addresses to these annual meetings, collected by Sudhoff in a special volume in 1922, were one of his most important means of influencing the opinion of German physicians and scientists on a nationwide scale.

In the winter of 1847/48 a typhus epidemic devastated famine-ridden Upper Silesia, a Prussian province inhabited by a Polish minority. The Silesian situation became a public scandal and the government was forced to act. Once more the administration gave Virchow an important assignment: to survey, together with *Geheimrat* Barez, the medical situation in Upper Silesia. As Virchow had always expressed his opinions freely, one wonders whether the bureaucracy was hard of hearing or suffering from an extreme dearth of competent men, or whether (most likely) the old school-tie feeling (he was in spite of all a product of *their* school, not just some civilian) blinded them to this extent. None of the occasional liberals in the Prussian bureaucracy seems to have been instrumental in Virchow's early career. Virchow was in Upper Silesia from February 20 to March 10 of the fateful year of 1848. Fifty-four years later Virchow called this trip "decisive" for the development of his convictions.[25] The event gave him a unique occa-

sion to crystallize his previous critical and constructive ideas in
the fields of politics and science into one consistent structure
to which he adhered from then on. It convinced him definitely
of the inadequacy of the old bureaucratic-feudal structure and
the necessity of its removal. It also made him and his ideas
known to a larger public beyond medical circles.

Although many of the ideas in Virchow's report [26] on the
Upper Silesian epidemic are based on earlier English and especially French work,[27] it is certainly quite an unusual and original document. Its fine clinical and pathological findings are
imbedded into an amazingly competent "anthropological" (sociological) and epidemiological analysis. The report squarely
blames the government for the catastrophe. Its recommenda-
tions are, not some new drug or articles of food for the one and
a half million paupers in Upper Silesia, but *full and unlimited
democracy*,[28] or *education, freedom, and prosperity* [29] (the
three "pillars" of the political program of the radical Struve
whom Virchow admired greatly). In practical terms this meant,
according to Virchow: admission of Polish as an official language, self-government, separation of church and state,
shifting of taxes from the poor to the rich, improvement of
agriculture, creation of "associations" (co-operatives), building
of roads.[30]

Virchow was hardly back from Silesia when the revolution
for which he had waited since 1846 broke out in Berlin. The
night of March 18 saw him fighting on the barricades.

My own share in the uprising was relatively minor [as he writes
regretfully to his father]. I helped build a few barricades, but then,
as I could get hold only of a pistol, I could not do much more. The
soldiers shot mostly from too great a distance, and hand to hand
fighting was impossible, due to the small number of citizens behind
our barricade.[31]

C. L. Schleich's memoirs also describe him as rushing into
the elder Schleich's office.

"Schleich, have you any weapons?"
"Only this old gun and a rusty sabre."
"Out with them! Off to the barricade!" [32]

Virchow's letters after the victory (although badly muti-
lated by the conservative father and later by the editing daughter) show him in a mood of tremendous elation. He enjoyed
to the hilt the "spring of the nations," this outburst of boundless democratic optimism and faith in 1848 of which most
Germans later talked blushingly as the "mad year," if they
talked of it at all.

There is something entirely new, and almost the most important
thing in the whole revolution that now we have gained self-esteem,
self-respect, self-confidence.[33]

For a long time I have been conscious of the fact that I stand free
and open-eyed in my times, and assimilate their trends early and
quickly. I have often misjudged people, the times never. This has
given me the advantage of being now not half a man, but a whole
one whose medical beliefs fuse with his political and social ones.
As a natural scientist I can be but a republican.* The republic is
the only form in which the claims, derived from the laws of nature
and the nature of man, can be realized.[34]

Virchow was now drawn into a whirlpool of activities. He
served in several electoral colleges. He refused to be a candidate for the Frankfurt Constitutional Assembly and he looked
at its future with suspicion. He was too young to accept his
actual election (as a man of the extreme left) in the district of
Ziegenrueck into the Prussian Diet. He participated in democratic meetings and clubs. Together with L. Bamberger,
Corvin, Kinkel, and A. Ruge, he was a member of the Democratic Congress in Berlin in October, 1848. He caused much
trouble for his teacher, Johannes Mueller, now rector of the
university, as a leading spirit in the meetings of rebellious
Privatdozenten and associate professors; and through the medical reform movement he caused even more trouble to his
former mentor, J. H. Schmidt, who devoted to him a very personal pamphlet. Virchow felt that "the few young men who
have found real recognition from the administration are there-

---

* In European parlance the terms "republican" and "democrat" have
no party implications and mean only "devoted to the ideals of a republic
and a democracy" as compared to monarchist, fascist, etc.

with *personally* indebted to certain officials. But this does not mean that they have surrendered their good right to oppose the administration as a body and its principles." [35]

A cholera epidemic put heavy demands on Virchow's time as a clinical physician and a researcher. He continued his teaching routine. With Reinhardt he continued his *Archives*. Together with another friend and collaborator of the *Archives*, the psychiatrist R. Leubuscher, he even published (from July 10, 1848, to June 29, 1849) a weekly, *Die medizinische Reform*, as the Berlin mouthpiece of a nationwide medical reform movement that tried to parallel scientific with administrative progress.

This great German medical reform movement of 1848,[36] expressing itself mostly in meetings, journals, or pamphlets, is now largely forgotten. As Virchow reprinted most of his articles from *Die medizinische Reform* in his collected papers in 1879, they are almost its sole surviving traces that are accessible with relative ease. Hence one might be misled into thinking that Virchow was the lone originator, theoretician, and leader of this movement. Actually this movement was so large that a history of it, omitting Virchow's contribution, would still show its essential traits. It had been growing ever since the 1820's in Germany and had received many inspirations from parallel English and especially French movements.[37] Virchow was by no means alone in this endeavor. Many of his most catchy slogans actually stemmed from friends, especially Salomon Neumann, another collaborator of the *Archives*. Within these limitations Virchow's contribution should not be underestimated. In wielding the chaotic reform ideas into a consistent whole in articles which are literary masterpieces, in organizing the movement with his characteristic energy, industry, and courage, he furthered it tremendously and became undoubtedly one of its leaders.

The common fight brought him closer to his above-mentioned friends, especially Carl Mayer. It brought him new friends like the Hegelian philosopher, J. C. F. Rosenkranz, and the Sanskrit philologist, Th. Goldstuecker, with whom he kept faith long after the happy hunters became the hunted again.

After the first great victory of the reaction in November, Virchow did not abandon politics, but intensified his activity.

My participation in politics till November was more accidental, only work of my spare time. It was natural that I could not stay aside where everything pressed forward and where it seemed possible to sow scientifically reasonable principles in fertile soil. . . . Since November many things have changed. In the period where moving forces were almost entirely lacking, I felt it to be my simple duty as a citizen to step into the foreground of agitation. As a member of the central committee for popular elections, as vice-president in the third district, I have not shied away from an energetic and open opposition to the cabinet of Brandenburg [one of the illegitimate uncles of the king].[38]

On March 31, 1849, under the continual clamor of the reactionary press the unavoidable happened: the government suspended Virchow. But on April 15, 1849, submerged by protests of students and medical circles, it reinstated him as prosector "on probation." He remained deprived of the free room and board in the Charité that he had enjoyed previously.

During the whole crisis Virchow behaved in a calm and dignified way. It is true that he had vague hopes of a professorship in Giessen or Wuerzburg. But there the same forces that had driven him out of his job in Berlin were at work to bar him. It took five more months of painful waiting till the Wuerzburg professorship was eventually confirmed. The bureaucracy tried to remove him from Berlin by offering him a professorship in Koenigsberg, or to silence him with a special "research grant." He refused both. He did not make any of the then fashionable "declarations of repentance." After the second dissolution of the Prussian chamber in April, 1849, reaction triumphed completely and there was no prospect for fruitful political work. But Virchow did not give up. To him a defeat was never final, always only a temporary setback. He continued publishing the *Medical Reform*, till in June, 1849, this was no longer feasible. In one of its last numbers (No. 48) he declared that "the violation of justice is bound to lead the people to the barricades." In the last number he stated: "We have not lost our faith in the final victory of the people which rests on our conception of world history." [39] He wrote to his father in May, 1849: "I do not hesitate to state that were this situation to recur, I would act again, as I have done hitherto, and as circumstances demanded." [40] And in 1851: "You seem to conclude from my silence that I have come to consider my former opinions as erroneous. I do not abstain from politics because I deny my former ideas, but only because I want to abstain, because I do not want to be active in politics *now*." [41]

Virchow was by no means the only medical man of his generation to be involved in the events of 1848. On the contrary, most of them were—to mention here only the names of Remak, Traube, M. Schiff, Koelliker, Oppolzer, Semmelweis, and Griesinger. But he was probably the only one to republish his 1848 articles thirty years later with approval.[42] A kind fate hid from him the fact that the defeat of the only modern spontaneous German democratic revolution was far more definitive and decisive than anybody could see then, implying in the last instance the catastrophe of 1945.

Throughout his life Virchow felt that his participation in public life was not dictated by personal ambition, but had happened to him rather despite himself.[43] He wrote Bardeleben in March, 1849: "I have no intentions of becoming a professional politician. . . . I did not push my way into politics. The events pushed me into it. . . . I hate all waste of strength and time, and if I can do something better than politics, I stick to it. Thus far I entertain no political ambitions, no political fanaticism, but profound political convictions." [44] His lack of ambition at the time is confirmed by the testimony of detached observers like Bischoff and Wegscheider.[45]

In November, 1849, Virchow left Berlin for Wuerzburg, becoming engaged on the day of his departure to Rose Mayer, a girl eleven years his junior. In his words, "the probably most decisive year" of his life was over. Through good luck and strength of character he had avoided catastrophe that befell so many in this year. His life, never quiet, was now nevertheless to proceed in calmer channels. He was twenty-eight years of age and his apprenticeship was finished. He had overcome the handicaps of his lowly origins and had risen to a respected position. He had launched the *Archives* and formulated his basic scientific philosophy and program. If we summarize with Von Recklinghausen his contribution in pathology in the four words thrombosis, embolism, cellular pathology, metaplasia, then two of his main contributions were already made. In Upper Silesia and in the revolutionary meetings in Berlin his ideas on public health, epidemiology, self-government, and anthropology had crystallized. He was no longer alone; he had won a group of faithful and devoted friends. The storms of the revolution called forth only more strongly those personal traits that made him a leader of men, wherever he went.

In the 1850's general political remarks disappear from Virchow's letters to his father. In the heyday of reaction there was no opportunity to be politically active.* The early fifties were so hopeless that even Karl Marx withdrew from practical politics to devote himself to scientific research.[46] Virchow was a Prussian "foreigner" in Catholic Bavaria; and Philistine Wuerzburg, where there were no poor,[47] offered little stimulus to political action. He and his friend Koelliker mostly disregarded the venomous attacks devoted to them by the romantic Von Ringseis and other Bavarian reactionaries. Virchow was happy with his quiet young wife Rose, who understood him "better than anybody else,"[48] and the three of his six children who were born in Wuerzburg. He concentrated on his scientific work, and his seven years in Wuerzburg were probably the period of most creative professional activity in his life. Together with the histologist Koelliker, the chemist Scherer, the obstetrician Kiwisch, and the clinician Rinecker who had brought the others to Wuerzburg, he formed a congenial team, in spite of the fact that Virchow had criticized the scientific work of several of these friends before and continued to do so. They re-established the reputation of a once famous medical

* The bacteriologist Ferdinand Cohn wrote the following lines in his diary under date of September 25, 1849 (quoted by Leikind in *Bull. Hist. Med.*, VII [1939], 51): "Germany dead; France dead; Italy dead; Hungary dead; only cholera and court martials immortal. I have retired from this unfriendly outside world, buried myself in my books and studies; seeing few people, learning much, only inspired by nature. . . ."

school, ruined through reactionary persecutions in the 1830's. They founded a very active "physico-medical" society, the transactions of which reveal their intensive endeavors. Virchow's and Koelliker's fame as scientists and teachers drew hundreds of students to Wuerzburg, not only from the farthest corners of Germany, but even from abroad (Great Britain, Scandinavia, Russia). Virchow's newly created chair in Wuerzburg was the first chair in pathological anatomy in Germany. Among the best-known of Virchow's pupils in the Wuerzburg period are: the pathologists Rindfleisch, K. E. E. Hoffman, Grohé, E. Klebs; the anatomists Otto Beckmann,[49] Wilhelm His, Sr., V. Hensen, Gegenbauer, E. Haeckel, J. N. Czermak, Lachmann, Deiters; the clinicians A. Kussmaul, N. Friedreich, H. Ziemssen, and C. Gerhardt. His Wuerzburg pupils alone would make Virchow one of the greatest teachers in medical history. Two of them, Klebs and Haeckel, were to become his main opponents in the late 1870's in rather bitter discussions about bacteriology and evolutionism. But even they would always remember gratefully their years of apprenticeship, the little table-railroad, a special contraption on which Virchow would pass around the demonstration microscopes, and the master's persistent admonition: "Learn to see microscopically!"[50]

In Wuerzburg Virchow became engaged in two large-scale literary undertakings. In 1851 he became coeditor with Scherer and Eisenmann (the famous medical martyr of the period preceding 1848 who had spent seventeen years of his life in prison) of the *Jahresbericht ueber die Leistungen und Fortschritte der Gesamten Medizin (Yearbook of Accomplishments and Progress of Medicine)*, later known as *Virchows Jahresbericht*, which he edited from 1866 to 1893 with August Hirsch and from 1893 to his death with C. Posner. In 1854 he started the publication of a six-volume *Handbook of Special Pathology and Therapeutics*. Most of the first volume he wrote himself. The others were done by authorities like Griesinger, Hasse, Julius Vogel, Hebra, Lebert, Bamberger, Friedreich, Biermer, and Veit. This was one of the first and the model of the German collective *Handbuecher* that have earned well-merited fame in scientific circles all over the world.

Virchow's greatest accomplishment in Wuerzburg was the elaboration of his conception of "cellular pathology," and the collection of the numerous details underlying the conception. It was from Wuerzburg, in an editorial of the eighth volume of the *Archives* in 1855, that he first launched the famous slogans "cellular pathology" and *omnis cellula a cellula*. In the same year he went for the first time to Paris to see the International Exhibition and old friends (like Goldenstuecker and L. Bucher) then in exile. He also assisted at the International Statistical Congress.

Virchow did not lose contact with epidemiology and public health in Wuerzburg. In 1852 the Bavarian government sent him to explore a famine in the Spessart region. Fortunately there was no typhus, only some typhoid. His report was milder than the one on Upper Silesia, as was the situation, and yet it ended literally with the same demands as Virchow's 1848 Silesia report: education, prosperity, freedom.[51]

In Wuerzburg Virchow also started his work in physical anthropology with studies on the skulls of cretins in 1851. Here he did most of the work for his book, *Researches on the Development of the Cranial Basis*, one of his most important contributions to anthropology.

In his vacations Virchow usually went with his family to a seacoast resort in his Pomeranian homeland. But, alas, even there he could not stop his research urge and made observations on the "physiology of sea bathers."

Virchow refused several calls to other universities while in Wuerzburg. He was happy and satisfied. But when in 1856, after the premature death of H. Meckel von Hemsbach, the call for Berlin came, he accepted immediately. He was not the man to refuse a return without conditions, nay on his own terms, where he had been more or less driven out seven years ago and had even been the subject of a police expulsion in 1850,[52] on the occasion of his wedding. It was Johannes Mueller who had mainly engineered this call and who wanted Virchow to succeed him in the teaching of pathological anatomy.

Virchow instinctively took the right direction. It is easy to see that, had Virchow stayed in Wuerzburg as his friend Koelliker did throughout his long life, he would probably have made some more contributions to pathological anatomy, but he would never have become Virchow the scientific and political leader.

One of Virchow's conditions was the erection of a special building for a Pathological Institute. This building lasted during Virchow's forty-six years in Berlin. A new building was half finished when he died. In this old building he trained generations of doctors and scientists, many of whom he was to outlive. His first assistant was Felix Hoppe-Seyler, the father of physiological chemistry in Germany. Although Virchow himself no longer engaged in chemical work, he still regarded "pathological chemistry" as the avenue of the future; and his institute became through Hoppe-Seyler's successors, O. Liebreich, W. Kuehne, Alexander Schmidt, and Salkowski, one of the starting points of German biochemistry. Virchow's second assistant was Von Recklinghausen. After him the institute trained in the 1860's and 1870's among others such well-known men as Cohnheim, Hueter, E. Klebs, Baginsky, F. Busch, P. Langerhans, Jr., Ponfick, Grawitz, J. Orth. Virchow's influence as a teacher goes, of course, far beyond those who became his assistants. Chr. Baeumler, Marchand, Martius, F. Hueppe, O. Kuestner, Th. Gluck, and W. Roux have testified in their memoirs [53] to the great amount of inspiration and information they received from Virchow in their student days in the 1870's. C. Weigert and the clinicians, Aufrecht, Leyden, and Nothnagel, also were pupils of Virchow. Besides there was a multitude of less famous pupils. There were also numerous foreign students. Botkin, Andrew H. Smith, A. R. Simpson (the nephew and successor of Sir James), and Wilson Fox came in the late fifties. Cornil arrived in 1862 with a letter of introduction from Claude Bernard. H. M. Bernheim was sent by his teacher Kuess. The sixties saw, among many others, Moritz Roth, Tommasi-Crudeli, Reginald Heber Fitz, Raph. Lépine, and Axel Key. A young Canadian doctor, William Osler, stayed for three months in 1873 and was profoundly influenced, not only in his pathological, but also in his public health interests. Although

Virchow's production of pathologists was such that Rindfleisch could claim in 1893 that his scientific sons and "grandsons"— Cohnheim, Von Recklinghausen, etc., had been very productive in turn—held more than half of the chairs of pathology in Germany, it is characteristic of Virchow's teaching and orientation that among his pupils there were also many who became outstanding in other fields of medical science or as surgeons or medical clinicians.

Virchow himself asked for and retained up into the 1870's a clinical division. It is there that his assistant O. Obermeier discovered the spirillum causing relapsing fever in 1868. Cooperation in the Charité was not furthered by the eternal feud between the two clinicians Frerichs and Traube, whose assistants were not supposed even to greet each other. Virchow sided with his old friends, Traube, Langenbeck, and Graefe, while Frerichs was supported by Reichert. In spite of Virchow's friendly relations with Traube, he never formed a team with him as Rokitansky had with Skoda, or Henle with Pfeufer. Like Lebert, who eventually became a clinician himself, he apparently tried to be his own clinician. Virchow's knowledge of technical details in medicine and surgery seems to have been quite impressive.

It was in the nature of things that many of Virchow's assistants and associates shared his political convictions, as, for instance, Friedreich and Pagenstecher, Recklinghausen and Cohnheim. Hensen sat with him in the Prussian Landtag of 1867/68; Hueter became his colleague in the Reichstag in 1881, only to die in 1882.

Lubarsch has alleged that Virchow had no outstanding pupils during the last twenty years of his life.[54] This is not entirely fair to men like D. von Hansemann, Walter Kruse, Robert Langerhans, Oskar Israel—or Lubarsch himself. A certain decrease in the number of famous pupils is not so surprising in view of the fact that for psychological and practical reasons men in their twenties tend to cater to men in their forties rather than to sexagenarians, especially if the latter have acquired a reputation for handling their assistants in a somewhat arbitrary manner.* It also should not be forgotten that Virchow's interest in these years had very obviously shifted from pathology to anthropology, and the interests of the younger generation from pathological anatomy to bacteriology.

During the first seven years of his second Berlin period Virchow brought out some of his major pathological books: *Cellular Pathology* in 1858, the three-volume work on tumors that began appearing in 1863, and the little book on trichinosis in 1863.

This is all the more amazing in view of the fact that in 1859 Virchow had re-entered political life, this time as one of the main actors of the drama, and that up into the 1870's his political activity was, in the context of his total biography, the most significant of his many endeavors.

In 1859, on the suggestion of his old friend Doctor Salomon Neumann, Virchow was elected into the city council where he served up to his death. But this assignment was only semipolitical, as in the city council Virchow concentrated primarily on health matters. His work was facilitated by the facts that from 1863 to 1872 the mayor of Berlin was his brother-in-law Seydel and for many years the president of the city council was his old friend Doctor Paul Langerhans, Sr. Virchow was also able to promote sanitary reforms in Prussia by becoming in 1860 a member of the *Wissenschaftliche Deputation* (Council of Scientific Advisors to the Prussian government).

In 1861 the democratic forces in Prussia had recovered to the point where they founded again a party of their own, the *Deutsche Fortschrittspartei* (German Progressive Party). Virchow was among the founders, together with Von Forckenbeck, Schultze-Delitzsch, Von Hoverbeck, P. Langerhans, Franz Duncker, and Th. Mommsen. In 1861 he was elected into the Prussian diet and came just in time to lead the desperate fight of the constitutional forces against Von Bismarck, called in 1862 as prime minister by William I. Between 1862

---

* Virchow's attitude toward his assistants was decidedly paternalistic. While he paid fair salaries and had them publish under their own names, he had very personal opinions as to their rights to marry, to teach, or to leave him.

and 1866 Bismarck enforced Prussian rearmament against parliament and constitution and was thus able to realize his program of German "unification" by "blood and iron"—that is, the conquest of Germany by Prussia in the three *Blitzkriegs* of 1864, 1866, and 1870. Bismarck was so annoyed by the little professor that he tried to get rid of him in 1865 by a challenge to a duel. (Bismarck was an experienced duelist.[55]) Virchow declined the honor.* The tremendous ovations Virchow received at the *Naturforscherversammlungen* of 1861 in Speyer and 1865 in Hannover were directed as much at the opposition leader as at the scientist.

In 1868 Virchow founded with Holtzendorff the *Sammlung gemeinverstaendlicher wissenschaftlicher Vortraege (Collection of Popular Scientific Lectures)*, an important instrument in bringing science to the masses. He was very much attached to this series, for which he wrote several numbers and which he edited for thirty-three years. Its disappearance in 1901 caused him acute chagrin.[56]

In these years he also started his international activities. In 1859 the Norwegian government invited him to study the leprosy situation. In 1867 he went to the first International Medical Congress in Paris, at which Bouillaud presided, and to the Prehistory Congress in the same city.

The wars of 1866 and 1870 put Virchow into a difficult situation. As a sincere patriot he could not but wish for the victory of his country. But he could not overlook the fact that this victory would also be the victory of Bismarck and what he stood for, and the source of new conflicts. Virchow found an appropriate field of activity in building military hospitals and in equipping the first hospital trains for a progressive philanthropic organization. He profited much from United States' publications after the Civil War, for which he had the highest respect. In 1870 he himself led the first hospital train to the front. His magazine manager was Eugen Richter, who later replaced him as the leader of the Progressives. Two of his sons,

* That these duels were not mere formalities is evidenced by the case of Virchow's colleague K. Twesten, whose right arm was destroyed at such an occasion by E. von Manteuffel in 1861.

who accompanied him as orderlies, came down with typhoid.

In the 1870's Virchow's interest concentrated more and more on anthropology, not that he withdrew from politics. Even in 1880 he was still popular and interested enough to be elected to the Reichstag, where he sat till 1893. He maintained his seat in the Landtag to the time of his death. But the essential battle with Bismarck was over, and it was the *Junker* who had won. In addition Virchow lost the leadership of his party. Blinded by his traditional anticlericalism, he sided with Bismarck in his (unsuccessful) fight against the Catholic Church, for which Virchow even coined the name Kulturkampf. Virchow used the prosperity in the New Reich in these years to effectuate his main municipal reforms in Berlin.

Virchow also continued his medical activities. He continued publishing original observations up to the very last; in 1874 he published his standardized autopsy technique. But his main role in medicine became now more and more that of the arbiter of international medicine. He participated in international leprosy and cholera conferences like those at Moscow in 1871 and at Stockholm in 1874; he made a leprosy survey of Spain and Portugal in 1880. He was no longer a leading figure only in the German *Naturforscherversammlungen*, but also in the International Medical Congresses of London (1881), Copenhagen (1884), Berlin (1890), Rome (1894), Moscow (1897), and Paris (1900). His linguistic abilities—he knew not only Latin, Greek, Hebrew, and Arabic, but spoke fluently English, French, Italian, and Dutch—were very helpful at such occasions.

Virchow's tremendous international influence is reflected in the story of Ramon y Cajal's entrance into the Spanish Academy. In 1897 Virchow asked a Spanish dignitary passing through Berlin, "And what is Ramon y Cajal doing now?" The dignitary, who had never heard of Cajal though the latter was by then already internationally recognized, informed himself immediately after his return and had Cajal elected into the Academy. Cajal used to say jokingly that he had entered the Academy "on the nomination of Virchow."

Virchow had friends, pupils, and admirers in every European

country (especially in Russia). He repeatedly expressed his great admiration for Pasteur, made great efforts to work for a German-French reconciliation, and above all was closest to Britain and the British, to whom he felt congenial in every respect and where real friendship united him with Lister, James Paget, Wilson Fox, and Pye-Smith. He made repeated trips to England, where on one visit he met Robert Browning at a tea party and had a long talk with him about Paracelsus.[57] He studied English sewerage systems on the spot in 1884, delivered the Croonian lecture in 1893 and the Huxley lecture in 1898.

Virchow received the two great scientific movements of the seventies and eighties, bacteriology and Darwinism, with sound scientific scepticism—an attitude which we can well appreciate today, yet which did not make for popularity then. But Virchow was never interested in popularity for popularity's sake. Nevertheless he maintained his grip on people through his tremendous abilities as an organizer and administrator, through his courage, his intellectual superiority, and his extraordinary power of observation. Aschoff was surprised to see in 1897 with what respect his teacher Von Recklinghausen, not exactly a humble person, approached the seventy-six-year-old master.[58] He did not know then of a small, but chastening experience Von Recklinghausen had had a few years earlier, told later by Waldeyer in his interesting memoirs.[59] On a visit to Strassburg, Von Recklinghausen had shown Waldeyer a skull, the lesions of which he was unable to identify; neither was his eminent visitor. While they were talking, Virchow, who was also on a visit and working in another room, walked through, saw the skull from a distance, and said, "Oh, you have there a nice case of such and such." Von Recklinghausen commented somewhat peevishly to Waldeyer: "The old man still sees more than both of us together." *

* He impressed Osler by a similar snap diagnosis of four Northwest Coast skulls that the latter brought him in 1884; see Osler in *Boston Medical and Surgical Journal*, CXXV (1891), No. 17, 425–27. Also see Schleich, *Besonnte Vergangenheit*, pp. 186 and 289, for Virchow's diagnostic acumen.

In 1882 Virchow—or *Geheimrat* Virchow as German publications called him since 1894—took over the presidency of the Berlin Medical Society as a provisorium. This very active provisorium lasted till his death twenty years later. Only in 1893, at the age of seventy-one was the "dangerous" man entrusted with the rectorship of the University of Berlin.

In 1888 Virchow performed what was probably his last autopsy under rather tragic circumstances. The "case" was no less than the German Emperor, Frederick III, who had succeeded his father William I as a dying man and who succumbed to laryngeal cancer after a reign of one hundred days. Frederick III was the only member of the Hohenzollern family ever to show any liberal leanings and was encouraged in this direction by his wife, a daughter of Queen Victoria. Virchow had therefore been on friendly terms with the couple, who had helped him to found the first children's hospital in Berlin and a workman's association. When the then crown prince showed the first signs of disease, a violent discussion had broken out among his three physicians, the English consultant claiming a benign and the two Germans a malignant growth. A piece submitted to Virchow had actually shown no signs of malignancy.[60] Virchow's report had thus strengthened the position of the wrong party. Although Virchow was innocent of the tragic outcome, it was no less saddening to him. Frederick's son and successor, William II, the *Kaiser* of 1918, was a true reactionary Hohenzollern.

As mentioned above, Virchow's main interest after 1870 was anthropology. Typically enough, all his contributions in the Prussian Academy of Science, which he entered in 1873, are of an anthropological nature. At an age when many other people have long given up active research, Virchow tackled an entirely new field. He felt that, now that pathological anatomy was a going concern and ably carried on by his pupils, it was but reasonable for him to concentrate on this very young and chaotic field. These characteristics of the field are one of the reasons why Virchow's scientific accomplishments in it cannot be compared to those in pathology where he was the heir of centuries of progress.

Virchow was active in the founding of the German Anthropological Society in 1869 and founded, in the same year, the Berlin Society of (physical) Anthropology, Ethnology, and Prehistory, over which he presided to the time of his death. The journal of the latter, the *Zeitschrift fuer Ethnologie,* which became the leading German journal in the field, was edited by him almost singlehanded (proofreading included) throughout the rest of life. He was a guiding spirit in the national and international meetings of these new sciences.

Physical anthropology was closest to Virchow's professional background. In this field he had worked previously. Here he carried through in the 1870's the nationwide racial survey of school children, the first of this kind ever undertaken.

Virchow's interest in German archeology dated from his student days. His activities now spread out into the Near East. Sponsoring Schliemann, the self-made discoverer of the ruins of Troy, and providing him with trained help, he made Schliemann scientifically respectable—and saved his collections for Germany. Virchow excavated with Schliemann in Hissarlik in 1878. In 1888 he went with him and Schweinfurth to Egypt. In 1881 and 1894 he did his own field work in the Caucasus.

He was least active as a researcher in ethnology, where his friend Bastian took the lead, but furthered this field tremendously in an administrative way in sponsoring expeditions, and especially in obtaining the erection of the splendid Berlin Ethnological Museum in 1886 and of the Folklore Museum in 1888.

It is consistent with Virchow's role as a "symbol," almost an idol, that toward the end of his life every possible anniversary of his should be celebrated as a world-wide ritual: his seventieth birthday in 1891 (which was also that of Helmholtz), the fiftieth anniversary of his doctor's promotion in 1893 (which coincided with that of Du Bois–Reymond), and above all his eightieth birthday in 1901. Banquets were given all around the world; in the United States faithful friends like Abraham Jacobi and William Osler extolled his virtues. International authorities—like Lord Lister, Stokvis, Armauer Hansen, and the

Italian minister, pathologist, and clinician Baccelli—flocked to Berlin to celebrate the master.

The little retrospective article that the octogenarian wrote as an expression of thanks to all his friends is extremely characteristic.[61] The many congratulations had mirrored to him his "whole, rather restless life."

The course of my researches has not only brought different countries and their inhabitants into the compass of my investigations, but according to circumstances my studies have also dealt with medicine and the sciences, anthropology and archeology, occasionally even with literature, philosophy, politics and social structure.

I did not bring about this mixture arbitrarily. Decisive for it was a mission on which I was sent by the Prussian minister of medical affairs early in 1848. I was to survey the grave epidemic of so-called famine typhus in Upper Silesia. In analyzing the causes of this epidemic I became convinced that the worst were the consequence of social evils, and that these evils could be fought only by ways of deep going social reforms. . . . I want once more to recall to memory that it is unavoidable to relate practical medicine and political legislation, as tried then in the *Medizinische Reform* (1848–49). . . .

He goes on to describe his efforts in epidemiology and sanitation, especially in Berlin. He is particularly proud of the honors he has received from city representations in connection with this work. There is no analysis of his pathological work.

He reviews the honors bestowed upon him at the occasion of his eightieth birthday by the medical profession in Austria, Australia, Switzerland, Great Britain, Italy, Sweden, Norway, Finland, France, Holland, Russia, Japan, and Germany.

My feeling of obligation is too strong to express it in adequate terms. I am too old to promise new accomplishments which would be a worthy compensation. *I will not tire of working as long as my forces last.* All I can promise is to try bringing several larger projects, started when I was young, to an end, useful to the world. . . .

Even if it were true that the world is ungrateful, it would be very ungrateful on my part to recognize ungratefulness as a common human quality. Nobody can count on finding or ask for more affection than I have found in all classes of our nation and even abroad. I did not ask for such affection, it was given voluntarily; I did not count on such affection, but all the more did it surprise me pleasantly and oblige deeply.

Of all the celebrations he enjoyed most the one in the Workman's Association *(Handwerkerverein)* he had once helped found.

Such is the gratefulness of the people, and that is why I say to everybody: trust the people, work for them; the recompense will not be lacking, as much as the destruction of many institutions, the disappearance of many men, the complete change of our public life reminds us of our mortal nature. This is my faith, and this, I trust, will suffice me, as long as I live.

Virchow seemed indestructible. He bore the strain of the 1901 celebrations very well. But on January 4, 1902, he broke his femur when jumping from a streetcar. The fracture united as he had prophesied, but in the forced inactivity of the sickbed he declined rather rapidly and died from cardiac disease on September 5, 1902. He was survived by his wife, three sons, three daughters, and nineteen grandchildren. The city of Berlin, for which he had done so much, gave him a public funeral attended by large masses of the population.

Ein Leben voller Muehe und Arbeit ist keine Last,
sondern eine Wohltat.

We shall not see him anymore in the flesh . . . : the little, slightly bent, lithe man with the parchment-like, somewhat yellowish, much wrinkled face and the slightly grizzled hair, which remained practically unchanged during the thirty years I have known him, with the small, piercing eyes covered by spectacles, which he always pushed up when reading or when about to make one of his caustic remarks; with his dry, sarcastic, somewhat monotonous voice; with his rapid gait, with his quiet, unostentatious demeanour. . . .[62]

Tremendous as Virchow's scientific contribution is, to the observer familiar with the work of others preceding and following him it is likely to become more the link in a great chain than a lonely monument. Virchow, though certainly never underplaying his contribution like Helmholtz, was himself fully aware of how much he owed his predecessors and contemporaries.[63] The historian is likely to be impressed less by Virchow's discoveries than by his ability to make men accept his ideas.

What seems most unique in Virchow's contribution is his ability to do outstanding work in so many fields simultaneously —an ability in general lost in nineteenth-century scientists—the Faustian urge to explore continuously new things, and the extraordinary quantity of his achievements. Besides his research, crystallized in more than two thousand papers and books, besides his academic and popular teaching, his traveling, his political and administrative work, besides his editorial and organizational activities, he still found time to arrange and label with his own hands more than twenty thousand preparations and four thousand skulls for his Institute collection. There is something inhuman or superhuman in this dynamism, this tireless energy, this ceaseless work. Although his life looks in many ways uneventful in its regularity, security, and continuity, the incessant movement that fills it gives it an almost demonic quality. And at that, Virchow seemed never to be in a hurry! [64]

Virchow was favored by nature, not only through superior intelligence, but through an iron health. He never was seriously ill before his eighty-first year. When hiking with him in 1901, the sixty-five-year-old Waldeyer found himself no match for his eighty-year-old friend.[65] Virchow's most precious gift from nature was perhaps his abnormally low need for sleep. He could do with five hours, occasionally with no sleep at all. This easily added twenty more years to his active life.

Virchow's work was apparently never arrested by fear or by doubts in his abilities and in the righteousness of his cause.*

---

* One has to be cautious though with such affirmations. Virchow said in his Croonian lectures (BKW, XXX [1893], 321) rather abruptly: "How often did I find myself in a state of discouragement with the definite feelings of a depression." Yet it seems unlikely that a document will ever be found from Virchow's hand similar, for example, to Th. Mommsen's testament (September 2, 1899; published by his grandson Konrad Mommsen in Die Wandlung, III [1948], 69) that contains the following amazing statement: "In spite of external successes I have not achieved

His extraordinary self-confidence was strengthened through his religious faith in science. ("I do not hesitate to say that to us science has become religion. . . ." [66]) As he died twelve years before the outbreak of World War I, he found his faith continually confirmed by reality. Although the one or the other scientific theory might fail and fall, science itself was progressing steadily and with ever-increasing speed. So was the society that seemed to be more and more guided by science. Wars seemed to become rarer, shorter, and less cruel. The lower classes, from which Virchow had risen so dramatically and to which he remained faithful, were improving their standard of living and increasing their political powers steadily, in spite of all temporary defeats. His country—politically, economically, scientifically a poor parent in the European concert when he entered life—had within a few decades become in every respect the strongest power on the continent. The Berlin in which he lived experienced a golden age in science and thought and was transformed, partially through his own efforts, from a semi-barbaric frontier city into a true metropolis.

All this made Virchow, not only a courageous, but also a proud man. When the other scientists that had risen to fame from the lowly *pépinière* became "Von Helmholtz," "Von Leyden," "Von Behring," Virchow refused the titles of nobility, feeling correctly that the assimilation into a class which owed its position to birth, not to accomplishment, could not increase, nay would rather diminish, his stature.

Historians have been impressed by Virchow's uninhibited pugnacity in scientific discussions.[67] He showed often a somewhat naive surprise when he was paid back in the same coin.

---

the right thing during my life. Accidents made me a historian and philologist, although my education and talents for both disciplines were insufficient. The painful feeling to appear more than I actually was has never left me throughout life. . . . I never had nor sought a political position or influence. Yet at my innermost and with the best I had in me, I was always a 'political animal' and wanted to be a citizen. But this is impossible in this nation where the individual, be it the best, cannot transgress the service in the ranks and the political fetishism. This internal conflict with the nation to which I belong has determined me not to present my personality to the German public for which I have no respect. . . ."

How little he knew himself is evidenced by the following tragicomic remarks at the occasion of his fiftieth graduation anniversary:

I have fought many battles in my life but nevertheless I can say that fundamentally *I have always been a man of peace, that is of peace between those who represent the same interests.* . . . Our interests are those of science and humanity. . . ." [68]

He did not mind, though, the accusation of being restless, of bringing unrest into science.[69] He had not come into this world to bring peace.

Virchow's self-confidence is also reflected, according to his son, by the fact that he wrote his papers in one sitting *(in einem Zuge)* and did not change them afterwards.*

A certain coldness of character probably facilitated his task. It enabled him to analyze people or a situation objectively, to determine clearly what he wanted and what he could obtain. It allowed him to use people, join them, or separate from them independently of his feelings. Only an unusually detached individual could co-operate with a Schliemann for any number of years.[70] It gave his considerable critical inclinations their power to strike. In a discussion he would usually demolish an adversary without even raising his voice.[71] This detachment, this reserve would tremendously depress and irritate persons of a different make-up, like his own father [72] or his onetime assistant Ernst Haeckel.† It would be congenial to men of a similar complexion, like the late Franz Boas, who liked to quote Virchow's recommendation of "icy enthusiasm," [73] a formula that characterizes both men, Virchow and Boas, so well.

Without a certain dryness Virchow would have been unable

* This is confirmed by the fact that the eleven manuscripts of articles published in *A*, now in the Thor Jager collection, show practically no changes or insertions.

† Haeckel, *The Story of the Development of a Youth: Letters to His Parents, 1852–1856*, pp. 373, 383, 384, 387, and 416. Haeckel's student letters are one sided, but probably next to Virchow's own letters the most relevant documents on Virchow's character. Poor Haeckel, who found it so "sweet to be attacked for Virchow's sake" (p. 363), suffered intensely from the "divine coolness, calmness, and consistency" of his master from whom he could never elicit either praise or blame.

to carry his tremendous load of work. A little anecdote, told by Martius, is rather characteristic in this respect. Martius, then a young army doctor, had sent a manuscript to the editor of the *Archives*. Receiving no answer for months, he went one day to Virchow's apartment. Virchow's study was filled with what seemed a complete chaos of papers, books, and journals.* Virchow shrewdly interpreted the facial expression of his visitor. "You think I don't know where your manuscript is? There." And he produced it from one of the disturbing piles. "It is a serious scientific production. I will publish it. Good-by." [74]

It will surprise nobody to hear that Virchow was a strong believer in will power. Significant is his answer to his (mediocre) anatomist-son Hans: "Stop fussing about your bad memory. One remembers what one has decided to remember!" [75]

Virchow had no time for sports and hobbies. He was most modest, almost ascetic, in his personal habits, his dress, the coaches he used. (The Berlin students were wont to say he used second-class coaches only because there were no third-class ones.) He was simple and democratic in spite of the fact that he must have been wealthy in later years and could easily have been rich, had he wanted to be.

Nothing would be farther from the truth than to assume that Virchow was a complete introvert, cold and inhuman. His popularity with his fellow scientists, and especially with the masses, his successful work in organizations would have been impossible under such conditions. He had to a high degree the "feeling for corporation." [76] He was easily approachable. After meetings he liked to sit down with friends and students for a glass of beer or wine and some singing. He snuffed tobacco; when young, he liked to dance. In his vacations he would bowl, swim, climb mountains. He was hospitable, inviting not only his peers, but also his assistants, and going to their homes. He could be very gay, especially among his family, who adored him. As a good German, he could be deeply moved by music.[77]

---

* As a matter of fact, Virchow's home office was so filled with books and the Institute office so filled with bones that he had to go to a hotel for consultations. (Letter to Volkmann in *Janus*, LV [1941], 16.)

He could be particularly warm with the lowly and the sick.* He was the only one of Schleich's teachers that ever showed compassion with an experimental animal.[78] He is one of the very few pathologists whose sympathy with the "case" sometimes breaks through the objective form of their case reports.[79]

He was perhaps never better characterized than when his friend Bastian called him "der Grosse Gaertner" (the Great Gardener). The word evokes so many of his traits: the eternal combination of pruning and planting, his industry, simplicity, thoughtfulness, mental and physical vigor.

As a whole, he was shockingly lucky all his life long and shockingly normal. There is in his life no psychosis or neurosis, no major character defect or vice or suffering, not even an unhappy marriage that so many other great men offer to reconcile us with their greatness. He had the rare ability or luck to channel all his tremendous energies (or sublimate, as the fashionable expression goes) into rational outlets, into work, the "search for truth." In typical German fashion he would look at his work as "doing his duty."

He also felt very strongly about the two corollaries of this German "work-duty" ideal: justice and order. There is the famous passage in the Preface of the *Cellular Pathology:*

I insist on my rights, and therefore I respect the rights of others. This is my standpoint in life, in politics, in science. We owe it to ourselves to defend our rights, because this is the only guarantee of our individual development and of our influence on the community.[80]

It was lawlessness that shocked him so deeply in Bismarck. Virchow's sense of "order" was highly offended even by the use of a path which was *verboten.*[81] The pedantry into which his strong sense of logic and order had hypertrophied was feared even by his friends. This made him a simply ferocious examiner.[82] His pedantic insistence with students on trifles like

* See Orth's (A, CCXXXV [1921], 41) description of Virchow treating an orderly suffering from cholera, or Haeckel's (*op. cit.*, p. 407) surprise from Virchow's behavior in Haeckel's own disease. See also A, LXXVII (1879), 180, on the popularity he acquired while treating peasants at the Hissarlik excavation.

color shades, etymology, or holding glasses the right way is well known.

Still he was a tremendously popular teacher in his earlier years, as testified even by men who entertained a rather ambivalent attitude toward him, like Klebs, Haeckel, Billroth, or Orth—and this in spite of the fact that his teaching was probably never simple, elementary, or systematic.[83] In a manuscript *curriculum vitae* of 1860 in the Thor Jager collection, Virchow points proudly to the fact that the number of medical students in Wuerzburg increased from 98 (42 non-Bavarians) in 1849 to 388 (276 non-Bavarians) in 1855. Even in the last two decades when an often described unpunctuality, caused by his many other obligations, seriously interfered with his teaching, it was still greatly enjoyed by the thoughtful.[84]

It was biologically almost unavoidable that some of his qualities should degenerate at an advanced age into negative traits. His uprightness might turn at times into unreasonable stubbornness. While it is but natural to remember that he furthered so many worthwhile things, it should also not be forgotten that he retarded quite a few out of obstinacy. For years, for instance, he blocked chairs in hygiene, legal medicine, and medical history in Berlin, not because he underestimated these disciplines, but because he felt they were well taken care of by his teaching. He also was, for instance, opposed to feminine emancipation.[85]

He was often called a "pope" or a "pascha" in his later years, and his attitudes were undoubtedly often authoritarian. Rebels who come into power have rarely exhibited much meekness. Pathological anatomists, who by the nature of things are always right, as they have the last word, have as a group never had a reputation for extreme humbleness. On the other hand, the "pope" position of Virchow was actually never as absolute as has sometimes been claimed, nor was it primarily his fault that so many mentally inert people preferred taking his word as ultimate truth. His continued friendship with such colleagues or pupils as Lebert, Koelliker, Waldeyer, or Von Recklinghausen, who had opposed some of his most cherished theories, proves that there is much truth in his declarations: "I respect the rights of others," or "Those who know me, know that I bear no grudges." [86] His very coolness allowed him often to eventually recognize his own mistakes. The famous democrat was, after all, not quite as undemocratic as some people, furious at their own previous spinelessness, tried to make the lion look—after he was dead. Historians are not obliged to take the belated eruptions of "Oedipus complexes" at face value.

If we try to weigh fairly the negative side of his record—which I have tried to report just as conscientiously as the rest—against his positive accomplishments and his virtues, his faults dwindle almost into insignificance. To a man of such courage, humanity, and intelligence even much more could be forgiven.

It is quite possible that the most important trait in Virchow was his "cold, firm, very strong character," as young Haeckel once saw it; that not so much what he said and did, but what he was, made him the power he became.[87] Yet, especially at our present stage of psychological ignorance, to the historian this "essence" of personalities is practically inaccessible; it dies with them. Historians remain bound to the lowly sphere of what people say and do, their works, which may not or, more often, may transgress the personality. We therefore take leave now of Rudolf Virchow, the man, and his long and glorious career, and turn to what, even when the story of his life will long have been forgotten or dissolved into mythical shadows, will survive—his works.

The Doctor

General Ideas

FROM THE BEGINNING to the end Virchow was a "whole man." Into how many fields he might move during his long life, the goal, the underlying ideas were essentially the same. From his first programmatic speeches in 1845, through his little philosophical treatise "Attempts at Unifying Scientific Medicine" ("Die Einheitsbestrebungen in der wissenschaftlichen Medizin") with which he closed his Berlin period in 1849 and which he put again in front of his *Collected Scientific Essays* in 1856 at the end of his Wuerzburg period, to his testament "To My Friends" of 1901, there is one straight line of unified thought and action. He not only preached the ideal of the "whole man," he succeeded in living it. Although his consistency might sometimes lead him into errors which less consistent people would have avoided, as a whole this combination of many-sidedness and unity of thought was to him a source of great strength. Some, like Aschoff, have regarded this unifying power of his thinking as his greatest contribution.

This quality of Virchow makes it, on the other hand, impossible to separate completely the discussion of the technically different fields he cultivated. It makes it desirable to examine at least briefly his general ideas in the fields of philosophy and medicine before entering a discussion of his more specialized biological and medical work. "We did find our method not without some philosophy." [1] There is no lack of published material for any period of Virchow's life for such an inquiry.

43

Virchow did not suffer from the inhibitions that made a Claude Bernard come into the open only toward the end of his career with general considerations that, as we see now from his note-books, had troubled and puzzled him throughout his life.*

We gain a glimpse of this unifying thought in the last sentences of Virchow's "Attempts at Unifying." "If medicine is to fulfill her great task, then she must enter the political and social life." [2] His epicritical remark in the *Medical Reform,* "The medical reform that we meant was a reform of science and society," [3] is to be taken very literally. Freedom and science are natural allies. To him the revolution of 1848 was obviously as much a scientific as a political event:

Eventually the days of March arrived. The great fight of criticism against authority, *of natural science against dogma,* of the eternal rights against rules of human arbitrariness, this fight which had already twice shaken the European world, broke out for the third time and victory was ours.[4]

This unification of medical and politico-social thought made Virchow ask for "political" therapy for Upper Silesia, where he was to suggest a "medical" one. It made him, on the other hand, suggest a medical approach where so far a political had been customary (as in the handling of criminals, in education, care for the unemployed and employed).[5] It made him fill his primarily political journal *Medical Reform* with medical items like the pathology of cholera and of phosphorous poisoning, like diabetes treatment, chloroform anesthesia, cancer metas-tases ("Virchow's gland"), etc.[6]

This attitude is by no means limited to the 1848 period when he shared it with the whole medical reform movement.[7] It accompanied him throughout his life, when this attitude was more and more lost by scientists. His continuous parallels be-tween political, scientific, and biological phenomena are some-times illuminating, sometimes not far from the ludicrous, like similar parallels of other contemporaries (Karl Marx, etc.).

---

* These differences in Virchow's and Bernard's work were first noticed by Chauffard (*Le Correspondant,* p. 205) and were discussed by Vir-chow himself in *A,* LIII (1871), 23 ff.

When examining the medicine of his time, Virchow looked for the "vanguards of the different [political] parties in medicine." [8] Stahl's animism was to him a reflex of monarchism; the following doctrine of the "formative force" was "a little more democratic." [9] Teleology, which attributed to the white cells the role of sheriffs, was an absolutistic way of looking at things.[10] The followers of Rademacher's therapeutics formed a "party of populist progressives." [11] Science was bourgeois in nature, now and forever.[12] The "rational medicine" of his competitor Henle was speedily assimilated to religious rationalism and the "Gotha" party, a spineless liberal group of the 1850's.[13] Rokitansky's humoralism once menaced medicine like socialism the state.[14] Later this comparison to socialism was applied to Haeckel's transformism.[15] In this latter discussion Virchow identified himself for the first time with the "right" side of an issue as against the "left." [16]

His theory of cellular pathology was important to Virchow, as it seemed to show objectively in the human body a situation he strove for and regarded as "natural" in society.[17] Just as the theory of the "internal milieu" seemed to Claude Bernard an answer to his philosophical as well as his physiological problems, just as Darwinism seemed to Marx the biological foundation of his sociology, thus cellular pathology was to Virchow far more than a biological theory. His political and biological opinions reinforced each other mutually at this point. Cellular pathology showed the body to be a free state of equal individuals,[18] a federation of cells,[19] a democratic cell state.[20] It showed it as a social unit composed of equals, while an undemocratic [21] oligarchy [22] of tissues was assumed in humoral, or solidistic (neuro) pathology. Just as Virchow fought in politics for the rights of the "third estate," thus in cellular pathology he fought for a "third estate" of cells (connective tissue) not duly recognized in their value and function.[23] Is it a mere accident that we have moved away simultaneously from the ideas of the independence of the cell in the body and of the individual in society?

Although Virchow's political opinions on democracy preceded in time his medical opinions on the "democracy of cells," in terms of the hierarchy of sciences he put medicine and physiology into the first rank. "The last task of medicine is the constitution of society on a physiological basis." [24] "Although verbally medicine is only the art of healing, it has always been, and was bound to be the task of scientific medicine to contain the unified science of man." [25]

If we examine in the light of these quotations the two famous slogans of Virchow, "Medicine is a social science, and politics nothing else but medicine on a large scale," [26] and "The physicians are the natural attorneys of the poor, and the social problems should largely be solved by them," [27] we immediately realize that they do not mean exactly the same as our present-day claim that "medicine is a social science." They actually mean that *social science is a subdivision of medicine,* which is "the highest form of human insight." This latter idea was widespread among French hygienists of the 1820's—like Fodéré, Marc, Rostan, Georget, Réveillé-Parise, and Virey—whose work was known to Virchow and his friends in the medical reform movement like S. Neumann and Leubuscher. (The latter translated, for example, Calmeil's book on the historical implications of mental disease.) It was equally accepted by Saint-Simon, one of the founders of social science. It was first suggested by Descartes and later developed by Cabanis, the spiritual father of the French clinical school and of French novelists like Stendhal and Flaubert. It is based on the assumption that the knowledge of physical man brings about automatically the knowledge and understanding of psychological and social man.

Only through A. Comte our present ideas on the particular nature of social science have developed. This older concept of medicine as the "mother of the social sciences" [28] (which historically she was to a certain extent through W. Petty, Quesnay, Villermé, and Buchez) was an important stimulus and moral reassurance for medical men to participate in social movements and politics. [29] Virchow's continual attempts to derive ethics from the biological sciences [30] and to make the latter the basis of public school education are only other consequences of this fundamental approach. [31]

Virchow, born into a generation of reformers, was a reformer himself. He preferred the expression "reformer" to "revolutionary," as it seemed to him the better characterization for the combination of destruction and construction, of criticism and respect for past accomplishments which he stood for. That his "reform" would occasionally not abstain from revolutionary means is evidenced by his behavior in 1848.

He tried to define his general goal as "humanism" or "anthropology."

The claim of humanism is to explore the nature of man, and to give to the individual the largest possible opportunities for natural development. From this certain consequences do stem for public and private life, for the education and handling of people, therefore also for therapeutics and prophylaxis.[32]

The basis of humanism is natural science, its proper expression anthropology.[33]

This anthropology was, of course, much more than the technical subject Virchow was to cultivate later under the same name. It was the "total empirical science of man," incorporating even philosophy. The unrest of his days would come to an end only when all had accepted "the cosmopolitan point of view, the point of view of a humane, scientific policy, the point of view of Anthropology or Physiology (in its largest sense)." [34]

In groping for a characteristic label for his endeavors, Virchow often chose the phrase "method of the natural sciences." This method implied criticism of, freedom from, and fight against, mere authority. Virchow was critical by temperament, by being a reformer, and by being a pathologist. He had "that critical turn of mind that characterizes pathologists more than any other group," [35] and that had been conspicuous already with Morgagni. Freedom and freedom of science were values he continually emphasized.[36] The "method of the natural sciences" implied, on the other hand, the absolute respect for the impersonal laws of nature,[37] which were to him the true miracles of nature.[38]

To bring medicine and the natural sciences together again

after the aberrations of the romantic "natural philosophers" and "natural historians" was his ever-repeated goal since his 1845 speeches. The method of natural sciences was eventually to become the method of the nation.[39] His period was to be the period of "natural science," his school the school of "natural science." In reading Virchow one cannot always escape the impression that in a way he claimed a monopoly for himself and his school on the "method of the natural sciences." [40] This was, to say the least, an exaggeration. This method had been long before the watchword of his teacher Johannes Mueller, of all pupils of Mueller (Traube and Henle included), of Rokitansky, of Wunderlich and Griesinger, not to speak of foreign authors like Magendie.

Virchow's actual definitions of this magic method are rare and short. Often it is identified merely with "autopsy" (in the wider sense of direct observation). In 1855 he summarized it as "criticism of formulas and systems, positive empirical experience, emancipation of pathology and therapeutics from auxiliary sciences, authority of facts, right of the individual, domination of natural laws." [41] Obviously one of the main elements of this message was the often repeated "this is not the time of systems; this is the time of research of details." [42] It is not that synthesis and hypothesis were by him entirely read out of science, as they had been by the French empiricists; [43] but emphasis was and remained, especially as far as the training of pupils was concerned, on research of details.

It is consistent with Virchow's total approach that, ever since his 1845 speeches and the programmatic articles of the first volume of the *Archives,* he was opposed to the notion of "pure science." Science had to be useful. It was even one of his main arguments against the three competing schools of Wunderlich, Rokitansky, and Henle that they were "neither helpful nor even concerned about the good of the people." [44] Henle retorted by calling Virchow "one of these modern mob-courtiers." He would be avenged by Klebs and Behring, who used the utilitarian argument against Virchow in the 1880's and 1890's. Of the three adversaries of Virchow, actually only Rokitansky upheld the position of "pure science." [45]

Philosophically speaking, Virchow was and remained a "sensualist." [46] He started from the assumption which, since Locke, Condillac, and Cabanis, has guided so many medical scientists—that sense impressions are the primary elements of mental life. Virchow started as a mechanist and antivitalist pure and undiluted. This is witnessed by the title and contents of his 1845 speech. ("Life is but the expression of a sum of phenomena, each of which follows the ordinary physical and chemical [that is mechanic] laws. We deny the existence of an autocratic vital or healing force.") He was then completely in tune with the antivitalism of such contemporaries as H. Lotze, M. J. Schleiden, E. du Bois–Reymond,[47] with his whole generation which in 1886 he himself characterized as the generation of the "mechanical analysis of nature." [48]

This mechanistic attitude explains his great early interest in "pathological chemistry." [49] As a matter of fact, it is in this field that he first acquired a reputation. The University of Zuerich considered appointing him in 1849 for his accomplishments in pathological chemistry, not microscopy! [50] As much as he might repudiate the encroachment of chemists into medicine, it is through chemistry that he first tried to solve the fundamental problems of biology: even if it were possible to make the blood or the nervous system the seat of special life-phenomena, *the catalytic movement would still remain as something higher and more general above nerve and blood.*" [51] Even when Virchow himself was no longer active in chemistry, his interest remained strong enough to make him, if not the father, at least the "grandfather" of modern biochemistry in Germany through Hoppe-Seyler and other pupils. In 1885 he made the remarkable statement concerning bacteriology: "This originally purely botanical problem becomes more and more a chemical one." [52] He also remained always on the lookout for a chemical theory of tumors.

It is a corollary to his mechanistic attitude that in earlier years he scorned the notion of "cellular force," [53] assimilated cell formation to crystallization,[54] adumbrated a general law equally applicable to star formation, crystallization, cell formation, and formation of the psyche.[55]

This changed when Virchow began to elaborate his cellular pathology. In the first article where he suggests this theory he also talks about his *new vitalism* (A, IV [1852], 377). It was not long and the romantic "life force" was back on the job too.[56] Now, of course, the comparison of cell and crystal formation became impossible.[57] The cell theory was no longer a mechanical but became a biological theory.[58] Only a few, like Rindfleisch and G. Bunge, followed Virchow on this vitalist road.

Virchow's change from mechanism to neovitalism was not the only change brought about in his general positions by the formulation of cellular pathology. Like the rest of his generation he opposed "ontology," a tendency to see in diseases organism-like entities instead of mere mental constructs.[59] Ontology, according to Virchow, was only preached by those who were fond of authoritarian systems! [60] Ontology had taken in German romantic medicine special forms, so far only known from primitives or Paracelsus. The German medical rebels who preceded Virchow in the early 1840's had taken their clues against ontology from the French, especially Broussais. The latter had fought in the second decade of the century a much more rational form of ontology, that of Pinel, derived from Sydenham. Virchow's earlier writings are full of polemics against ontological reasoning. Now cellular pathology suggested to Virchow not only a new vitalism but also a new ontology. The cell became the Paracelsian "body of disease," [61] and by 1895 Virchow found it appropriate to tie up cellular pathology directly with the Paracelsian-romantic brainstorms:

This opinion is clearly ontological. It is its virtue not its fault. There is really an *ens morbi,* just as there is an *ens vitae.* In both cases it is a cell or a cell complex that deserve this name. The *ens morbi* is also the parasite of the natural history school.[62]

While we can very well see today the untenable position of the pure "anti-ontologists," it is hard to understand why Virchow felt compelled to relapse into the antiquated formulas of romanticism. It would be, on the other hand, a misunderstanding to make Virchow an all-out romantic on the basis of such quotations. He came closer to the romantics in his older days, but in many respects he remained faithful to the mechanistic and anti-ontological ideas and prejudices of his youth and generation.

Virchow, like his whole generation, gave a "physiological" definition of disease. He taught all his life that disease is nothing qualitatively different from life, that it is only "life under changed conditions." [63] Disease is a vital process. In general he traced this idea back to Boerhaave and Gaub. He gave J. F. Meckel the credit he undoubtedly deserves. He might have gone as far back as Servetus and Fernel or even the Hippocratic treatise "On Ancient Medicine," or have mentioned the very obvious fact that this idea had already been effectively promoted by the French (for example, Bichat, Magendie, Broussais). Yet in one of his occasional paroxysms of nationalistic blindness he once even made the very unsubstantiated claim that this was a "German idea" and the French and English had not even a word for the disease process.[64] This is not without piquancy when one remembers that in his early criticism of Rokitansky he had (rightly) accused the latter of somewhat ungenerously hiding his indebtedness to the general concepts of Laennec, Cruveilhier, and Magendie.

Virchow had no use for teleology in pathology: "The teleological purists were always forced to go back to original sin,* without finding this way much recognition." [65]

We found Virchow to be an agnostic as early as 1845. Although he had nothing but scorn for transcendentalism, he never advanced beyond agnosticism into philosophical materialism.

Faith cannot be argued in scientific terms; both are mutually exclusive. Not that the one makes the other impossible or vice versa, but within the limits of science there is no faith, and faith can begin only where science ends. It cannot be denied that, if these limits are respected, faith can have real objects. It is therefore not the task of science to attack the objects of faith. It should only mark the limits

* To make disease the result of original sin had actually been the scientific contribution of such romantic physicians as Windischmann, Heinroth, Leupoldt, and Ringseis.

which can be reached by human understanding and establish within these limits a unified consciousness.[66]

He attributes this attitude to the influence of Kant, who had so clearly shown the limitations of human insight.[67]

There was another German philosopher who left a less acknowledged, but no less deep, imprint on Virchow—Hegel. It is true that Virchow had no use for Hegel's idealism; he repudiated Hegel's school too because it had given up only the idealistic principles, but not the speculative method.[68] He was perhaps not even conscious of the fact that—like so many of his anti-Hegelian contemporaries, like a Marx, a Klencke, a Feuerbach—he was all the more deeply affected by Hegel's other invention, dialectics. Neither his style, especially in his 1848 articles,* nor his continual operating with antitheses (like science-practice, vitalistic-mechanistic, humoral-solidistic) that are "resolved" by his "syntheses" (cellular pathology or pathological physiology) leaves any doubt in this direction.

Virchow regarded early as one of the main difficulties for going beyond agnosticism the fact that human consciousness is scientifically incomprehensible.[69] In his discussions of agnosticism he anticipated to a large extent Du Bois–Reymond's famous arguments of the "limits of natural science" (1872) and the "seven world riddles" (1880). Virchow wanted, therefore, philosophically rather to be called a "realist" than a "materialist." [70] It might not be without interest to mention here that Rokitansky was a straight philosophical idealist, strongly influenced by Schopenhauer, as was, by the way, Virchow's rebellious pupil E. Klebs.

Before raising the banner of "cellular pathology," Virchow tried to characterize his goal as "pathological physiology." The expression seems to occur first in Portal; it can be found in Bichat, Corvisart, and Magendie.[71] It was quite common in

---

* In 1847 (A, II [1849], 6) he says directly, "It is as if this age of peace, which negates itself in order to deliver from its entrails the social reformation, wants to confirm the paradox of the philosopher that the being comes into being through negation." On the "dissolution of antitheses in a higher synthesis," see *Vier Reden ueber Leben and Kranksein*, p. 33, and *ibid.*, p. 60, on Hegel.

French medical literature in the 1830's, perhaps as an aftermath of Broussais' teaching. It gained wider circulation in Germany only in the 1840's with medical reformers like Wunderlich. Herman Lebert, whose influence on Virchow is undeniable, published his *Physiologie pathologique* in 1845. Although technically a pathological anatomist, Virchow, unlike the Paris school, fully realized the limitations of pathological anatomy and the impossibility of basing pathology, the science of disease, exclusively on pathological anatomy.[72] This separated him from Rokitansky who, though using too the expression "pathological physiology," was primarily a pathological anatomist continuing the Paris tradition of Laennec, Cruveilhier, and Louis. Virchow saw a connection between this latter attitude and the therapeutic nihilism of the Vienna school, which he repudiated. Virchow felt that the notion of "pathological physiology" also separated him from the "physiological medicine" of Wunderlich and Griesinger and the "rational medicine" of Henle and Pfeufer.[73] He was closer to the truth when he occasionally admitted that no difference of principle existed between the three groups.[74] Wunderlich's studies on temperature changes in disease are perhaps more literally "pathological physiology" than anything Virchow ever did. Varied personalities and the spirit of "free competition" were carried by all participants into the discussions of these three groups, which, in spite of their differences, we now all group together under the heading of "physiological medicine" [75] or "laboratory medicine." [76] German particularism—the antagonism between Prussia, southern Germany, and Austria—gave these matters a good deal of their special and not very pleasant flavor.

Pathology, according to Virchow, should be autonomous and develop primarily out of itself.[77] It should use all sciences, but not become subservient to any single one—as it would be to gross pathological anatomy with Rokitansky, to histology with Henle, to chemistry with Liebig, or to physiology with Wunderlich. It should become a biological science itself. It should be based on a combination of clinical observation and animal experiment (Report of 1846), or a combination of clinical ob-

servation, animal experiment, and necropsy (Address of 1845).*
Therefore Virchow and Reinhardt's *Archives* were not called
Archives of Pathological Anatomy, but *Archives of Pathological
Anatomy and Physiology, and Clinical Medicine.* As the pros-
pectus of 1846 said, practical medicine should become applied
theoretical medicine, and theoretical medicine should become
pathological physiology. This goal was never entirely forgotten.
As long as Virchow lived, the *Archives* still carried a number
of clinical and therapeutic contributions. Virchow's programmatic article in the first number of the *Archives* ended:

Pathological Physiology is to be a fortress of which pathological
anatomy and the clinic are only the forts.

Pathology or pathological physiology was thus to be the ultimate synthesis of scientific medicine:

It is not an esoteric science that runs besides medical practice like
a little doggy that gives joy and pleasure to his master in the latter's
idle hours. In looking for the eternal laws of organic life it belongs
to the innermost nucleus and essence of medical knowledge.[78]

Virchow's earlier work (for example, that on thrombosis and
embolism) was largely experimental and followed rather
closely the lines of this program. As to providing the general
formulas for which Virchow was looking, it was not very effective. In his 1849 attempt, for instance, to bridge the contradictions between solidistic and humoral pathology, Virchow had
nothing more specific to say than that "the whole life" should
be taken into consideration.[79]

Virchow placed great stock on the "genetic principle," to him
an essentially German idea.[80] This implies the use of embryology as well as the analysis of pathological data as processes.

When Virchow appeared on the scene, "pathological microscopy" was nothing new; according to Virchow himself, it had
been used already too widely and so badly that it began to fall
in discredit.[81] Nevertheless, Virchow strongly urged the use of
microscopy from the very beginning, not so much as a diag-

* This is, by the way, also the approach of Bichat (*Anatomie générale.*
I, v) or of Lebert (Introduction to *Physiologie pathologique*).

nostic panacea, but as one of the means to gain new insights into the pathological process.[82]

It is necessary to advance our opinions to the same extent that our ability to see has increased through the microscope: the whole of medicine must come 300 times closer to the natural processes.[83]

Yet microscopy was to become much more to him than just one technique of pathological physiology among others. It proved to be the avenue toward his new system of cellular pathology, which has dominated pathology far into the twentieth century. He and his school were to turn more and more from physiology and experiment toward morphology and microscopical pathology. Of all his pupils, only Cohnheim was overwhelmingly an experimentalist and even seems to have exhibited a somewhat scornful attitude toward pure morphology.[84]

Virchow insisted, of course, that cellular pathology was not a system, only a method (as did Karl Marx for "historical materialism"). The notion of systems was so discredited by this time that he could hardly do otherwise. Compared to older systems, it was undoubtedly far more realistic and far more elastic, which made for its longevity. In its all-embracing aspirations, which correspond to a profound and ever-recurring need of human thought, cellular pathology bears nevertheless all the earmarks of a system. When Virchow developed his cellular pathology, which will be discussed in detail in later chapters, he followed the same romantic urge toward synthesis that had led Rokitansky ten years before to construct his pseudochemical system of "crases." Virchow showed greater discrimination and better luck in resting his synthesis on a less basic, but more tangible and far better developed common denominator—cellular histology.

Had Virchow remained faithful to his older antisystematic theories and to his slogan "details first," as did his pupils and for that matter most medical men of the second half of the nineteenth century, as he did himself in his completely atomized anthropological work, he would never have created cellular pathology. Virchow was a mechanist and a modernist. But he had also grown up in the shadows of German medical romanticisms which cultivated systematic aspirations at a time when in France, for example, such aspirations had ceased to be respectable. Most of Virchow's teachers were romantics or ex-romantics and Virchow was therefore familiar with medical romanticism. Thus in 1852 his romantic background was still strong enough to make him strive through details toward one basic, all-embracing principle.

Walter Pagel, the son of the great German medical historian Julius Pagel and an outstanding medical historian in his own right,[85] has the merit of having first examined this rather unexpected romantic background of the antiromantic Virchow.[86] Paul Diepgen has criticized Pagel's work by raising different more or less relevant questions of detail.[87] In "discovering" that synthetic movements existed in medicine before romanticism, Mr. Diepgen has missed the most essential historical issue of the whole argument: that *at the time when Virchow created his cellular pathology the striving for synthesis was in medicine a romantic trait and survival.* It is only through recognizing this fact that we can understand why Virchow, through the inner logic of his synthesis, was as a medical theorist closer to the romantics in his later than he had been in his earlier years. It can only thus be understood why, in spite of the application of what seemed to be the same principles, Virchow created a synthesis, while those who took such pronouncements literally or, being younger, had no romantic background created none. How much the finding of cellular pathology satisfied Virchow's synthetic urge is evident from the fact that after 1858 general editorials (up to then a regular feature) almost disappear from the *Archives.*

Virchow had already in his 1845 address called the cell the fundamental unit of life. But as long as he was an adherent of the cellular theory of Schwann, which regarded the amorphous blastema as the forerunner of the cell, this was a rather inconsequential statement. Others (for example, Donné, Lebert, Klencke, Julius Vogel, J. H. Bennett, A. H. Hassall, Johannes Mueller and his pupils Henle, Gluge, Gueterbock) had studied pathological changes in cells before him, under the premises of Schwann's blastema theory. Virchow's main discovery was actually not a pathological, but a biological one. The really new thing in Virchow's "cellular pathology" was not the reduction of pathology to cells, but the reversal of Schwann's blastema theory through empirical work, on a much broader basis than it had been done by John Goodsir or Koelliker and Remak, and the creation of a new cell theory (*omnis cellula a cellula—* each cell stems from another cell). On the basis of this new cell theory he then transformed the study of pathological changes of the cell into a system.

Tremendous progress in scientific medicine was brought about by this system, which is still basic to much of our medical thinking. In order to appreciate its value, one has but to realize that up to this time people had still thought of disease primarily as either an affection of the blood or the nervous system. Every symptom had been ultimately interpreted in this direction. That its great successes made the Germans and their pupils largely identify "pathology" and "pathological anatomy" is obvious through a comparison with French and English medicine. There the clinic remained more independent, physiology the more important medical science; and there "pathology" retained therefore a larger meaning. That like all systems cellular pathology had certain inherent dangers was seen clearly by some of Virchow's contemporary critics. There is some truth in Spiess's prediction that cellular pathology would mean a turn from physiology and mechanism to anatomy and vitalism.[88] Wunderlich's fears of a new dogmatism and a "renaissance of the poison of empty phrases and romanticism"[89] were not entirely unfounded. Virchow defeated his critics nevertheless with relative ease as in general they had nothing to offer but criticism, while he would compensate for his shortcomings through all his tremendous contributions.

Since his 1845 address Virchow had held it proven that spontaneous generation did not exist. Obviously this conviction would move him almost automatically into the direction of *omnis cellula a cellula.* An equally important early conditioning towards the finding of cellular pathology was Virchow's pronounced simultaneous belief in localism. "We want to localize everything."[90] "A substance, even when absorbed into the blood stream, is pathologically irrelevant as long as it does not affect an organ." [91] It was the early localism of Broussais that made Virchow say a good word for the old systematist [92] when the latter was no longer regarded as scientifically "respectable." * Virchow adhered to localism at a time when he was still believing in dyscrasias [93] and blastemas.[94] His localism was more sophisticated than that of Rokitansky insofar as he realized that not every local pathological disturbance might leave an anatomical lesion.[95] Virchow's insistence on localism made him paradoxically enough one of the driving forces toward modern specialization, which he so wholeheartedly disliked.

That in his early period Virchow gave much thought to therapeutics is reflected in the first two volumes of the *Archives*. Therapeutic nihilism was incompatible with his active approach. What is the good of medicine, if it does not try to cure? This attitude prevented him from drawing "nihilistic" conclusions from the physiological concept of diseases, as many others did. He realized that at the given stage of science therapeutics had to be developed primarily out of direct therapeutic experience, had to be empirical. This approach even made him show some sympathy and understanding for Rademacher's radical neo-Paracelsian empiricism. His rejection of disease-specific therapy was consistent with his physiological, anti-ontological concepts.[96] He believed, on the other hand, in the existence of organ-specific drugs.[97] This made him say: "Everywhere we have to attack the specificists, and yet we hope for the specific." [98]

In the Preface to his *Handbook* Virchow proudly acknowledged his "mistake" to believe in therapeutics. His numerous actual therapeutic suggestions in the *Handbook* are not worthwhile enough to be discussed in detail. Even occasional horrors are not missing.[99] Behring was right to tag his therapeutics as "radical symptomatic." But nobody had anything but symptomatic treatments to offer in the 1840's and 1850's.

Virchow believed strongly in the "specificity" of the indi-

* The influence of Broussais on Virchow was actually a much larger one and is easily detected (e.g., in Virchow's ideas concerning ontology, irritation, phthisis, physiological medicine, etc.). See also *H*, I, 50 and 63.

vidual patient, in the "mysterium of individuality." He therefore advocated individualizing treatment, the much-maligned
"practical tact." [100] He realized that the importance of the practical tact was indirect proof that therapeutics was no exact
science yet, even no science at all.[101]

Virchow's therapeutic ideas never developed beyond the
generalizing stage. His original program was too wide to be
fully realized even by a man of his breadth and dynamism. In
later years therapeutics was rarely mentioned. He consoled
himself with the tremendous progress in surgery that had been
stimulated by cellular pathology, and with the progress of
prophylaxis—so common a consolation with therapeutic skep-
tics or nihilisits. "What we lose in reliability of our curative
agents [through critical scientific analysis] we win through a
more complete knowledge of our health-preserving agents,
through better prophylaxis, hygiene and dietetics." [102]

Pathological Physiology

WHEN VIRCHOW started independent scientific research in 1844,
his teacher Froriep charged him to check the statement of the
then leading French pathologist Cruveilheir, "Phlebitis dominates all pathology" ("La phlébite domine toute la pathologie"). This idea that originated with John Hunter must be
seen against the background of the average autopsic material
of that time, when a high percentage of hospital cases of any
type of surgical operation or complicated fracture, even of
ordinary childbirth or venesection, would turn up in the autopsy room riddled with abscesses, their veins filled with infected disintegrating thrombi.

Such an assignment corresponded well with Virchow's
mental make-up. Among scientific discoverers two extreme
types may be identified. (The types of the majority are, of
course, "mixed.") The one type shows little interest in polemics
and rather sets out into uncharted regions to dig out new facts

from virgin soil; the other takes up previous work and, in criticizing it, finds clues for new discoveries. To call the latter type less "creative" than the former is an arbitrary assertion of people who do not like criticism. Virchow definitely belonged to the second, "critical" type of discoverers. The task of challenging the leading French pathologists attracted him the more as it involved also a critical examination of the pet theories of the leading Austrian pathologist Rokitansky on inflammatory exudation as the basic pathological process.

Virchow approached his problem in a very thorough, and what often seemed roundabout way; yet when he published his results in 1845 and 1846,* not much was left of phlebitis as the queen of pathology. He first made it his task to examine coagulation and its substratum fibrin. The obvious reason for this choice was that he wanted first to gain full understanding of the coagula, or thrombi, so prominent in phlebitis. A second, less obvious reason was that the "fiber" had been regarded since Erasistratus (and even more so since Fallopius, Glisson, and Haller) as the basic structural and functional element of the organism, even by those who occasionally had seen "cells." [1] The still very prevalent therapeutic habit of bloodletting continually drew attention to fibrin, the supposed source of fibers. John Hunter had made fibrin the "actual stuff of life." To examine this "stuff" again in the light of the cellular theory (then not even ten years old) with improved microscopes and chemicals seemed worth the effort.

Morphologically Virchow confirmed the results of those who claimed that the fibrin coagulum was originally not fibrous but homogenous, and that "fibers" in clots were either artefacts of the microscopists or the result of later unequal contraction. He demonstrated that no "corpuscles" were formed in coagulation; the accused corpuscles were found also in blood maintained liquid through addition of neutral salts. These results were im-

---

* Virchow himself published all his earlier work (insofar as it had not appeared in the *Archives*) in his *Gesammelte Abhandlungen zur wissenschaftlichen Medizin* of 1856. He could very well have called the volume *Essays in Pathological Physiology*. Specific points in the following can therefore easily be looked up by the interested and reference footnotes have been kept at a minimum.

portant, as they largely negated the then existing theories of tissue formation, notably the "blastema" theory. (See pp. 11 and 82.)

Coagulation was not a "vital," but a "physical" phenomenon. (This term "physical" includes in the technical language of the time our notion of chemical.) The one outstanding physical property of fibrin was its elasticity. Its viscosity had been much exaggerated. Adhesion of fibrin, for instance, to the valves of the heart was not due to its viscosity but primarily to ulceration of the surface.

Extensive chemical analysis of fibrin by others and by Virchow yielded no more definite results than that fibrin was a polypeptid. Its presence could not be shown chemically, but only by actual coagulation. Virchow opposed the attempts to "complete" clinical or anatomical disease pictures by the discussion of fictitious chemical blood changes, as Rokitansky had done. On the basis of numerous experiments Virchow demonstrated that the existence of fibrin, the "stuff of life," in muscles or other cells, especially of the blood, was totally unproven. He was far ahead of his time in interpreting the frequent formation of the buffy coat on coagula in inflammation, especially tuberculosis, by an increased sedimentation rate of the erythrocytes, a mechanism which we have learned to use prognostically in these conditions.[2]

Attempts to analyze chemically the decomposition products of fibrin did not give any more definite results. Virchow disagreed with the notion that there were different kinds of fibrin. When it came to coagulation, it was always the same fibrin. But he suggested in 1847 (A, I, 381) that most of the fibrin in the body was actually *fibrinogen*, a term which we have retained although with a slightly changed meaning. Fibrinogen was probably activated by oxygen. It was probably formed in the lymphatic and connective tissues; therefore in the case of inflammation formed locally, according to Virchow, it could not penetrate the intact walls of vessels.

These first studies of Virchow show, not only his own extensive interests in blood chemistry, but an even far more extensive chemical interest on the part of his medical contemporaries. We must not forget that with Rokitansky and Andral humoral pathology was again dominant, and blood chemistry therefore seemed to hold the key of pathology. The meager data on increase or decrease of fibrin in certain diseases (so-called hyperinosis and hypinosis) had been made the basis of a whole medical system of "crases" or "dyscrasias." This humoral pathology, which like the simultaneous anticontagionism looks now so "medieval" to us, appeared to contemporaries as ultra-modern, progressive, and scientific. The exertions of medical men in blood chemistry decreased rapidly around 1850 through Virchow's own success in re-establishing solidistic pathology. Most of the organic chemists gave up blood chemistry in despair because of its complexity at about the same time. Only the 1870's saw a renaissance of these studies.[3]

Virchow's first direct studies on "phlebitis" were those on obstruction of the pulmonary artery, published in 1845, 1846, and 1847. (Virchow continued to experiment and publish in this field up to 1856.) The obstruction of branches of the pulmonary artery by thrombi was interpreted by Virchow's contemporaries as a local phlebitis.[4] Virchow now made his first great discovery in showing that the thrombi in the lung had nothing to do with a local phlebitis—that they had not been formed there, but were parts of thrombi, mostly from the veins of the lower extremities and the pelvis, that had been torn loose and transported by the blood stream. He showed from his autopsic material that such transportation of thrombi into the lung took place in six out of ten cases of extensive local thrombosis. The "riding" of the thrombus over the ostia of two vessels, the absence of thrombi in smaller peripheral vessels or capillaries confirmed his hypothesis. He named this new pathological phenomenon, discovered by him, *embolism*. In many cases he could demonstrate where the thrombus had been torn off. This happened with particular frequency when the thrombus grew from a smaller into a larger vessel and started softening. He showed how thrombi differed in structure from ordinary coagula and studied their history, which ends either in decomposition or organization (vascularization and canalization). The "mechanical" symptoms would vary from sudden death to dyspnea to no symptoms whatsoever. The "chemical" consequences would depend on the nature of the embolus and could be atrophy of lung tissue, pneumonia, gangrene, or infarction.

In a large series of experiments on dogs Virchow was able to produce pulmonary embolism artificially by inserting fibrin, coagula, muscle, elder marrow, and rubber into the subclavian vein. To his great surprise the foreign bodies, or thrombi, arising from them passed through the right heart without symptoms. All his material, except the rubber, being contaminated, inflammation and necrosis of the lung would appear after embolism in his experimental animals; whereas it was absent in most of his human cases that had bland emboli. The gruesome developments in Virchow's case histories as well as in his experimental animals illustrate the dangers of pre-antiseptic surgical techniques.

Pulmonary parts behind his bland rubber emboli were, to his surprise, not anemic, but hyperemic. This hyperemia was, according to Virchow, due to collateral circulation from the bronchial artery.

Virchow attributed death in pulmonary embolism to arrest of coronary circulation. He also experimented with embolism by injection of air, fat, starch, and mercury.

On this occasion Virchow dismissed the supposedly newly formed "inflammation cells" as mere degenerating epithelia, an apparently minor but very consequential observation in regard to cellular theory. The assumption of inflammation cells formed from amorphous material was an orthodox application of Schwann's then dominant "blastema" theory. Virchow's observation reversed the whole sequence.

After eliminating thus a whole group of so-called "phlebitis," Virchow tackled the problem of arterial inflammation, a favored cover-all of German and Austrian pathologists, and pursued it by clinical, autopsic, and experimental studies. He showed (thus invalidating Rokitansky) that in arterial or endocardial inflammation no exudate was formed on the inner wall, but through slowing of the bloodstream or endoarteritic change of the wall thrombi would be formed, which again could give rise to embolism. Total obstruction of a small artery was usually due to embolism. Virchow demonstrated arterial embolism in the brain, eye, etc., mostly in cases of endocarditis.

Virchow did not deny the existence of phlebitis or "phlogosis" (inflammation) of blood vessels in general, but he believed that in most cases the primary condition was not the inflammation but a mechanical event—the formation of the thrombus, which he called *thrombosis*.* Virchow inherited from Laennec the mechanical explanation of thrombus formation on the basis of a slowing bloodstream. Only a certain percentage of thromboses would ever turn into phlogoses through infection of the thrombus. A primary phlogosis with secondary thrombosis was very rare.

Thrombosis was for him due primarily to the slowing down of the blood stream. The seven main forms of thrombosis were: marantic thrombosis, thrombosis due to compression, thrombosis due to dilatation of the vessel, traumatic thrombosis (especially in venesection and amputation), (physiological) thrombosis in the newborn, (physiological) thrombosis in the puerpera, and secondary thrombosis through inflammation of the wall of the vessel.

Phlebitis had been of overwhelming interest to medical scientists as the starting point of pyemia, an all too common condition. Virchow showed that the white cells in disintegrating thrombi were not newly formed "pus cells," but pre-existing leucocytes. Pus cells in the inflamed tissue surrounding the vessels could enter the circulation only in the rare cases when the wall of the vessel was damaged. Only in these cases one could legitimately speak of "pyemia" (pus in the blood). It was impossible to speak of pyemia only on the basis of the presence of "pus cells" in the blood because the latter could not be differentiated from leucocytes. (It was not clear at that time that they were not only morphologically but also genetically identical.)

Whereas a number of pathological phenomena, classified

* The modern concept of phlebothrombosis seems a revival of this concept of Virchow.

up to that time as either phlebitis or pyemia, had been accounted for by Virchow through the mechanical means of embolism and as derived from thrombosis, there was another important group which he regarded as a chemical disturbance, "ichorrhemia" (this neologism of Virchow did not stick), or as an infection (that is, a toxic contamination of the blood, our modern septicemia). The grave symptoms of "pyemia" and the fatal results could be thus observed clinically and produced experimentally without the presence of either phlebitis or pus. Virchow's experiments followed here the earlier attempts of Magendie.

With the various roles attributed to white cells in phlebitis, the main subject of his early studies, it is obvious that Virchow should closely watch these bodies, which up to Ehrlich's invention of specific dyes were very elusive. This particular attention was rewarded by a discovery that was to open up a whole new field of pathology. In 1845 Virchow made the autopsy of a fifty-year-old female cook who had suffered from splenomegaly and epistaxis. The blood looked "white" because, as the microscope showed, the proportion between white and red corpuscles was reversed. Virchow recognized immediately that the condition was a particular disease, "white blood," not a "pyemia" as it was claimed by Lautner and J. H. Bennett, the able Edinburgh microscopist and pupil of Donné, who had made a similar observation at about the same time. Virchow came to his conclusion because the clinical picture resembled in no way "pyemia." It was gratuitious to call the corpuscles "pus cells," as microscopically "pus cells" and leucocytes were not distinguishable. Eventually "pus cells" or leucocytes could, according to Virchow, not penetrate the wall of vessels (a pet error of Virchow, corrected by his pupil F. Cohnheim in 1867,* which in this case helped him to find the truth). In 1847 (A, I, 563) the anti-ontologist, who through history's irony had

---

* Diapedesis had been seen by Dutrochet in 1824, M. Barry in 1841, Waller in 1846, W. Addison in 1849, and Zimmermann in 1852; but only Cohnheim's results found recognition. W. Addison also published a *Cellular Therapy* in 1856.

discovered a new disease entity, named the new disease "leukemia."

Virchow realized that in numerous pathological and physiological conditions a more limited increase of leucocytes took place, which he called "leucocytosis." He showed how leucocytosis could be demonstrated in the buffy coat of the coagulum. He felt that determination of leucocytes in a given disease would be more relevant than the chemical fibrin analyses of his time.[5] In 1846 when the leading German text in microscopical pathology by J. Vogel did not even mention leucocytes, Virchow wrote: "I vindicate for the leucocytes a place in pathology." [6]

Experience with new cases enabled Virchow in 1847 to differentiate the splenic and the lymphatic forms of leukemia and the two kinds of leucocytes involved respectively. Virchow believed disturbances in the spleen and lympathic glands, perhaps also in the liver, to cause the disease. Extensive chemical analyses of leukemia (A, V [1853], 43 ff.) remained unproductive.

In 1849 (A, II, 594) Virchow described "melanemia," confirming an observation of H. Meckel of 1847 concerning the occurrence of a dark pigment in unidentified blood corpuscles. Virchow suspected a connection between the condition and intermittent fever (malaria), but further examinations of old intermittens cases failed to show the phenomenon. Only the discovery of the malaria plasmodium in the erythrocyte by Laveran in 1880 explained Meckel's and Virchow's observations and confirmed the latter's hunch.

Some early studies of which Virchow was very proud, probably because of their chemical character, and which are now completely forgotten are his 1846 papers on "Uric Acid Excretion in the Fetus and the Newborn." Schlossberger had described in 1842 the so-called uric acid infarction of infants between the second and nineteenth days of life, when the epithelial channels of the kidney were filled with the crystallized salts of uric acid. He regarded the phenomenon as the result of intestinal affections. Virchow confirmed Schlossberger's findings but gave them a very different interpretation and application. During the first days of life a revolution (the term stems from Bichat, another scientist whose terminology was heavily colored by his time) takes place in the body of the newborn with extensive decomposition of blood elements. The increased excretion of uric acid is one expression of this revolution, just as the icterus neonatorum is another one. Uric acid infarction is a valuable sign in forensic medicine insofar as its presence proves that the infant has lived. If uric acid infarction takes place prematurely in fetal life, it brings about hydrops renalis, a form of cystic kidney. If in such infants the question of infanticide arises, it can be safely stated that they were not viable.

These early papers of Virchow reveal an unusual gift of observation, a phenomenal memory for retaining details of old observations and autopsies, an ability to remember them at the right moment, a very sharp logic, an extraordinary familiarity with the older and the contemporary international medical literature, and an unlimited willingness to attack and criticize statements no matter by whom they were made.

Virchow's interest in the chemical aspects of pathology was by no means limited to his years in Berlin. It still continued throughout the Wuerzburg period. These results can be found only in the *Archives* and are not incorporated into the *Gesammelte Abhandlungen*. In 1851 Virchow gave a first report on corpora amylacea (found by Purkinje in the brain) and on what he called *amyloid* formations in kidneys and ovaries, mostly summarizing the work of others.[7] In 1853 he was able to find color reactions that made it possible to identify and differentiate both bodies. The corpora amylacea would become blue under iodine, and purple, like cellulose, when sulfuric acid was added.[8] The amyloid substances would show a red color under iodine and also turn purple under sulfuric acid.* With his new reaction Virchow was able to identify the strange sago spleen (lardaceous or waxy spleen of others) in chronic cachexias, that had puzzled him for almost a decade,[9] as amy-

* This somewhat primitive method of differentiating tissues by pouring on them all kinds of chemicals had come down from Bichat to Virchow via Johannes Mueller.

loid degeneration. Virchow was still doubtful whether the substance did not contain proteins, although the chemical reaction
induced him to classify it with the carbohydrates. He showed
that amyloid was different from the so-called colloid in thy-
roids, from amylum (Donders), and from cholesterin, with
which it had been identified by H. Meckel.[10] In later papers
Virchow demonstrated its presence in the liver, kidneys, cartilage, the wall of vessels, and lymphatic glands. It was particularly frequent in bone diseases of long duration. He was
undecided whether it was the result of local degeneration or
of infiltration.[11] Virchow's amyloid degeneration is still an important phenomenon. We know more today about its chemical
(protein) character,[12] but the fundamental mechanism of its
formation is still unknown.

In 1854, Virchow described the occurrence of a chemical
substance, which forms the nervous marrow, in the diseased
lung and ovary and in the normal spleen and adrenals. He
called the substance, which we now range with the lecithins,
"myelin." [13] In 1854 he published on alkaline albumines and in
1855 on leucine and tyrosine.[14] In 1857 he started extensive
analyses on the chemistry of the adrenals, which he apparently
never completed.[15]

In omitting all papers referring to cellular problems from his
1856 *Collected Essays,* Virchow probably planned already at
that time a special book summarizing his work in cellular anatomy and physiology. To us his early studies on pathological
pigments, which he obviously regarded as part of his cellular
studies, are so much of a chemical nature that we prefer to
discuss them in this chapter.

In his long article on pathological pigments in the first
volume of the *Archives* (pp. 379 ff.) Virchow differentiated essentially three: colored fats, bile pigment (cholepyrrhin, now
bilirubin) and blood pigment (haematin). The latter, leaving
the erythrocytes, can infiltrate other cells or amorphous materials. It can be found in a diffuse, in a granular (in the typical
pathologically pigmented cell), and sometimes in a crystal-
line state, described by Virchow in unprecedented detail. Its
presence indicates old hemorrhages and extravasations.

Extensive chemical investigation of these pigments was poor in results. How unreliable chemical methods still were is evident from the fact that the presence of iron could not always be ascertained by Virchow in haematin.[16] Pigment crystals derived from haematin nevertheless showed one constant reaction—a color change into green, blue, purple, and red under sulfuric acid—which put them in close chemical vicinity with bile pigment (bilirubin). Virchow named such pigments *haematoidin*.[17] Their identity with bilirubin has been demonstrated since.[18] To Virchow these reactions suggested the derivation of bile pigment from blood pigment and the possibility of what we now call hemolytic icterus. Breschet had first drawn attention to the existence of icterus without disease of the bile ducts.* Black pigment was often the consequence of contact with hydrogen sulfide.

Virchow studied the occurrence of pathological pigments in the Graafian follicle, the spleen, vessels, the brain, and the lung. He described the pigmented epithelia in the lung especially in mitral stenosis, still regarded as pathognomonic, and called the lung condition brown induration.[19] Unlike Natalis Guillot, he did regard the black pigment of the lung as pathological and as a derivative of haematin, not coal.[20] The normal pigment in the uvea and hair was, according to Virchow, probably not derived from haematin. As to the pigments of melanosarcomas and melanocarcinomas, Virchow doubted their connection with haematin, the more as it was alleged by Rokitansky in a somewhat "dogmatic and categoric manner." Virchow, like Remak, denied the formation of cells around agglomerations of erythrocytes, as claimed by Ecker and Koelliker on the basis of the then dominant blastema theories.[21] He thought the erythrocytes had entered the cell after its formation.

The study of pigmented cells convinced Virchow that these

---

* It is characteristic of the change brought about in Virchow's thought by cellular pathology that in 1865 he almost regretted these statements and tried to replace them by some localistic theories (A, XXXII [1865], 117). On this occasion he also coined the notion of icterus catharralis, only recently replaced by a revival of that of infectious hepatitis.

cells, like the cells with fatty granula, were not formed by "envelopment" and that "the Schleiden-Schwann [cell] theory can no longer be maintained in its old form." [22] That was written in 1847; Virchow then attempted a chemical theory of cell formation in this very article which obviously satisfied himself so little that up to 1853 he still repeatedly resorted nevertheless to the old Schleiden-Schwann theory.

On the Road to Cellular Pathology

VIRCHOW illustrates well I. B. Cohen's statement that great scientists usually make more than one contribution! [1] Even the accomplishments of his first three productive years in Berlin, which form essentially the contents of the foregoing chapter, are not limited to his studies on leukemia and on the chemistry of fibrin, pigments, and the newborn, or to his observations and experiments on thrombosis and embolism. There are, furthermore, contributions that I omitted because of their relative insignificance (on female physiology and gynecology); there are studies on parasitism which will be reported later; and there are microscopical and morphological studies on cancer and tuberculosis, bone and connective tissue, and on parenchymatous inflammation which, developed in his Wuerzburg years, would form the basis for his famous *Cellular Pathology*.

Before discussing these details, it seems necessary to give a short summary of the development and status of cellular knowledge and theories at the time when Virchow entered the field.* It is well known that the expression "cell" was coined by

* For more detailed recent studies on this subject we refer (in addition to Berg's "Die Lehre von der Faser," A, CCCIX [1942], 333 ff.) to Rich in *Bulletin of the Johns Hopkins Hospital*, XXXIX (1926), 330; the articles of Karling and Conklin in *Biological Symposia* (ed. J. Cattell), I, Part I, 37–57 and 58–66; Schlumberger in *Archives of Pathology*, XXXVII (1944), 396 ff.; Wilson in *Isis*, XXXV (1944), 168, and XXXVII (1947), 14 ff.; Baker in *Quarterly Journal of Microscopial Science*,

the seventeenth-century microscopist R. Hooke for the cavities he observed in cork. "Cells," "globules," or "vesicles" were also seen by other seventeenth-century histologists like Malpighi, Leeuwenhoek, and Grew in plant or animal tissues. The mere seeing of cells does not, of course, imply a "cell theory," which is an opinion regarding the cell as the basic unit of organic structures. The basic unit of that period was the fiber. We might perhaps regard as "Cell Theory No. 1" the opinion, proferred toward the end of the fiber era by numerous authors between Prochaska (1797) and J. Berres (1837), that fibers originate from small globules. This opinion was obviously a compromise of traditional theories, actual observations, and optical illusions created by the poor microscopes of the time.

The idea of an ultimate unit was largely overshadowed during the first decades of the nineteenth century by the twenty-one basic tissues of Bichat, who was curiously indifferent toward microscopical structures. Elaboration of the atom theory in physics and chemistry served, on the other hand, as stimulus to look for the smallest unit in organic life. Ideas of cell structure have, in turn, later on influenced the ideas of atomic structure.

In the beginning of the nineteenth century a second cell theory was propounded which has quite rightly been called the "globule theory" by Baker, since the authors speaking of the cell or the globule as a basic structural element thought of a formation which is far more primitive than both our own or even Schwann's notion of a cell. We encounter this cell theory, for example, with Oken (1805), the Wenzel brothers (1807), Meckel (1808), and Heusinger (1822).* It was particularly well developed by the botanists Mirbel (1809), Treviranus (1816), Meyen (1828), and Mohl (1831). In France it

---

LXXXIX (1948), 103 ff., and XC (1949), 87 ff. and 331; Diepgen and Rosner in A, CCCVII (1940–41), 457 ff.; Krumbhaar in *Annals of Medical History*, 3 ser., I (1939), 427 ff.

* Gerould (in *Scientific Monthly*, XIV [1922], 273) made Lamarck one of the fathers of the cell theory on account of Lamarck's utterances on "cellular tissue." This error, copied repeatedly since, springs, as Wilson has shown, from Gerould's unfamiliarity with the fact that connective tissue was up to the 1830's called "cellular tissue" by histologists.

was prominent with Milne-Edwards (1823), Dutrochet (1824), Raspail (1826), and Royer-Collard (1828). Some of this work has been dismissed as optical illusions due to poor instruments; for example, Henle, Virchow, and Rich dismissed that of Milne-Edwards. In some of this work the fiber theory still loomed large. Some was overwhelmingly speculative, like that of Oken. But most of it was based on actual, though incomplete, observation. In this respect all these men are precursors of Schwann. It seems just as arbitrary, for instance, to make Dutrochet, only because he was a great scientist in general, *the* precursor of Schwann, as it is mythological to make Schwann *the* creator of the cell theory.

The technical possibility for a third and better cell theory was provided through the introduction of much improved microscopes around 1830. The cellular nucleus—seen before by Hewson, Fontana, and Purkinje, but not recognized in its generality and importance—was discovered as a normal and essential cell element with such a new instrument by the English botanist Robert Brown in 1831. By means of these new instruments and concepts we obtain the first satisfactory descriptions of cells by men like Purkinje (1834), Valentin (1835), Schultz (1836), Joh. Mueller (1836), Donné (1837), Henle (1837), and J. Vogel (1838).

On the basis of this work, his own observations, and the (not too original) 1837 statement of his friend, the botanist Schleiden, that all plants consist essentially of cells, Schwann proferred in 1838 the third cell theory, often erroneously regarded as *the* cell theory. The elementary parts of animals and cells, according to Schwann, were the same. "There is one universal principle of development for the elementary parts of organisms, however different, and this principle is the formation of cells." [2] As to the genesis of cells, Schwann unfortunately adopted the "free cell formation" (or watch crystal theory) of Schleiden and others, even worsening it a little. In the amorphous "blastema" the granulae coagulated into a nucleus around which the rest of the cell was formed.

There is no doubt that Schwann, even if he knew little of them, had an abundance of forerunners in the cell theorists of the "globule" period and later. Valentin could claim that most of Schwann's basic theses could be found dispersed in his writings.[3] A common structural principle for animals and plants had been claimed not only earlier by Malpighi, C. F. Wolff, or Haller, but in the immediate past, for example, by Dutrochet, Raspail, Purkinje, Turpin, Valentin, and Johannes Mueller.

The "blastema" hypothesis was a very serious handicap. It produced a lamentable relapse into humoralism (Rokitansky, etc.). That Schwann resorted to this hypothesis, disregarding what had been already made known about cell division by Dumortier, Mirbel, and Mohl, can be partly explained by the mechanistic bias of his generation. It is obvious from his *Microscopical Researches* how eager he was to find a process of cell formation resembling crystallization.

Nevertheless Schwann and nobody else swung the general scientific opinion in favor of the cell theory. This was first of all due to his own merits. His work was based on excellent observations and descriptions. Although his image of the cell was still incomplete—the notion of the protoplasm was developed only later by Purkinje, Mohl, and Remak—his nucleated cells were no longer mere globules; they looked at least like what we today call cells. His illustrations can be identified with actual structures, a statement that can hardly be applied to the "globulists." But Schwann's success was also due to the fact that "the time was ripe" for his theory, not the least perhaps on account of the long preparation by the "globulists." [4]

All this is not said to detract from Schwann's merits. Schwann was a great scientist (discovery of pepsin, 1835; disproof of spontaneous generation, 1836; proof of the organic nature of yeast fermentation, 1837) and the third cell theory is as much or as little "his discovery" as most of the discoveries attributed to individuals in the history of science. "Culture heroes" that create everything from nothing exist only in the mythologies of savages or popular writers.

Schwann's discovery served as a tremendous stimulus to pathological research. The manifestations of disease in and through cells were now studied by a host of observers like Johannes Mueller, Henle, Gluge, Gueterbock, Rokitansky, Raspail. A series of books was written on the subject by J. Vogel (1842), Donné (1844), Klencke (1844), Lebert (1845), Robin (1845), Mandl (1845), Guensburg (1845). A new cellular pathology was born, which we might call "Cellular Pathology No. 1." Because it was based on Schwann's cell theory, it was prior and inferior to Virchow's cellular pathology ("Cellular Pathology No. 2"). Again we see that, contrary to the popular myth, Virchow is by no means the unprecedented creator of cellular pathology in general. It was not through Virchow that the interest in pathology shifted from the tissue of Bichat, which in turn had superseded the organ of Morgagni as basic unit in pathology, toward the cell. Virchow only completed, systematized, and definitely established this orientation.

Before the second cellular pathology could be created, Schwann's "cell theory" based on the "blastema" had to be replaced by a new cell theory based on the continuity of cell life—the fourth in turn, which in honor of its main protagonists we might call the "Remak-Virchow Cell Theory."

Virchow's first "cellular" paper with the lengthy title, "On the Evolution of Cancer with Remarks on Fat Formation in the Animal Body and on Pathological Resorption," [5] opened a long series of studies on malignant tumors. It was "orthodox" in the sense of the Schwann theory in stating repeatedly that cancer (carcinoma) arises from amorphous material. It repeated Johannes Mueller's ideas on the three elements of cancer: the connective tissue stroma, the epithelium-like cancer corpuscles, and the cancer serum. Like Mueller, Virchow denied the existence of specific "cancer cells" ("tailed bodies") claimed by Vogel, Bruch, Lebert, etc., and stressed the similarity of cancer tissue and embryonic tissue. His relation to Lebert is not without interest. In view of the time of their meeting and their close personal friendship, there is no doubt that Virchow picked up many tricks of the trade from Lebert, who was older and a far more experienced microscopist. Despite this Virchow did not take over any of Lebert's doctrines concerning specific tubercle or cancer cells.

The paper becomes more original when Virchow starts an analysis of the "retrograde" (degenerative) processes in cancer.

Then cells with fatty granulae were found which looked like Gluge's "inflammation globules," supposedly formed in inflammation from amorphous exudate. But these "globules" were, according to Virchow, no recent formations. They were old cells undergoing fatty metamorphosis (degeneration). They could occur in any nutritive disturbance, not only inflammation. They were, for instance, physiological in colostrum. The long list of tissues which Virchow gives, in which he or Reinhardt had shown the occurrence of this degenerative process in cells (leucocytes, epithelia,[6] ganglion cells, pus cells, sarcoma cells, cartilage cells, fibers, muscle fibers, etc.), shows the great importance the two friends attributed to their "law" of fatty degeneration in old cells. They were obviously unaware at this moment of the larger implications of this demonstration. It actually removed one of the crown witnesses of "blastema" cell formation from the scene.

This fatty metamorphosis produced tubercle-like formations in cancer. The resorption of this material left the connective tissue skeleton and produced the local "cancer scar" (central depression), which was no sign of a stopping of the cancerous process as a whole ("cure"). Virchow nevertheless believed that he and others had seen cases of arrested liver cancer.[7]

Virchow discussed at length whether the fat appearing in fatty metamorphosis was infiltrated or pre-existing in the cell or locally formed out of protein. After extensive chemical excursions he inclined toward the last alternative. Numerous chemical discussions are one of the characteristics of this paper. Another outstanding trait is the "anti-ontological" tendency of the author, which in the desire to minimize the "specific" character of cancer (carcinoma) leads him to compare cancer not only with tuberculosis, but also with pneumonia, the ovary, etc.

In a paper on "Endogenous Cell Formation in Cancer"[8] written in Wuerzburg Virchow described "breeding spaces" in carcinoma which he compared with the lacunae or cavities of cartilage. Still an adherent of Schwann, he could explain the appearance of several nuclei in such a space, filled originally only by one cell, only by endogenous formation of nuclei from blastema inside the cell. This was possible, according to Schwann, but very rare. From Virchow's description and his reference to observations of the botanist Naegeli,[9] it is obvious that *he observed actual nuclear division without recognizing it as such.* In the description of a malignant "composed myxoid cystoid tumor" (myxosarcoma?) [10] in 1853 Virchow still adhered to the idea of nucleus formation from intracellular blastema.[11]

In Wuerzburg Virchow took up again the problem of cancroids (epitheliomata) and papillary tumors [12] that he had tackled already in Berlin.[13] Cancroids started as simple hypertrophies like warts and papillary tumors. The great difficulty consisted in determining when they had passed from the hypertrophic benign to the malignant stage and were able to form metastases—a quality some prominent authors denied to cancroids. Virchow's criterion was the formation of alveoli at the base of the tumor. As an example of a tumor mixing hypertrophy and cancroid, Virchow discussed the cauliflower tumor of the os uteri. Virchow followed Lobstein in recognizing the possibility of combination tumors and tumor transformation.[14] This was especially found in enchondromata, colloid tumors, and cancroids of the sex glands, where "the particular energy of the formative processes produces the catalytic irritation that is the basis of neoplastic formations." [15] In the era of tumor dyscrasias Virchow maintained the opinion that tumors are *local* events before they become constitutional.

In reappraising Johannes Mueller's "cholesteatoma" ("pearl tumor"),[16] Virchow underlined that the cholesteatoma should not be confused with cholesterine cysts or atheromas. It was characterized by polyhedric cells and pure cholesterine contents. Cholesteatoma might occur combined with cancer or cancroid. But in his anti-ontologic and morphological fervor ("Formations have to be deprived of their specific character" [17]) Virchow threw together with cholesteatoma the same forms, atheroma and cancroid, which he had just differentiated. All were, according to him, epitheloids stemming from connective tissue. (The *epithelial* origin of cancroids had been stated by Holland in 1843 and Remak in 1852.) At this occasion Virchow claimed the "law" that repeatedly misled him: "Connective tissue is the essential place of origin of heteroplastic neoplasms." [18]

In 1850 Virchow observed for the second time (the first observation was Rokitansky's) the occurrence of striped muscle in malignant tumors and named the variety "myosarcoma." [19] He also discussed benign and malignant neuroma repeatedly and extensively during these years. [20]

Virchow had already in 1847 dealt in his habilitation lecture with bone pathology. In Wuerzburg he undertook detailed microscopical investigations of bone structure in health and disease. Schwann, Donders, and Koelliker had occasionally seen nuclei in the so-called "bone corpuscles," that together with their canaliculi were generally regarded as either empty or filled only with amorphous liquids. Through new preparation methods (cooking and chemicals) Virchow was able to show that they contained cells. [21] Virchow was furthermore able to demonstrate how these bone cells developed out of cartilage cells. [22] This was seen more easily in pathological (especially rachitic) tissues where the transformation was not obscured by previous calcification as in normal bone. [23] When ossification proceeded not from cartilage but from membranes (Virchow had defended this mode of ossification already in A, I [1847], 135), Virchow was able to demonstrate that connective tissue cells were directly transformed into bone cells. Showing thus the close relation between cartilaginous and periosteal bone growth, he came in 1851 to the following generalization, which he later regarded as a milestone on his way to cellular pathology:

Bone, cartilage and connective tissue consist *in the same way* of cells and intercellular substance. The cells appear round, oval, lentiform, tailed, branched and forming anastomoses; the intercellular substance appears hyalin, granular, bandy and fibrillated. The former resist cooking, the latter becomes first homogenized, then dissolved. [24]

Virchow, who in 1846 still had written "no histologist has been convinced of the cells of cellular tissue and it has therefore been called, on Johannes Mueller's suggestion, connective tissue," [25] was now able to demonstrate far more cells in connective tissue than any of his predecessors had demonstrated. This involved him in long and bitter polemics with Henle. From then on connective tissue was always in the center of his interest.[26] There is no doubt that Donders and Remak came to the same conclusions about simultaneously,[27] but published later. Virchow's ungenerous and trenchant remarks on this priority discussion are not to his honor.[28]

Virchow regarded the interconnected bone and connective tissue cells as a system of nutritional tubes.[29] In the same paper he also insisted on the differentiation of mucous tissue as an immature variety of connective tissue. It is interesting that he still (1852) thought connective tissue to rise from "blastema." [30]

Virchow gave a detailed analysis of the microscopic pathology of rickets, characterized according to him by abnormal proliferation of the preosteoid cartilage and the premature formation of medullary (marrow) spaces in the absence of calcification.[31] Curvature of bones was mostly due to incomplete fracture. Rickets was not identical with osteomalacia. None of the existing bone "softened" (decalcified) in rickets; only "hardening" (calcification) of new parts was retarded. Virchow also analyzed pathological atrophy of skull bones in old age (malum senile).[32]

Virchow's extensive macroscopical studies on bone development during his Wuerzburg period will be discussed in the chapter on physical anthropology (pp. 195 ff.).

To Virchow his work on tuberculosis during the Wuerzburg period was so important because again it replaced a "dyscrasia" by a local process, and it uncovered a cellular process where a formation out of exudate had been assumed. Virchow showed that Gluge's and Lebert's tubercle "corpuscles" were not new cells, rising out of some "blastema," but end products, degenerating cells. The process started with hypertrophy of connective tissue by endogenous formation of numerous cell nuclei. Then caseous degeneration set in with atrophy and desiccation.[33]

Virchow's very real merits in elucidating the microscopic

anatomy and genesis of the tubercle can unfortunately not balance the fact that his anti-ontological, purely morphological, nonclinical approach led him in this more than in any other field to produce errors, confusion, and contradictions. Nowhere is the extensive and mostly detrimental influence of Broussais on Virchow more visible than here: not that Virchow was worse than most of his contemporaries in abandoning the great unitarian concept of Laennec in favor of dualist or pluralist theories of tuberculosis; but because of the overwhelming authority he was to acquire soon, his mistakes were more durable and more influential than those of a Lebert or a Rokitansky.[34]

According to Virchow, tuberculosis could be diagnosed only where actual tubercles were visible, and "tuberculous metamorphosis" (which he later called "caseous") was also seen in cancer,[35] sarcoma,[36] pus formation, typhoid,[37] and glanders. Tuberculosis was therefore neither something specific nor a disease unit. It did occur in all kinds of organs (lung, kidney, lymphatic glands) and diseases, though most often in "scrofulosis," [38] next in glanders and typhoid. Scrofulosis in turn was nothing very specific either. While producing tuberculosis in the lung, it produced "colloid" in the thyroid or ovary. (Virchow, in spite of occasional criticisms, up to 1854 shared with his contemporaries the respect for the strange, originally Hippocratic "exclusion" theories of Schoenlein, Rokitansky, *et al.*: malaria "excludes" tuberculosis, goiter "excludes" tuberculosis, etc.) Tuberculosis was not an inflammatory process. (This last statement is in straight contradiction to Virchow's theory of inflammation as a degenerative process.)

"Phthisis" (our pulmonary tuberculosis) was therefore separated by Virchow from "tuberculosis." [39] It was a chronic pneumonia; tubercles appeared only sometimes as a secondary complication. (This "discovery" of Reinhardt and Virchow was a precious heirloom from Broussais.) Or, as Virchow's follower Niemeyer formulated it so aptly, "The greatest danger to most phthisical patients is the development of tubercles." [40] The susceptibility to acquire phthisis was hereditary. It was based on a constitutional weakness of the lungs, located in the "solids," not the humors. Phthisis was therefore no dyscrasia.

A dyscrasia might be produced secondarily out of the local seat of the disease.

Virchow's excellent morphological observations on early tuberculous bronchitis and secondary gland affections are a small compensation for all this. His paper, "Formation of Cavities in the Lung," [41] is also primarily destined to destroy the "ontological" belief in tuberculous cavities. It contains, nevertheless, valuable data on the differentiation between simple bronchectasias and cavities with ulceration (tuberculosis, gangrene, abscess). The occurrence of lung tissue in the sputum announces ulceration.

For a pathological synthesis Virchow needed consistent views on the basic process of inflammation beyond the results available from his phlebitis studies. He approached the problem again in his "On the Dilatation of Smaller Vessels," [42] and he showed that inflammation was more than dilatation of vessels under nervous influence, as was generally assumed. On the contrary, dilatation of vessels was nothing specific in inflammation, but occurred in a host of other physiological and pathological conditions. He stated that the changes in small vessels paralleled those in large vessels. He subdivided dilatation of vessels into the following groups: (1) simple (generalized) ectasia as in inflammation and pregnancy; (2) ectasia of varicosis; (3) ampullary ectasia (aneurysms, etc.); (4) dissecant ectasia; (5) cavernous ectasia.[43] Any permanent dilatation of vessels presupposes or produces a change in the wall of the vessel. Hyperemia becomes inflammation only through additional involvement of all other parts concerned (nerve, tissues).

The "anti-ontological" dig at the role of vessels (and their controlling nerves) in inflammation made it necessary to look for another basic carrier of inflammation. Virchow found it in the cell. He renovated the old concept of "parenchymatous inflammation," giving it the meaning of inflammatory swelling inside the cell as opposed to the interstitial exudation of Rokitansky. Normally parenchymatous inflammation would be combined with vascular and nervous changes, but it could occur without them. The famous hyperemia of the French and the exudation of the Austrians were expendable.

How early the idea of parenchymatous inflammation became important to Virchow is evident from the fact that in his famous 1852 article (A, IV, 261 ff.) no less than three unpublished 1847 papers on the same subject are incorporated (his *Naturforscherversammulung* address on parenchymatous inflammation, his *Probevorlesung* on muscle inflammation, and a paper on Bright's disease). Inflammation being a nutritional disturbance, either resorption or absorption became deranged and swelling resulted. Virchow showed how in the muscle (on which Gendrin had done yeoman work) this led to softening, fatty metamorphosis, eventually scar (callosity) formation. Virchow studied muscle inflammation (including the heart) in rheumatism, syphilis, puerperal fever, glanders, and "putrid infection." [44] His particular attention was, of course, directed towards the study of parenchymatous inflammation in parts lacking vessels like the cornea, cartilage, the inner wall of vessels, or connective tissue (studied similarly by Kuess in 1846).[45] Virchow developed here his idea that pus is an inflammatory product of connective tissue. Virchow also described parenchymatous inflammation in nerves, and in the liver and kidneys, where he decomposed the complex "Bright's disease" into catarrhal, croupous, and parenchymatous inflammation. His studies impressed him with the ultimately degenerative character of inflammation.[46]

Virchow regarded later as a first general formulation of his cellular pathology the article, "Nutrition Units and Disease Foci," published in the same year of 1852 (A, IV, 375 ff.). Pathological processes were primarily disturbances of nutrition. It was therefore necessary to gain clarity as to the smallest nutritional units. These were not the territories of a nerve or vessel (that were "anatomical" or "circulatory" units of a higher order) but the small "vegetative" units formed by cell groups: the cell territories. The cell was the focus of life. It was itself a nutritional unit (J. Goodsir). *New cells or cell derivates were the results of cell division.*[47] (The blastema remains here unmentioned for the first time as a source of cells.) Cell groups were nutritionally to a certain extent independent of nerves and vessels, as grafting experiments or such structures as the umbilical cord or the lens showed. (Had Virchow known tissue cultures, he would have had even more striking examples at his disposal.) The elementary disease foci were in turn simply the diseased elementary nutritional units: the cell territories and cells. The main elementary disturbances of these foci were: fatty and "earthy" (calcification) metamorphosis, pigment degeneration, colliquation, induration, waxy degeneration.[48]

Both Virchow and Rokitansky had based their search for a synthesis on Schwann's cellular theory. But while Rokitansky had concentrated on its most perishable element, the blastema hypothesis, which he interpreted in pathology as the exudate that in turn had led him toward the dyscrasias, Virchow developed more and more that positive aspect of Schwann's heritage that saw in the cell the basic biological unit. Numerous detailed observations had convinced Virchow of the untenability of the governing blastema hypothesis. What were supposedly new young cell forms, crystallizing out of blastema in inflammation, tubercle, and cancer, had been identified as old degenerating cells. Instead of exogenous cell formation out of blastema, he had observed endogenous cell formation and cell division. Where there was supposedly only amorphous material in the connective tissue, he had seen cells. What had seemed original material, blastema, the intercellular substance, was actually an end product of cell activity. Cells in cartilage and bone developed, not out of the blastema "chaos," but out of the other connective substance cells. In parenchymatous inflammation, in the inflammation of tissues without vessels or nerves, the cell appeared able to react as an independent unit.

Thus from omission of the blastema in 1852 Virchow advanced in 1854 to the statement, "There is no life but through direct succession." [49] And when this statement seemed still too vague and seemed not to have the desired clarifying effect, he published an editorial in Volume 8 of the *Archives* in 1855, a kind of manifesto of what he modestly called *the pathology of the future,* entitled "Cellular Pathology" and containing the famous aphorism *Omnis cellula a cellula.*[50] These cells, all direct descendants of other cells, none born in Schwann's blastema chaos or Rokitansky's specific exudations, were the ultimate units of life and disease. "They are the last constant link in the great chain of mutually subordinated formations that form tissues, organs, systems, the individual. Below them is nothing but change." [51] They and not only the nervous substance are endowed with that basic vital quality of irritability.[52] "They form a free state of individuals with equal rights, though not equal abilities, which persists because the individuals depend on each other and because there exist certain centers of organization, without the integrity of which the parts cannot obtain the necessary amount of nutritive materials." [53] The new cellular pathology would unite in itself the old solidistic and humoral pathologies. In this respect Virchow would live up to his promises. He would never discard the possibility of a "dyscrasia" for mere dogmatic reasons.

We have mentioned already that Virchow was not the first to look for pathological changes in the cell. He was the first to make this procedure a system. He was not the first, either, to claim that cells descended only from cells. This opinion was entertained in the "globular" period, for instance, by Raspail who in 1825, after all, preceded his treatise "Developpement de la fécule" with the motto *Omnis cellula e cellula.* It was expressed by John Goodsir in 1845.[54] The botanist, H. von Mohl, and Koelliker were strongly inclined in this direction since 1835 and 1844 respectively, but did not dare to rule out entirely "free cell formation." It was stated with great clarity by Remak in 1852.

The extracellular genesis of cells in animals seemed to me, ever since the publication of the cell theory [of Schwann], just as unlikely as the spontaneous generation of organisms. These doubts produced my observations on the multiplication of blood cells by division in bird and mammalian embryos (*Med. Zeitg. d Ver. f.*

Heilk. in Preussen, 1841, No. 27) and on the division of muscle bundles in frog larvae (*Fror. Not.* 1845, No. 768). Since I have continued these observations in frog larvae, where it is possible to follow the history of tissues back to segmentation. Only in the spring of 1851 I have succeeded in finding that all embryonic cells multiply by division. . . .

These results are just as closely related to pathology as they are to physiology. It can hardly be denied that pathological tissues are only variants of normal embryonic developmental types and it is unlikely that they should have the particular privilege of extracellular cell formation. The so-called "organization of plastic exudates" and the earliest history of malignant tumors has to be revised in this direction. Based on the confirmation of my doubts of many years standing I dare to suggest that pathological tissues just like normal ones are not formed in an extracellular blastema, but are descendants or products of normal tissues of the organism.[55]

After having given due credit to Virchow's predecessors (which, by the way, he did occasionally himself [56]) it is but fair to state that he reached his conclusion independently, inductively, and in his own way. This is probably the reason he reached it so late. But it is probably also the reason his statements had an unprecedented influence on the mass of doctors. Virchow did not have the extensive interest in comparative anatomy or embryology that characterized the other pupils of Johannes Mueller or a John Goodsir; if he had had it, he would probably have made his discovery earlier but would have produced just as small a reaction in the medical profession as Remak did. Working always almost exclusively on full-fledged pathological material, he reached his conclusions later; but they had far more meaning and immediate applicability for the medical profession. In addition to the fact that Virchow's findings were more meaningful, he propagated them with that tireless zeal and almost sinister energy in which nobody has ever excelled him.

Before analyzing the further elaboration of his cellular pathology in his second Berlin period in a following chapter, we must mention, among the many disconnected valuable detailed observations of his earlier period, at least a few that are of more than average interest.

The great prevalence of abdominal complaints in everyday medical practice provoked Virchow's extensive study, "Historical, Critical and Positive Comments on the Doctrine of Abdominal Affections" (A, V [1853], 281 ff.). These complaints, which seemed to reflect mostly dyspepsia, muscle spasms, or hyperesthesias, he explained pathologically by veinous hyperemia (due to liver, heart, pulmonary disease, fecal retention, etc.), intestinal dislocation, adhesions and partial peritonitis, or catarrh of the mucous membranes. Although recognizing the psychological element in these "hypochondrias," he did not regard them (like Romberg) as purely "cerebral" diseases but as actual abdominal disturbances overemphasized for psychological reasons.[57] In this article he claimed for the first time that gastric ulcer is not merely a result of hyperacidity but of a concomitant local circulatory disturbance in the mucosa.[58]

In a survey of the pathological anatomy of syphilis,[59] Virchow showed that Ricord's theory of three stages was a purely clinical notion. Anatomically "secondary" phenomena could be found in "tertiary" syphilis and vice versa. How much good this critical "anti-ontological" analysis, so famous in its time, did to practical syphilology, in spite of all brilliant detail observations, remains open to doubt. Virchow explained the return of syphilis after successful treatment by the fact that the "poison" survived in some local foci, especially lymphatic glands.

In an interesting study of calcium "metastases" (diffuse calcification) in the lung, kidney, stomach, etc., occurring in connection with tumors and other affections of the bone, Virchow found kidney damage in all his cases. He wondered whether "normal" senile calcification might not equally be referred to a combination of the senile decalcification of bones and kidney damage.[60]

In 1857 he interpreted certain types of subdural hematoma

as inflammatory and coined the term and notion of "pachymeningitis hemorrhagica." [61]

In 1846 Virchow described for the first time a special type
of what he felt to be connective tissue in the brain and nervous
system. In 1856 he named it "neuroglia." [62]

Synthesis

VIRCHOW'S so very successful synthesis, the book of 1858 on
cellular pathology, was not his first attempt in this direction.
His *Attempt at Unifying Scientific Medicine* of 1849 has also
been mentioned. Some of its formulations were so general as
to defeat the purpose of synthesis. (See pp. 46, 47, 49, and 54.)

A second, far more serious and extensive departure in this
direction was the introductory chapters covering four hundred
pages that Virchow wrote in 1854 for his *Handbook of Special
Pathology and Therapeutics*. He started out with some general
statements on life and disease: cells are the real foci of life, the
vital elements. These elements have a certain independence,
but are mutually dependent and form higher units. Such units
are maintained through common circulation, common nervous
supply, and continuity or contiguity of cells. The latter relationship has been neglected. Life can exist only through continuous stimulation, irritation. Disease is always a weakening
of life characterized by danger. Each disturbance of life
starts locally. Pathological phenomena are not qualitatively
different from ordinary vital phenomena; they are not heterologous, in the strict sense of the word, but are vital phenomena
occurring at the wrong time (heterochrony) or in the wrong
place (heterotopy).

Normal relations can be re-established by nervous regulation,
by the blood and circulatory system, and through tissue reaction. In the latter context Virchow took over from John Simon
the idea that organs excrete substances into the blood that act
on other organs.[1] He also emphasized the effect of the sexual

glands * on the thyroid, milk gland, and larynx.[2] This is one of the not too rare premonitions of internal secretion in this period, a concept that gained full elaboration only in the 1880's through the work of Brown-Séquard, Schiff, and others.

In a chapter on fever Virchow reviewed extensively the older and current theories and adopted a neuroparalytic one. In a chapter on inflammation Virchow stated that inflammation is one of the general forms that local diseases can take. Irritation is a reaction that is not yet inflammation. It is not limited to parts that have a nervous supply. Virchow surveyed the paralytic, spastic, stases, and attraction theories of inflammation. The local circulatory disturbances, hyperemia, are not the basic elements of inflammation. (Virchow used here the results of Claude Bernard's experiments on sympathectomy, which he repeated and modified.) The basic phenomena are a local disturbance of nutrition and the parenchymatous swelling. There are only quantitative differences between irritation and inflammation. When nutritive changes are added to the functional disturbances of irritation, we can speak of inflammation. Destructive tendencies differentiate the inflammatory disturbance of nutrition from other disturbances of nutrition.

The second part of this treatise consists of a discussion of local disturbances of circulation. It deals with local anemia (named "ischemia" by Virchow), active congestion, passive congestion (or fluxion), thrombosis and obstruction (here Virchow reported mostly his own experimental results on thrombosis and embolism), hemorrhage, and hydrops (dropsy). In the last, transudation occurs at the level of the capillaries. Only material that is in a true state of solution transudes. Albumines that are only in a state of suspension (we would say colloid today) do not transude. Hydrops is nothing static. There is a continuous change through evacuation, absorption, and new transudation.

The third part of this discussion deals with general disturbances of nutrition: necrosis and gangrene, atrophy and degeneration, and hypertrophy and neoplasias.

* See his 1848 aphorism, "Woman is a woman only through her sex gland" (GA, p. 747).

This synthesis was still entirely conceived in the spirit of "pathological physiology." Very little morphology and practically no microscopy enter the picture. The second part (on local disturbances of circulation), for instance, was an able and very extensive discussion of all aspects of hemodynamics as then known. The very intelligent analysis of hydrops was overwhelmingly mechanical and chemical. Even the approach to atrophy was chemical. "Unfortunately we do not know anything in detail concerning the chemical process which would be the most important in either senile or atrophic processes." [3] This frustrating fact unfortunately prevailed for most of the subjects discussed and made for the highly abstract and somewhat vague character of this synthesis, undertaken along the lines of a still very rudimentary mechanical and chemical physiology.

Developing his subject in the framework of a traditional text on general pathology, Virchow had to cover many fields outside his direct field of action. He had little opportunity to report on his own experiences or to develop his own basic ideas, which, by the way, were not yet fully crystallized. (See, for example, his hesitations to confirm Remak's absolute denial of free cell formation.[4]) He was forced to report mainly the observations and theories of others. This gives the text great historical interest today, but has deprived it of the dynamism and authority that a good synthesis needs in order to gain general acceptance. A great deal of space was also taken up by not very original discussions of the therapeutics to be applied to the conditions described.

Thus, to the great chagrin of the author, this synthesis was never much noticed, even by his enemies, and left little impression on his contemporaries. Some of its elements reappeared in his third synthesis, the famous book of 1858 on cellular pathology. Here Virchow consciously or unconsciously avoided the tactical shortcomings of the *Handbook* articles. Now he followed another plan, subjective, but new and entirely his own. Now he dealt primarily with *his* observations and discoveries, *his* now matured basic ideas. The abstract discussions of incompletely known physiological relationships were replaced by the reassuring and authoritative concreteness of morphological microscopical data immediately visualized by a wealth of illustrations. The original form of the book, a series of lectures, provided a form of expression far more direct and impressive than the all too dignified "handbook" style. Thus Virchow eventually realized beyond expectation his long-sought goal to give medicine a successful synthesis.

The exact title of Virchow's famous book is *Cellular Pathology Based on Physiological* [!] *and Pathological Histology*. It was originally the stenogram of a series of lectures given early in 1858 to an audience of Berlin medical practitioners and destined to acquaint them with the basic opinions and findings of the new professor of pathology. Virchow rightly stated in his Preface that the book contained little that he had not published during the previous twelve years in special articles or the chapters of the *Handbook*. But in order to be fully appreciated, the book has to be read in its entirety. It is available in a good English translation.[5]

Virchow set out with a description of the cell (Chapter 1) as then known (protoplasma, nucleus, nucleolus, membrane), a short historical review of previous cell theories, and a statement of his own two basic tenets: *Omnis cellula e cellula*, and that the cell is the true unit of all living organisms. The animal is a sum of cell territories and a kind of social organism.

There are three groups of normal tissues (Chapters 2 and 3): those consisting only of cells (like the epithelia), those consisting of cells and intercellular substance, and "higher" (that is, specialized) tissues (like muscle, nerve, vessels, blood), which are all properly described. Virchow freely admits that the second group, the connective substances, interests him above all others.[6] It consists of connective, adipose, and mucous tissue, cartilage, bone, teeth, and neuroglia. The intercellular substances of this group differ chemically. In all of them the cells form a system of channels.

Unfortunately morphology does not always enlighten us as to function. One function (for example, movement) can be connected with different forms (muscle, spermatozoon, ciliated epithelium); one form (glandular epithelium), with different functions (secretions). The author differentiates between permanent, temporary, and mutant tissues. In the latter the cell may persist, but the tissue changes its character. The relationship of tissues has to be based on common origin in the embryonic period. Then we will understand the substitution of certain tissues by their "histological equivalents."

All pathological tissues (Chapter 4) are essentially neoplasias and have physiological models. We know neoplasias of the epithelium, of the connective substance, and (rare ones) of the specialized tissues. There are histoid (composed of one tissue), organoid (composed of several tissues), and teratoid formations. Heterology is essentially either heterotopy, heterochrony, or heterometry (difference in size). *Heterology is therefore not identical with a malignancy.* It is obvious that Virchow's concept of heterology is new and different from the traditional "heterology" concepts of Laennec, Lobstein, Lebert, and Carswell, who saw, in "heterologous" tissues, tissues without physiological parallel or precedent.

One should differentiate between simple *hypertrophy* (increase of the original element in size) and *hyperplasia* (another neologism of Virchow, meaning numerical hypertrophy or increase in number of constituent elements). In pathology as in physiology we encounter heterologous substitution. The same tissue (for example, bone) can be formed in several different ways.

In nutrition (Chapters 5 and 6) the vessels have been too exclusively regarded as the only existing pathways. The density of vascular supply varies, as shown by numerous examples, all the way down from abundance to absence of vessels. Below the vessel territories we encounter cell territories as nutrition units. In bone, cartilage, tendon, cornea, umbilical cord, mucous and connective tissues, the nutritive substances progress through the above-mentioned intracellular channel system. The cell is not simply "fed" (that is, inundated with nutritive material), it feeds itself in selecting from the nutritive fluids. This is particularly clear in the fetus or in transplantation material.[7]

The vessels (Chapter 7), as the larger pathways of nutrition, are examined anatomically. Congestion is viewed as the relaxa-

tion of the vascular wall after initial contraction. The elastic
elements of the media maintain an even flow. Aneurysm and
varix are the consequences of their destruction. Exchanges
between blood and tissues do not proceed on a purely mechanical basis. There exist chemical affinities between certain tissues
and certain circulating substances. Hyperemia is not identical
with inflammation, as shown by Claude Bernard's sympathectomy experiments, which were followed by hyperemia but
not by inflammation.

In the chapters on the blood (Chapters 8 and 9) Virchow
incorporates most of his research on fibrin, haematoidin, leucocytes, and leukemia. He maintains that fibrin is locally produced in inflammation and that hyperinosis results from its
transport into the blood from the inflamed part via the lymphatic system. Pyemia (Chapter 10), properly speaking, does
not exist. Pus cells cannot be absorbed. Liquid substances are
absorbed which irritate lymphatic glands into increased leuko-
cyte production. The lymphatic apparatus is not limited to
the glands, but comprises also the lymphatic elements of the
intestine, tonsils, etc.

In the chapter on infection and metastasis (Chapter 11)
Virchow reports his work on thrombosis and embolism, the
latter being the prototype of a metastasis. Other metastases are
the deposits of silver salts, uric acid, and calcium. Virchow
gives thus a new and modern meaning to the old humoralistic
term of metastasis. The affections of the spleen, liver, kidneys,
and heart muscle, so frequent in infectious disease, must be
caused by circulation of toxic liquids. The "metastatic" pleuritis
and arthritis in ichorrhemia might be caused by such liquids.
Perhaps also the transport of diseased cells, or "micrococci," is
involved. Virchow nevertheless was skeptical as to the occurrence of cellular metastases in cancer (carcinoma), as he found
metastases there often not in the direct line of circulation.

As to the theory of dyscrasias (Chapter 12), Virchow does
not deny their existence in acute conditions as the above shows.
Pathological conditions can be mediated by the blood. What he
emphatically denies is the existence of chronic dyscrasias as in
cancer, tuberculosis, leprosy. The basic error is the assumption

that blood is a permanent and self-perpetuating material, which it is not. Chronic "dyscrasias" depend, therefore, on the existence of foci in the solids. From such foci substances enter the blood which either damage its cellular elements and interfere with its function, are carried by the blood to organs and damage those, or affect the regular replacement and formation of elements of the blood. In this chapter Virchow defends the idea of heterologous (besides homologous) infection, which now sounds so strange. (Cancer poison, for instance, can produce tuberculosis.[8])

After having thus dismissed the exclusively humoral pathology of his time, Virchow turns to the refutation of the exclusively solidistic pathologists (Spiess, Henle), who in his time were "neurists," referring any physiological and pathological phenomenon in the last instance to action of the nervous system. A detailed histological analysis of the peripheral nervous system (Chapter 13), and the brain and spinal cord (Chapter 14) seems to reveal poor bases for such a theory, inasmuch as the nerve territories are too large to explain all localized pathology, and inasmuch as the nervous system itself does not appear as an absolute unit but rather as a complex corporation of numerous small cellular centers.

In the chapter "The Life of the Elements: Their Activity and Irritability" (Chapter 15), Virchow asks the neurists: where is the nervous influence in the development of the egg, in the reactions of the cartilage, lens, vitrous body, blood corpuscles? Their ideas are mythological.[9] We experience our consciousness as an undivided unit. (That was the opinion in 1858!) We are therefore inclined to postulate similar physiological or anatomical units like the nervous system of the neurists. But these assumptions are rather the projections of this single experience into nature than the results of observations.[10] Virchow's arguments are very reminiscent of those used by Gall against the adversaries of cerebral localization.

Life depends on irritation. Often the existence of irritability is the only criterion whether a part is dead or still alive, as form can survive death.

Concern with irritation and irritability, which became so

dominant an element in his later teachings and one of his main legacies to modern pathology, appears relatively late with Virchow in the *Handbook* of 1852. His ideas on the subject are developed in a more elaborate form, paralleling much of the content of *Die Cellularpathologie,* for the first time in an article entitled "Irritation and Irritability" in the *Archives,* XIV (1858), 1 ff.

Bouchut [11] has rightly emphasized the fact that Virchow took over the concept of irritation from Broussais and in some cases confirmed through microscopic findings Broussais' hypotheses. Virchow did not add anything new to the concept. It remained with him axiomatic, destined primarily to fill a logical gap already discovered by Broussais. Broussais argued that when the ontological idea of disease is given up, what then does act on the organ? * Neither he nor Virchow knew a factual answer, which was later partly provided by bacteriology, and both introduced the hypothesis of irritation to fill this gap.

Irritation can provoke life activity in either of three directions: function, nutrition, or formation.†

Function can be produced through direct irritation without nervous intervention (for instance, in ciliated epithelium,‡ muscle, glands). Virchow does not deny "the high dignity of the nervous system" or that normally the majority of body actions is initiated by nervous action. What he does deny is that nervous irritability is the basic criterion of life. Study of unicellular organisms has shown, in their so-called automatisms, functional irritability without nervous mediation. The same cellular movements were observed in higher organisms by Virchow himself and Von Recklinghausen.

* "En effet, si ce ne sont pas les maladies qui agissent sur les organes, qu'est-ce donc qui agit?"—Broussais, *Examen des doctrines médicales,* II, 313.

† This attempt to break down life into some essential characteristics is, of course, not original with Virchow. It has been tried by most medical theoricians from Aristotle down to the present.

‡ Virchow was always very proud that he had found, in potassium and sodium, substances reviving the activity of such epithelia after Purkinje and Valentin had failed with hundreds of substances. See *A,* VI (1854), 133.

Nutritive and formative irritation are predominant in inflammation and neoplasia (Chapter 16). The minus processes of nutrition should be differentiated into aplasia, atrophy, and necrobiosis. Nutrition presupposes assimilation and fixation of the nutritive substances in the cell. Tonus is more than a neural notion. It implies the general nutritive tension of parts. A well-nourished part is able to function well. Nutritive irritants (stimuli) are manifold and not limited to nutritive substances or trophic nerves. Inflammation begins with increased intake of nutriment into the cell. Virchow names this stage "cloudy swelling." It tends toward degenerative processes, but it is often hard to differentiate from simple hypertrophy. It can occur in parts lacking nervous supply, like the cartilage, or only in segments of one nerve territory (skin). The swelling is not primarily due to vascular action either, as it is not due to an exudate but is based on parenchymatous, intracellular swelling and can occur in parts lacking direct vascular supply (cornea). Parenchymatous inflammation, the highest degree of nutritive irritation, might be defined as acute hypertrophy with a tendency toward degeneration. It is very frequent, as it accompanies the majority of infectious diseases (for example, acute exanthemata, typhus, and puerperal fever) in kidneys, liver, heart, muscles, etc.

The next steps are formative changes. Nuclear division sets in. We observe the "giant cells," named such by Virchow. "Nucleation" is then followed by "cellulation" (cell division) and proliferation. Inflammatory irritations are complex. They might produce all three forms of irritations in the same organ. In addition exudation and nerve irritation might exist. *But inflammation as such needs neither nerves nor vessels, neither pain nor exudation. It can exist as a simple nutritive and formative process, differing from other similar processes only through its acuity and danger.* This Virchow regarded as the most important medical result of his special histological researches.[12] The shift from a vascular to a cellular theory of inflammation was indeed one of the most radical departures from medicine's past.

Inflammation might end in nutritive or formative restitution. But it also might end in a passive process, a degeneration. In passive disturbances parts are either reduced in function through unfavorable external conditions or destroyed with consequent loss of substance. The most frequent form of degeneration is the so-called fatty metamorphosis (Chapter 17). This is not to be confused with intercellular or intracellular fat infiltration. It is the transformation of cells into corpuscles composed of fat granula and eventually fatty detritus, as first described by Reinhardt and extensively investigated by Virchow. Other forms of degeneration are amyloid degeneration and calcification, not to be confused with ossification (Chapter 18).

Inflammation is thus an active *and* passive process (Chapter 19). Fatty degeneration, a passive process, can occur by itself. But in the case of inflammation it follows an active process (cloudy swelling). Virchow regards the atheromatous processes in the arteries as an active-passive process. It starts actively as a sclerosis or endoarteritis; it ends passively in either atheromatosis or ossification.

Inflammation is not a particular process, unique and uniform, but a group of processes that become particular only through their special arrangement in time and space. Its essence is neither the hyperemia of French authors nor the exudation of Austrian authors. The point of departure in the analysis of inflammation must be irritation (Broussais-Andral). When a nutritive disturbance is added to the functional one (mere irritation), we can speak of inflammation. Though normally the part, irritated directly or via blood or nerve, will attract nutritive material from a neighboring blood vessel, this need not be the case, as the inflammation of parts lacking blood supply shows. Exudation is neither general in inflammation (already as a student Virchow had been struck by the absence of exudate in keratitis [13]) nor is the exudate always fibrinous (the author refers to the nonfibrinous exudation of mucous membranes, brain, liver). The inflammatory exudate in the old sense does not exist. The exudate we encounter in inflammation is a combination of locally formed materials and transudates of differing character. There exist two basically different forms of inflammation: the purely parenchymatous, and the secretory (exudative) inflammation of superficial organs. The former tends to change the functional and histological characteristics of the organ. The latter tends to relieve the tissues of noxes. The former can produce nutritive or formative degeneration; the latter, mucous, serous, fibrinous, or synovial exudate. Virchow himself felt later that his two types of inflammation did not do justice to the total reality of inflammation. It is obvious that an interstitial process like our present "serous inflammation" was nowhere taken into account. He therefore replaced his twofold classification of inflammation by a fourfold one (see p. 119).

The ways of normal and pathological tissue formation are illustrated primarily by the history of bone tissue (Chapter 20). In discussing formative irritation Virchow tells how his first doubts in the blastema theory were aroused when in the early stages of the tubercle and the typhoid follicles he found numerous cells and nuclei, hypertrophy instead of amorphous exudation, only later followed by amorphous caseous degeneration. His discovery of cellular elements in different "cell-free" divisions of the connective substance confirmed his doubts. He now feels that, instead of the "plastic lymph," the blastema, or the exudation, *the connective tissue and its equivalents should be regarded as the main germinative center of the body*.[14] His discovery of connective tissue in brain and liver explains the existence and character of neoplasias in these organs. New formations can proceed by simple cell division or by endogenous cell formation. He characterizes the former as the "growth," the latter as the "generative" type of tissue and neoplastic formation. Rapid multiplication produces very small indifferent cells: the stage of granulation. Hereafter heterology might set in. The more rapidly the elements develop, the more heterology is to be feared.

Virchow chooses the history of the osseous tissue as particularly graphic illustration for his notion of normal substitution of tissues and metaplasia. He draws again on his earlier studies on rickets and bone formation. Metaplasia was to Virchow actual transformation, not only replacement of cells.

In Chapters 21 and 22, Virchow deals with the pathological, especially the heterologous neoplasias. All neoplasias are in a way destructive. They are to be subdivided into homologous and heterologous. The heterologous ones are not necessarily malignant. Homologous ones (like the uterus tumors named "myoma" and "fibromyoma" by Virchow) can occasionally become quite troublesome. Pus, a neoplasia according to Virchow, is either formed by leucocytes or from connective tissue or epithelia. Degeneration in an ulcer sets in only when the connective tissue layer is affected. Pus is not the substance that "melts" tissue, but the end product of the melting of tissue.

What is commonly referred to as one tumor and regarded as a unit is actually a multiplicity, a sum of many small foci in different stages of their evolution. The last-affected zone actually reaches beyond the limits of the tumor discernible with the unaided eye. This explains many local recidives after extirpation. The infection of one focus seems to be carried by liquids, not by cells, into neighboring regions without intervention of vessels or nerves.

After discussing the merits and demerits of different tumor nomenclatures, Virchow gives his opinions on tuberculosis. In order to be understood, neoplasias have to be studied genetically. Virchow ends with short remarks on his cancer (carcinoma) theories that have occupied us already (pp. 74 ff.) and will occupy us in the next chapter in greater detail (pp. 104 ff.). He ends with a significant comparison with plant tumors that develop without the participation of blood vessels and nerves.

Cellular Pathology, though no easy reading matter, was an unexpected success with the public.* It found, according to its author, "numerous friends and lively enemies." Within one year a new edition was necessary; another one followed within two

---

* In 1858 Blanchard and Lee refused to publish a translation of *CP* by A. H. Smith on the grounds that such a speculative German text would not find enough readers among the practical inhabitants of the United States. See Smith in *Post-Graduate*, XVII (1902), 6.

years. It is still a classic. The author had not been alone in his yearning for a synthesis and he eventually formulated a comprehensive basis on which people could unite and work.

Tumors

VIRCHOW'S most ambitious literary undertaking was his three-volume book on tumors, *Die krankhaften Geschwuelste*, which started to appear in Berlin in 1863. Like *Cellular Pathology* it was based on a series of lectures, this time delivered in the midst of the hottest political battles of Virchow's whole life in the winter of 1862/63. The lectures were worked over so carefully that in the author's own words the stenographic record was eventually little more than the "red thread" around which the materials were grouped. Unfortunately this book, like the tumor book of Virchow's teacher Johannes Mueller, remained a torso. The second half of the third volume, which was to contain the last five of the thirty lectures and among them the one on cancer (carcinoma), failed to appear during the remaining thirty-five years of the author's life. It has been surmised that Virchow's doubts in his own connective tissue theory of cancer prevented him from finishing the job.

Even in its unfinished form the work is most impressive and unduly forgotten. Its eighteen hundred pages are a storehouse of information. No subject offered itself better to a discussion in terms of cellular pathology. As a matter of fact, cellular pathology had started with J. Mueller's and Gluge's work on tumors in the 1830's. Virchow's theory of cellular pathology obtained some of its finest triumphs in the field of tumors, changed this field more profoundly, and dominated it longer than any other theory. In the course of the years Virchow had piled up a tremendous number of observations, published and unpublished, on tumors in man and animals; his wide reading, especially his critical abstracting for his *Jahrbuecher*, had given him a very comprehensive knowledge of the literature, old and new. We

know from the foregoing how frequently Virchow had analyzed tumors and developed new concepts and terms in the
field. All this Virchow drew together into an imposing structure. The book reflects clearly the change that Virchow had
experienced from physiological pathology to pathological anatomy or morphology, not only microscopical but macroscopical.
Even the illustrations reflect Virchow's change toward macroscopical pathology. Virchow refers to, and polemizes continually against, Rokitansky throughout the book and it appears,
more than anything else Virchow ever wrote, a successful attempt to outdo the great Viennese "father" in his very domain
of gross pathological anatomy.

The influence that Virchow exerted on oncology is borne out
by the fact that many of his chapter headings and much of the
contents of his book parallel modern texts in the field. That,
on the other hand, much is dated in a book more than eighty
years old which belongs to the prebacteriological era is not
surprising. Much of what Virchow still discussed as true tumors
has since then been revealed as the product of chronic infection (like tuberculosis, syphilis, leprosy).

Virchow himself was fully aware of the provisory and arbitrary character of the "tumor" notion of his time. Why was a
hydrocele a tumor but a pleurisy not? His introductory chapter
contains the famous phrase: "I do not think that a living human
being can be found that even under torture could actually say
what tumors really are." [1] "Tumors" were not a well-defined
group, not identical with "pseudoplasms," but a classification
arising from practical needs. Only formations which presented
the danger of diagnostic errors were called tumors. Therefore
inflammatory swelling, abscesses, etc., had with increasing
knowledge already ceased to be "tumors."

As important as the question of benign or malignant was, it
could not form the basis of a scientific classification, as little as
a scientific classification of plants could be based on their being
poisonous or edible. A scientific classification of tumors had to
be anatomical and genetic. (Here Virchow went far beyond
his teacher Mueller, whose basic classificatory principle was
still that of benignity versus malignancy.)

In the second chapter Virchow explained his particular notions of homology and heterology. Heterology had meant with the older French and British authors a tissue never occurring normally (like the famous cancer cell) and was identical with malignancy. Such heterologous tumors did not exist according to Virchow. Heterologous with him meant only "heterotopical," "heterochronical," or "heterometrical." The same tumor could be heterologous in one, homologous in another place. Heterology was therefore not always identical with malignancy and there did exist degrees of heterology. A tumor of the connective substance group in another connective tissue was less heterologous than an epitheloid in the same setting.

Three factors existed in the formation of tumors: local cause, predisposition, and dyscrasia. Virchow recognized to a certain extent the role of predisposition. Dyscrasia, the fashionable explanation of his time and of the foregoing two thousand years, ranked lowest with Virchow. Without denying it completely, he minimized it at every occasion throughout the book. If dyscrasias played a role at all, they were mostly of a secondary nature. Virchow's continuous fight against dyscrasia appears today quixotic, but in the 1860's it was most necessary if he wanted to counterbalance the weight of the mightiest of all medical traditions. His battle was not only of theoretical, but also of the greatest practical importance. *The whole emphasis with Virchow was on local causes, local beginnings of tumors.* (See pp. 76, 91, and 97 of this book.) Moreover, Virchow was the first to emphasize local tumor causes in Germany.[2] This had the greatest practical consequences. To the partisans of dyscrasia, tumors were therapeutically a completely hopeless proposition: surgery was senseless; humoralistic surgeons were "knife-shy." The localistic approach, on the contrary, called for early surgical intervention.[3] Virchow's book shows clearly the boost surgery received from localism, even before the arrival of Listerism. It reflects Virchow's own great interest and not inconsiderable activity in the field of surgery even in his later years.[4] Virchow was fully conscious of the influence he had exerted through his concepts on surgery, especially through his personal friendship with such outstanding surgeons as Carl Mayer, A. von Graefe, and Langenbeck.[5] In the case of tumors Virchow had to fight only the humoral theory; his other target, neuropathology, was absent here, as practically nobody had ever produced a neuropathological theory of tumors of any consequence.[6]

"Mutiple tumors" were no proof of dyscrasia. They might be the result of tissue predisposition. In most cases the multiplicity and recurrence after extirpation were results of metastases. Metastases could be produced by tumor elements traveling along the lymphatic or blood vessels. Probably the more common cause of metastases was "infection." Infection was essentially a chemical notion with Virchow in this as in other cases. Infectious spread of tumors meant the transport of a chemical agent by blood or lymph from the original tumor into other tissues where this "poison" would again provoke tumor growth. Like many later theoreticians,[7] Virchow compared the effect of this tumor poison on distant cells to the effect of the semen on the ovum.[8] (The actual mechanism of fertilization was still unknown in 1863.) There was no essential difference between metastatic growth and growth of the tumor itself, as in the case of the large tumor one actually dealt with an agglomeration of "accessory nodules" provoked by the same agents that produced metastasis. The richer the supply of vessels and the "juicier" the tumor, the more the tumor was prone to metastasize.[9]

Predisposition of tissues for tumor formation could be either hereditary (in tuberculosis, melanoma, cancer, cancroid) or acquired (scars, chronic inflammation). Local irritation was a factor continually stressed by Virchow in tumor formation. The role of gross mechanical insult was admitted by Virchow as late as 1900.[10] Frequent irritation and predisposition probably accounted for the very obvious fact that tumors were much more prone to arise in certain parts of the body than in others. Virchow illustrated the existence of these "areas of predilection" with numerous statistics.[11]

All tumors tended to pass through certain initial stages of the indifferent granulation formation, a stage of "florescence," and a stage of regression. Virchow wondered whether the substances liberated in the regression state were also the infecting ones. His numerous experiments with glanders inclined him in this direction. The products of regression were often toxic.

In this context he mentioned "iodism." He actually referred to the hyperthyroidism observed in certain cases of goiter since the introduction of iodine treatment of goiter by Coindet in 1820. This complication brought the whole iodine treatment into discredit for many years. At this early date Virchow did not regard this "iodism" as a direct effect of iodine, but as an intoxication by substances liberated in the thyroid by iodine.[12]

Not all tissues were equally able to react by tumor formation, some being too highly differentiated. Tumor formation was mainly a quality of the connective substances.[13] There were two great subgroups of tumors: the "cystical tumors," arising mainly through extravasation, and the "pseudoplasm," based on actual new cell growth or proliferation. The latter tumors might be of either a histoid, organoid, teratoid, or combined nature. A tumor was not so much characterized in every element, but by its particular total arrangement.[14]

After six chapters of general introduction filling only 128 pages, Virchow entered the detailed discussion of different tumor forms. It is quite obvious that in the framework of this discussion we have to limit ourselves to little more than a mere enumeration of the tumors discussed by Virchow. Any attempt to report on even a few of the innumerable interesting descriptive details contained in the remaining nineteen chapters of Virchow's book would completely destroy the structure of this exposition and be inconsistent with its purpose.

In Chapters 7 to 12 Virchow described and discussed the tumors originating from extravasation: hematomata, hygromata (hydrocele, hydromeningocele cerebralis and spinalis), follicular cysts (atheromata, hydatids of the uterus and gastrointestinal tract), retention cysts of larger channels (gall bladder, female genitalia).

With Chapter 13 (fibromata) Virchow entered the field of the proliferative tumors, the "pseudoplasms." Besides nodulous and papillary fibromata he also discussed elephantiasis as a diffuse fibromatosis. Fibromata might be combined with can-

croids (what Virchow calls cancroid is epithelioma with us)
or develop into sarcomata. Chapter 14 is devoted to the lipo-
mata. In both chapters the fallacy of a dyscrasic theory is
discussed in great detail.

The lore of myxomata (Chapter 15) is entirely Virchow's
creation, as the mucous tissue was his "invention." Chondromata (Chapter 16) subdivided into homologous ecchondro-
mata and heterologous enchondromata are studied in particular
length, cartilage having always been one of Virchow's favored
tissues. Traumatism is discussed as a causative factor. Malignancy of chondromata seems rare.

The second volume starts with a chapter on osteomata
(Chapter 17). Chapter 18 discusses psammomata ("sand
tumors"—a group first described by Virchow), gliomata (another creation of his), and melanomata, which he had separated from the sarcomata. Virchow discussed at this occasion
tumors of the hypophysis and adrenals (and again in Volume
III, Chapter 22, pp. 78 ff.).

Chapter 19 is devoted to the sarcoma, "the real touchstone
of oncology." The creation of our present-day notion of sarcoma might indeed be Virchow's most important contribution
to oncology.[15] Sarcomata are connective substance tumors not
resembling any definite physiological tissue.[16] They might originate by metaplasia from fibromata, myxomata, chondromata,
osteomata, melanomata, or gliomata, but need not always pass
through such stages. The round-cell sarcoma might be confused with cancer, but it has no alveolae.[17] The sarcoma has a
histoid structure, while the carcinoma is organoid. Sarcomata
seem to metastasize through the blood, as in spite of extensive
metastases, especially of the lung, lymphatic glands are often
immune.[18] The sarcoma is an affliction mostly of the young.
Early operation is particularly indicated.

Chapter 20 comprises so-called "granulation tumors": syphilis, lupus, leprosy, and glanders. Virchow was fully aware of
the fact that he switched here all of a sudden from a morphological to an etiological classification. On purely morphological
grounds he would have to describe syphilitic manifestations as
fibroma, myxoma, tubercle, etc. And yet interestingly enough

they are all manifestations of one disease! [19] Virchow noticed the histological similarities of lupus and the tumor albus of articulations; but, still an "anti-ontologist," he insisted, of course, on its "nonscrofulous" nature.[20] In discussing leprosy he used the extensive firsthand experience acquired on his Norway mission of 1859.

The lymphatic tumors (Chapter 21) comprise lymphomata (especially in leukemia), lymphatic neoformations in typhoid or scrofulosis, and Hodgkins disease. They include tuberculosis (Addison's disease is extensively discussed under tuberculosis in Volume II, pp. 692 ff.), lymphosarcoma, and "Perlsucht" (bovine tuberculosis).

The published part of the third volume contains the chapters on struma (goiter—in Chapter 22), myomata (Chapter 23— another Virchow concept), neuromata (Chapter 24), and angiomata (Chapter 25).

The tumor book is silent on cancer (carcinoma), but we know already Virchow's earlier cancer concepts. In his last systematic survey of cancer problems in 1888 he emphasized as his main contributions his description of the alveolar structure of cancers (carcinomata) and his characterization of the epitheloid cell form in cancer.[21]

He avoided a definite statement of his theory on connective tissue origin of carcinoma.[22] The evidence produced by Remak (1854), Michel (1857), and especially Thiersch (1861) and Waldeyer (1867) for the epithelial origin of carcinoma had been too overwhelming. And yet up to the very end Virchow could not, on the other hand, convince himself entirely that connective tissue could not be transformed into epitheloid cells.[23] He still believed that he had observed the process in 1855.[24] This attachment to the connective tissue theory of cancer, which he had inherited from Bichat, is largely a function of Virchow's basic notion of metaplasia ("persistency of cells while changing their tissue characteristics") for which he had found so many examples in other situations and which he reaffirmed in his address on metaplasia at the International Medical Congress in Copenhagen in 1884.[25]

It is natural that in later years Virchow found comfort in

some of the endothelioma theories of others [26] which seemed to connect again certain carcinomata and connective tissue.[27]

Although he had often shown the similarity of embryological and tumor tissues, he refused to accept the embryological cancer theory of his pupil Cohnheim as "too exclusive" [28] and tinged with a certain "mysticism of the embryological." [29]

When the evidence for cellular spread of carcinoma metastases increased, he had nothing to recant, as he had always formulated his reservations very cautiously. He continued to feel that perhaps the last word in this question of the chemical nature of metastases was not yet said.[30] It is characteristic of his close co-operation with French scientists in general and with Velpeau in particular that he furnished the preparations that allowed the latter to prove, in the great Paris Academy discussion of 1855, the ability of "cancroids" (epitheliomata) to metastasize.[31]

Even Virchow's last systematic discussion of the cancer problem in 1888 contains an extremely sagacious and fertile new idea. In view of the fact that carcinomata have a tendency toward regressive metamorphosis, Virchow felt that therapeutic research should look for such substances that could induce or speed up this regression! [32] This has been exactly the goal pursued by radiation therapy during the last forty years. In spite of unavoidable errors, Virchow remained the great master of oncology up to the end.

Parasites and Bacteria

VIRCHOW's cellular pathology was hardly ten years old when a new star of the first order arose in the medical firmament— bacteriology. The old theory of the *contagium vivum* that had seen its lowest ebb between 1820 and 1850 [1] became again acceptable primarily on account of the proverbial swing of the pendulum. A more objective factor for this reaction was the increasing number of diseases that could be traced to parasites.

Though all these parasites were of a far greater magnitude than bacteria, they suggested that these smallest beings might have equally pathogenic qualities. Some such mistaken identifications between bacteria and diseases were immediately made by uncritical enthusiasts. It is significant that the bacteriological disease theory spread *before* the first important discoveries of Pasteur, Koch, and their followers in the field of human pathology in the 1870's. Only through these discoveries did bacteriology become the greatest medical accomplishment of the nineteenth century, especially when to improved prophylaxis were added Pasteur's immunizations of the 1880's and Behring's sera of the 1890's.

The myth that so often poses as history has it that Virchow "opposed bacteriology." The truth is considerably more complex, and it might even be claimed that Virchow made positive contributions in this new field which was of such great immediate importance to medicine. It is certainly true that his main contributions (as in the case of Claude Bernard, who showed a similar reluctance to embrace bacteriology) do not lie in this, but in a more basic, less immediately practical field. It is equally true that energies had to be channeled away from this field if bacteriology was to grow, that men like Klebs and Behring, therefore, had perhaps to attack Virchow, and that some of his early errors to which he clung (as in the case of tuberculosis and diphtheria) made him a fine target. Yet to take simply the affirmations of these rebellious "sons" as historical truth would be, to say the least, unwise.

Virchow was certainly ill prepared to adopt bacteriology. All those who did were, except for Pasteur, considerably younger than he was. Virchow had grown up in the shadow of an "anticontagionism" that was promoted by such first-rate scientists and sanitarians as Magendie, Andral, Bouillaud, and John Simon.[2] This movement, denying the contagiosity, not of all diseases, but of such important diseases as yellow fever, plague, cholera, leprosy, or influenza, denied automatically the idea of the *contagium vivum* of living disease germs. It was particularly congenial to the young Virchow, as he had elaborated in 1848 a new fundamental social theory of epidemic diseases.[3]

In 1848 he was therefore, like all leading medical men, an anticontagionist in the case of cholera [4] (to the pathological anatomy of which he made valuable contributions). His own research rather increased his skepticism as to the existence of a cholera germ. He had found numerous vibrios in cholera stools, but he found the same vibrios in dysentery (A, XLV [1869], 280) and arsenic poisoning (A, XLVII [1869], 524). While Virchow was too old and too "progressive" not to have once embraced anticontagionism, he was—unlike a Bouillaud or Ph. Ricord—still young enough to shake it off in later years. Thus he outgrew his anticontagionism, in the case of cholera analyzing critically in 1868 his own errors and declaring (published in A, XLV [1869], 279) that everything suggests a "fungus" as the cause of cholera. When Koch found the "fungus" in 1885, he defended him against his critics. As a matter of fact, he grew so enthusiastic about Koch's discovery that he called the cholera bacillus the *ens morbi* (the essence) of cholera, an opinion inconsistent with his general theory of infectious diseases.[5] And all this was in spite of the fact that the politically conservative Koch was continually played up against the radical Virchow by governmental agencies.

In the case of typhus Virchow was in 1848 one of the few "progressives" to doubt its contagiosity.[6] But by 1868 he had joined the contagionists also in the case of typhus.[7]

We know already the strong chemical bias of the young Virchow. In 1880 he confirmed [8] that on account of these chemical leanings his early sympathies were indeed with the "catalytic" theories of epidemic diseases promoted by Liebig and Berzelius, not the *contagium vivum*.

We are equally familiar with the problematic "anti-ontological" bias of Virchow and his generation. To the anti-ontologist "specific" diseases were anathema and bacteriological discoveries that confirmed the existence of such specific diseases were automatically a source of discomfort.

Virchow had just created with much labor and many difficulties cellular pathology. It is rather natural that this made him psychologically disinclined immediately to shift the emphasis into another direction (and into one whose lonely defender in Germany through decades had been his archenemy Henle!). Cellular pathology, furthermore, provided him with a notion of the role of "constitution," "disposition," specific body structure, and reaction that would see in infectious agents often secondary factors.

Under these circumstances it is not surprising that Virchow was somewhat reticent to embrace bacteriology. But it is surprising that he was able, not only to gain a balanced view of the subject in later years, but also to make important contributions to the first stages of the science of pathogenic germs— to parasitology. While the former is a fine testimony to the large amount of objectivity and self-control at his command, the latter is an expression of his often noticed sensitivity toward contemporary trends.

As a matter of fact, one of the earliest published contributions of Virchow (in Froriep's *Neue Notizen,* XXXV [1846], 323) is the first description of fungi (sarcina) in a (tuberculous) lung. Sarcina had been found in the stomach by J. Goodsir, Virchow's inspiration in more than one field, in 1842. It is furthermore typical of Virchow's early genuine interest in parasitic diseases that he himself undertook to write for his 1854 *Handbook* the chapters on diseases produced by plant parasites (I, 355 ff.) and by animal parasites (I, 366 ff.), and on infections produced by animal poisons ("Zoonoses": glanders, rabies, anthrax—II, Part 1, 337–413. Virchow reported here on his inoculation experiments with glanders). These are the only special chapters he contributed to the *Handbook.*

Virchow continued his research on fungi in 1855 with work on onychomycosis, for which he gave one of the first descriptions.[9] In 1856 [10] he coined the general term of "mycoses" that we still use and described other forms of pneumomycosis—for example, such caused by aspergillus. Here again he had had very few predecessors (among them his perennial competitors Bennett in 1842 and Remak in 1845). He regarded these mycoses as secondary, but as giving a new aspect to the disease process.

Virchow started original work on animal parasites in 1856 in showing that certain tumors of the liver, first described by Buhl in 1852 and diagnosed as colloid cancers, were actually multilocular echinococci.[11]

In 1857 he started a series of articles, "Helminthological Notes," [12] in which he discussed such problems as the geographical distribution of entozoa, the calcified bodies in the heads of taenoids, the so-called "worm-knots" around pentastoma or psorospermia, and the grapelike hydatids of the pia mater. In the course of these researches he became also engaged in the study of trichinae, where he made outstanding contributions.

Trichinae had been found post-mortem in the muscles of man by James Paget in 1835 and in those of the pig by Leidy in 1846. But nothing was known of the nature and life cycles of the animal or its pathogenic qualities. Feeding experiments by Herbst and Leuckart had failed to give conclusive or correct results.* This is where Virchow came in with his feeding experiments in 1859 and 1860 (reported in *Deutsche Klinik*, XI [1859], 430, and in *A*, XVIII [1860], 330 ff.). While Zenker showed in 1860 that trichinae were more than curious post-mortem findings and produced definite and dangerous clinical symptoms, Virchow, partly using material from Zenker's cases, unraveled the life history of the parasite. The larvae contained in the muscle would develop in the intestinal tract of the animal that had eaten trichinous meat into full-grown male and female trinchinae (not trichocephalus as Leuckart had assumed). They would mate and the female would produce living larvae that would penetrate the body of the same animal host and settle in the muscle (not leave via the stools and infect only the body of a second animal host feeding on the stools, as Leuckart had assumed—this being possible, but un-

* Priority discussions with Leuckart became possible only because Claude Bernard, on account of Virchow's abominable handwriting, had been unable to read a note to the French Academy when it was sent to him in July, 1859. Only by November was Bernard in possession of a readable version. Meanwhile Milne-Edwards had read in September a note on Leuckart's new experiments, which were actually later than Virchow's. See *A*, XXXII (1865), 335.

common). Virchow eventually was the first to describe the location of the trichina within the muscle fiber (not a small vessel) and the nature of its capsule formed by sarcolemma. Virchow also dealt with the problems of differential diagnosis of trichinae from other entozoa, their life duration, etc. In a short popular book in 1863 Virchow summarized his findings and started a vigorous campaign for proper prophylaxis—that is, meat inspection—which was eventually introduced into Germany in 1872–73. It is essentially due to Virchow's efforts that trichinosis has long practically disappeared in Germany, while in the United States human and pig infestations are even today still widespread.[13] Virchow rounded out his trichinosis work in the following years with smaller studies on trichinosis in wild animals, on psorospermosis, on actinomycosis in pigs, etc.[14]

With Virchow's experimental work on trichinosis in 1860 his creative activity in the new field of parasitic disease came to an end. He nevertheless played an important indirect role in furthering the beginnings of bacteriology. He published in the *Archives* (XI [1857], 132 ff., and XIV [1858], 432 ff.) the articles of Brauell, who together with Pollender and Davaine was the discoverer of the anthrax bacillus—the first well-established pathogenic bacterium. He also published Keber's article on the cocci that were long regarded as the causative agents of smallpox and cowpox (in A, XLII [1868], 112). It was Virchow's assistant Obermeier who, with his approval, published his discovery of the recurrens spirilla in *Centralblatt fuer die medizinischen Wissenschaften,* IX [1873], 145–47). In disproving the dogma of the hereditary nature of leprosy during his expedition in Norway in 1859, Virchow cleared the way for the discovery of the lepra bacillus by Armauer Hansen,[15] which was also published in the *Archives* (LXXIX [1880], 32). The *Archives* also published Loesch's discovery of amoebae in dysentery.[16]

Virchow dealt twice in the early seventies with the new bacteriological trends. In an address, "Lazarette und Barracken," in the Berlin Medical Society in 1871 he took up the relation between "infectious diseases" and microorganisms. Virchow had coined for himself the expression "infectious disease" as early as 1854, but with a different meaning from the one we attribute to it today. It would be best described as "general toxic diseases," and included, therefore, not only diseases like measles, smallpox, septicemia, typhus, but also uremia and bilemia (cholemia), while it excluded "local diseases" like pulmonary tuberculosis, tuberculous meningitis, "zoonoses" like anthrax, or parasitic diseases like trichinosis. It had now "with a certain justification" been claimed that all infectious diseases were caused by microorganisms and therefore were contagious. "As little as I deny the correctness of the idea that is at the bottom of these new researches . . . I must say that our present experiences are far from giving a solid basis for a general doctrine of infection and that much caution is indicated in the application of such a doctrine to certain disease situations." [17] The active substances might not be in the organisms themselves, but might be toxines produced by them (this was stated almost twenty years before the work of Loeffler, Roux, and Yersin on toxines!), or the same substances might also be produced in other ways. The air might not be the only way to convey microorganisms to wounds.

In 1874 Virchow gave again at the *pépinière* the Founders' Day address which he had given first in 1845. He dealt with "progress in military medicine, especially in the field of infectious diseases." The theory of a *contagium vivum* had been confirmed so far in the case of anthrax and recurrent fever. But what was the role of the "microcci" found in so many other infectious diseases? Many days would probably pass till scientific clarity on them could be obtained, "but we can well state that in the infections of man and animals a new, tremendous domain of independent life-phenomena has been opened up." [18] The technical difficulties are very great, due to the minuteness of the objects and the difficulties of differentiation. "Pure cultures" fail again and again. "Smallpox and cholera, typhus and dysentery, diphtheria and wound infections are all suspect to be caused by these minute plants." But are the bacteria and micrococci found in all of them the real cause or the essence of these diseases? Billroth refers all these vibrios, bacteria, etc., to one mother form, "coccobacteria septica." But do we actually deal only with one bacterium or several of them? And do they act directly or through toxine formation? Some might act in the former, some in the latter way. Experiments Virchow made with bacteria-free lymph in anthrax suggested in this case a chemical, toxic, not a mechanical, hypothesis. (A toxic hypothesis he had proclaimed already in 1845 from the same chair, introducing the notion of ichorrhemia.) Virchow was always strongly impressed by the similarity of certain intoxications and infections, as in the case of cholera and arsenic poisoning, of bone changes in syphilis and phosphorus poisoning. Could such toxines not occasionally be products of body cells?

The question cannot be settled morphologically. Even if we should continue to be unable to differentiate these microorganisms morphologically, they might be actually different. *In the case of infection the experiment alone will decide the issue.* Morphology is only one part of biology, and it cannot give the last answers concerning the nature of things.[19] That in 1874 Virchow's attitude toward bacteriology was progressive, not reactionary, is evidenced by the fact that probacteriologists like Weigert and Cohnheim would not go beyond these statements even years later.[20]

It was not Virchow who attacked the bacteriologists, but their erratic leader Klebs, who in an address *on cellular pathology and infectious diseases* at the fifty-first *Naturforscherversammlung* in Cassel in 1878 declared that the former had outlived its utility. Virchow answered in his "Krankheitswesen und Krankheitsurachen" ("The Essence and the Causes of Diseases," published in *A*, LXXIX [1880], 1 ff.). The *principle* of cellular pathology is not refuted by the demonstration of leucocyte diapedesis, of the epithelial origin of cancers, or of bacteria. All these are cellular processes. In disease the cell reacts to external irritants, external causes. As different cells react differently to the same irritant, we must also assume internal causes, predispositions. Insofar as Klebs claimed that "the so-called reaction of tissues depends essentially on external causes" (bacteria), he was wrong. One could discuss the more or less of external and internal causes. But Klebs had gone much farther. In claiming that all cell processes are passive, *he abolished internal causes and actually confused disease causes * and the resulting disease process.*[21]

One of Klebs's main arguments was that cellular pathology had not brought about cellular therapy. Virchow admitted that it had not given "cellular prophylaxis." A theory of the disease process is not at the same time a theory of disease causes. Therefore the etiological analysis is of a high practical value. (Virchow had actually expressed this point of view repeatedly, for example, in Frankfurt, 1867; see *DN* p. 67.) But without a nosology, etiological medicine remains a conglomeration of empiric statements of which a large part remains unintelligible.[22] Cellular pathology had nevertheless had a profound influence on therapeutics in reinforcing local therapy, surgery included.[23] Cellular pathology had, in the use of "general remedies," established the principle that there is a certain affinity between certain drugs and certain parts of the body and cells.[24] This became Ehrlich's guiding principle and therewith that of all modern chemotherapy.

In refuting, on the other hand, the embryonic tumor theories of another pupil, Cohnheim, Virchow found himself between two fires: Klebs, who made everything depend on external, and Cohnheim, who made everything depend on internal causes.[25] Klebs's main reproach was that there is no room in cellular pathology for the parasitary theory of disease and the infectious processes. But were all infectious diseases really produced by parasites? Virchow reminded Klebs of the bioplasm hypotheses of Beale and Drysdale. Virchow had never pronounced doubts where there was actual proof, as in the case of Brauell or Obermeier. But he took the liberty to have doubts concerning Klebs's "Bacillus malariae," "helicomonas of syphilis," and "helicomonas of rheumatism" (and right he was to do so). And are all contagious diseases thereby infectious diseases?

---

* Henle (*General Pathology,* p. 90) had already warned his followers in vain: "It is false that contagion should ever become disease in its development. . . . It is always only the morbific cause diffused in one body and transferable to others." Broussais had even earlier insisted on the differentiation between disease cause and disease process.

Are scabies and trichinosis and mycoses which are contagious therefore infectious diseases? Klebs had put the whole discussion on a false basis. Cellular pathology did not discuss parasites, as it did not discuss traumatisms and corrosions, because it did not claim to be a general pathology. It did not discuss, therefore, etiology, but only the behavior of body elements in the basic forms of disease, the disease process.

To know the microorganism did not mean to know everything. It did not imply (for example, in the case of the recurrens spirilla) knowledge of how the microorganism entered the body and how it produced disease in the body. This would have implied some knowledge of the pathology of cells. Virchow referred here to the suggestion of different possibilities of bacterial action that he had made in his 1874 address (mechanical, toxic, etc.). How did these bacteria produce immunity? Might there not exist another "infectious material" besides bacteria? [26] Experiments with dialyzed materials suggested the existence of toxines outside the bacteria. The action of some infectious diseases closely resembled that of poisons. Chronic interstitial hepatitis could be produced by alcohol, syphilis, malaria, phosphorus, and bacterial extracts. Phosphorus and syphilis could produce exostoses. [27] The "mycotic" origin of a number of infectious diseases was assured; it would probably be shown in more (like malaria and cholera). But the bases for a general mycotic theory of infection, as claimed by Klebs, were not yet given.

I have reported this sixty-page article of Virchow in some detail, as this seems the best way to enable the reader to make his own decision as to the myth of Virchow's basic opposition to bacteriology.

In 1885 (A, CI [1885], 1) Virchow, in an article entitled "The Struggle of Cells and Bacteria," again defended himself against the claim, this time coming from France, that cellular pathology was dead. The argumentation is essentially the same as in 1880. What has to be studied, according to Virchow, is the fight of the cells against the parasitic microorganisms. Virchow hails the phagocytosis discoveries of Metchnikoff (published in A, XCVI [1884], 177, and XCVII [1884], 502) that

are promising beginnings of such studies.* The new bacteri-
cidal sera are probably cell products too.[28]

In 1893 "Stabsarzt Professor Doctor Behring" introduced his
*Collected Essays on Etiological Therapy of Contagious Dis-
eases* with a seventy-one-page onslaught against Virchow and
cellular pathology. The "Stabsarzt" attacked with the same
arguments Klebs had used, but added the battle cry "Back to
Sydenham and humoral pathology." In emphasizing the desira-
bility of an etiological classification of disease, he did not tell
anything new to Virchow, who had stressed this point in
1867.[29] In order to win an easier victory, Behring preferred
"discussing" Virchow's publications of the 1840's to discussing
those of the 1870's and 1880's. Virchow didn't even answer.
Only when Behring completed his scientific attack by personal
smears in the general press, did he receive a well-deserved
short rebuttal from Virchow's pen.[30] That Virchow was not
only the greater intellect, but also the greater character is
graphically illustrated by the fact that at this very moment
Virchow publicly testified as to the value of the newly discovered Behring diphtheria antitoxin.[31]

Virchow's attitude in the bacteriology discussions of the
1870's and 1880's can be fully appreciated only by those who
know about the ruthless and uncritical enthusiasm that had
seized the bacteriologically-minded. In 1877 Virchow even
had to defend digestion as a chemical process against the attempt of interpreting it in purely bacteriological terms.[32] How
overwhelming this trend was, is perhaps best illustrated by the
fact that even so critical a man as Virchow himself fell for
some of the hundreds of "causative agents" that were then
announced every year. Virchow adopted Keber's smallpox
"bacteria" [33] as well as the "beriberi" bacillus.[34]

While Virchow's total attitude had little in common with the
myth of "total opposition" to bacteriology, it cannot be denied

* The very reason that endeared Metchnikoff to Virchow induced
Koch, not only to deny his discovery (International Medical Congress,
1900), but also to try some "character assassination" of Metchnikoff. See
the unpublished letters of Koch to Fluegge in the H. B. Jacobs collection
of the Johns Hopkins Institute of the History of Medicine.

that Virchow's critical conservatism was quite unreasonable in some specific cases.

It would undoubtedly have been wiser had he dropped his old notion of infectious diseases, dating from his anticontagionalist youth, instead of going into needless semantic exercises on the question up to the very end.[35]

Orth has already pointed out that Virchow's greatest failure in regard to bacteriology consisted in his unwillingness to draw the consequences of Koch's discovery for his tuberculosis theories.[36] His insistence, in tuberculosis as elsewhere, that the bacillus was not the disease was meritorious. That he did not encourage Koch at the occasion of the latter's visit in 1878 was a personal matter.[37] That, in a very objective way, he demonstrated the negative effect of Koch's tuberculin in 1891 was his duty.[38] That he repeated his pluralistic tuberculosis theories (see pp. 79 ff.)—for example, in 1865 [39] and in 1882 [40]—and that in 1880 he still denied the transmission of cattle tuberculosis [41] were most regrettable. That after Koch's discovery of 1884 he stated in 1885, "Phthisis has remained what it was," [42] that he upheld in 1901 that "tuberculosis" is not everywhere where tubercle bacilli are found [43] are inexcusable and completely inconsistent with his 1874 claims that morphology should cede to the results of experimentation. The morphological differences observed by him were real and had their meaning, but were of secondary importance after Koch's discovery.

Virchow committed the same morphological mistake in the case of diphtheria. In the anti-ontological, antispecific fervor of his youth he had expanded Bretonneau's clinical-anatomical notion of diphtheria into a purely morphological one.[44] Virchow's "diphtheria" was nothing but a superficial necrosis with membrane formation that therefore could be found also in cholera, dysentery, and other conditions. The discovery of the bacillus eliminated this morphological formalism and reinstated Bretonneau's specific notions. Virchow's tragicomic comment on this development in 1894 was still that this made "scientific analysis impossible." [45] This might have been said with more justice of his transformation of Bretonneau's notion.

Virchow has been justifiably blamed for not recognizing the merits of Semmelweis' great 1847 discovery and for having stuck to outmoded climatic and predisposition theories of puerperal fever. Semmelweis himself devoted some very caustic lines to Virchow in his book on childbed fever.[46] Kleine collected the few occasional remarks of Virchow in this direction in 1930.[47] Virchow's halfhearted admissions of Semmelweis' right in 1864 and 1879 [48] were certainly ungenerous. In all fairness it must nevertheless be stated that Virchow shares this blame with 99.99 per cent of his medical contemporaries and that his own personal role in blocking the spread of Semmelweis' discovery was extremely small. I have been puzzled by Virchow's affirmation in 1863 [49] that he had no cases of puerperal fever in his clinical ward, though handling corpses simultaneously. The riddle is solved by a passage in his 1854 Handbook,[50] overlooked by Kleine, from which it appears that he used and recommended Semmelweis' cleaning methods, though not adopting his theories in toto.

These episodic attitudes should not be taken as Virchow's total outlook on bacteriology. If we continue here our scrutiny where we left off, we find him in the 1880's in his medical report on an Egyptian archeological expedition as "germ conscious" as any child of the period. He praises his experiences with Listerism and tells of observing dysentery amoebas (under the guidance of Kartulis) and fly transmission of infectious conjunctivitis.[51] In Moscow in 1897 he calls the knowledge of bacteria, as compared to the knowledge of cells, "another, not less, perhaps even more important product of the scientific endeavors of our times." [52] Half of his Huxley lecture of 1898, "Recent Progresses in Science and Their Influence on Medicine and Surgery," is devoted to a positive review of the achievements of bacteriology. He emphasized the "immortal merits," the "stupendous success" of Pasteur's work that have "opened new avenues to medicine and technology." [53] He praised Koch's discovery of the cholera and tuberculosis bacilli (far more generous in this respect than Koch himself who, for instance, in his Academy reception speech did not even mention the name of Pasteur [54]). Virchow's last great medical address at the International Medical Congress in Paris in 1900 on "Traumatism and Infection" fully appreciates the role of bacteria, especially in osteomyelitis.[55] A warning not to refer all contagious diseases in advance to mere bacteria [56] has been fully justified by later developments.

Virchow's attitude toward bacteriology seems more properly defined as positive, thoughtful, and useful criticism than as "stubborn opposition." His insistence on social and constitutional factors, besides bacterial, in the causations of infectious diseases proved actually to be progressive, not reactionary. Virchow was confessedly more interested in the disease process than in disease causes. But to reproach Virchow for this, to blame a Virchow and a Claude Bernard that they were no Pasteurs or Robert Kochs, seems about as sensible a piece of historical criticism as to reproach grapevines that they don't bear apples.

Anticlimax

AFTER MORE than twenty years of most intensive creative activity in pathological anatomy, marked by dozens of discoveries, Virchow almost abruptly stopped making new contributions in pathological anatomy toward the end of the 1860's, before he had finished his fifth decade. Is this because most of his research was now devoted to anthropology, or did he turn into anthropology because he felt that in pathology he had reached certain limits? We shall probably never know.

In the late fifties and early sixties Virchow spent much time and energy defending his new cellular pathology against old adversaries like Henle,[1] Spiess,[2] Wunderlich,[3] and Robin.[4] Then he had to adapt his system to the new findings of friends and pupils like Von Recklinghausen (extracellular liquid circulation in connective tissue, migratory cells), Cohnheim (diapedesis of white blood corpuscles, vascular inflammation theory, embryonic cancer theory), Weigert (necrotic inflammation theory), and Waldeyer (epithelial origin of cancer).[5] Virchow's inflammation concept underwent, as Lubarsch has pointed out,[6] considerable change after 1871. His new point of view is most clearly developed in his address at the Twelfth International Medical Congress in Moscow, 1897, on "The Role of Vessels and Parenchyma in Inflammation." He then admitted the existence of four kinds of inflammation: (1) exudative, (2) infiltrative, (3) parenchymatous or alterant, (4) proliferant.[7] In the first and second hyperemia plays a dominant role. This subdivision of inflammation, on the other hand, made him approach the old idea of Andral to discard the concept of inflammation as a unit altogether.[8]

In the 1880's the attacks of the bacteriologists had to be answered. From 1858 to Virchow's death these more defensive actions were accompanied by a tireless propagation and interpretation of cellular pathology in numerous addresses and papers. Doctor Edith Heischkel-Artelt has quite rightly argued that part of Virchow's success in convincing his contemporaries is due to his propagandist skill, which he might have acquired in his early political activities.[9]

The last new discoveries Virchow made in pathology were those of ochronosis (A, XXXVII [1866], 212), congenital interstitial encephalitis (A, XXXVIII [1867], 129; XLIV [1868], 472), and heterotopy of gray matter (A, XLIV [1868], 138). In 1862 he named "parametritis" a condition which he had analyzed already much earlier.[10]

Of the well-known pamphlets of the 1870's, that on *The Value of the Pathological Experiment* is an attempt to help his English friends against the onslaught of the antivivisectionists; that on *Chlorosis* has largely lost interest due to the fact that the disease has not only disappeared, but that many suspect today that it never existed. *The Technique of Dissection* of 1875 was the codification of what Virchow had taught and practiced for thirty years. He had been (together with Rokitansky) a great innovator in the field of independent systematic pathological autopsy. So far the dissector had mostly opened only such organs as the clinician advised him to do. A. L. Smith had seen many dissections in New York, but never a systematic one, before he came to study with Virchow in the 1850's. Usage in Germany was apparently no better, as Klebs, who had studied in Koenigsberg before joining Virchow, reported the same experience.

Virchow continued, of course, his routine as a pathologist. He frequently demonstrated interesting pathological specimens—mostly tumors or rare conditions like polysarcia and progressive myositis ossificans—to medical audiences, especially the Berlin Medical Society, as reported in the *Berliner klinische Wochenschrift* or in the Charité *Annals.* He gave interesting and artful papers in the same society in the seventies and eighties on, for instance, bone formation, nephritis arthritica, fat embolism in eclampsia, and emphysema.[11] His old flair for new trends was still present when in the late eighties he became particularly interested in acromegaly [12] and myxedema,[13] although we can't blame a man of his age when he would no longer make great contributions in the new field of internal secretion and organ therapy (or "parenchyme juice" therapy as he preferred to call it [14]). Indirectly he is even linked to the great new acquisition (and fashion) of twentieth-century medicine—vitamins and avitaminosis—by having published the first papers of Eijkman on beriberi (*A,* CXLVIII [1897], 523; CXLIX [1897] 187).

The above-mentioned manuscript *curriculum vitae* of 1860 in the Thor Jager collection contains also a division entitled "Wichtigste Arbeiten" ("Most Important Research"). With the kind permission of Doctor Jager a complete translation of this important passage, which again shows to what extent Virchow's creative work in pathology was completed before 1860, is here printed:

First studies on the inflammation of vessels, particularly phlebitis. Started at a time when Cruveilhier had just stated: *La phlebite domine toute la pathologie.* First a great number of preparatory studies on fibrin, leucocytes, metamorphosis of blood, published separately. Doctrines of *leukemia, embolism, thrombosis, ichorrhemia.* New researches on pathological pigments, stemming from blood (discovery of *hematoidin*). Use of hemin crystals in forensic blood diagnosis. Furthermore studies on endocarditis and endoarteritis.

Just finished large series of studies on *genesis* of tumors: carcinoma, cholesteatoma, neuroma, tubercle, colloid tumor of ovary, enchondroma, myosarcoma, etc. Published in monographs.

New theory of *structure of connective tissue* in connection with more accurate description of cartilage, bone and mucous tissue. More accurate history of bone growth and *rickets*. Special study of skull formation and skull deformation, especially in connection with *cretinism* and mental diseases.

Discovery of *corpora amylacea* and *amyloid degeneration*.

History of *inflammation:* parenchymatous inflammation (Keratitis, chondritis, osteitis, Bright's disease, etc.). Fibrin formation as a result of tissue activity.

New theory of *irritability* of different tissues: Cellular pathology. *Omnis cellula a cellula:* continuous development and transformation of tissues.

In looking back now over Virchow's pathological work, all those even only vaguely familiar with pathology will realize how tremendous and lasting his contributions are. My students usually express this feeling in stating that he is "so modern." One might just as well say that we can afford to be rather old fashioned in those fields where he labored in maintaining the validity of many of his concepts and findings of one hundred years ago.

Of course, on some points new discoveries—like, for instance, Cohnheim's discovery of the diapedesis of leucocytes—proved Virchow wrong. On many others his views were not wrong, but they do look somewhat primitive, since through the work of his successors we have learned so much more about these fields. Ehrlich's staining methods, for instance, opened a whole new era in our knowledge of leucocytes. And yet the genesis of leucocytes is still controversial and discussed in the framework set by Virchow. We might now know better what amyloid is chemically, but we don't know its pathological meaning any better.

The scope of this book would be transgressed and the competence of its author would be taxed in analyzing systematically the status of Virchow's findings and concepts in the light of our present-day knowledge of pathology. But it seems worth noting that: arteriosclerosis is to many of us no longer an en-

doarteritis; [15] all fatty degenerations had till recently become
a kind of fatty infiltration ;[16] pus melts again instead of being
only a product of melting; our concepts of inflammation have
changed; [17] and the limits of metaplasia have become much
narrower. And yet just the case of inflammation or metaplasia,
where after an almost complete renegation of Virchow's concepts in the "second generation" we have again approached
his point of view, invites caution and respect for his findings
and interpretations in all those regions that are not definitely
settled. Later findings (like the reticulo-endothelial system)
have given greater validity to many of his hypotheses. It is
still a matter of wonderment how, a hundred years ago, he
could find so much with poor microscopes, without fixing or
staining methods, without tissue cultures or experimental embryology, with only rudiments of our present-day physiology
and chemistry, and without colloid or enzyme chemistry at his
disposal.

Rarely do we realize to what extent cellular pathology is still
with us. In the words of E. R. Long,

All fields of pathology were cleared by the new knowledge. The
physician of today can scarcely conceive how great a revolution
this was. One who from his earliest student days has heard every
phase of anatomy, embryology, neurology, physiology and pathology discussed in terms of cells, can hardly picture a state of medical knowledge in which these cells had no part. We are all cellular
pathologists today, taking our post Virchowian cellular sense for
granted.[18]

In spite of chemistry's successes going into and beyond the
cell, in spite of our increased knowledge of nucleus and protoplasm, the cell is still an ultimate biological unit. And cells still
arise only out of cells. *Omnis cellula e cellula.*

We have gone away from the strictly localistic approach that
Virchow had inherited from Morgagni, the limitations of which
were felt already by Bichat. We often feel that the strict localist ignores the forest in the study of trees. The pendulum has
swung again in certain respects from Cnidos to Cos, from
localism to holism. This is a result of our general change in
philosophical concepts, as well as of our increased knowledge

of the relations of organ functions. We feel that thus we have come closer to reality, though our concepts have often become rather hazy.

In the light of these changes we also look differently at the independence of cells. Virchow saw both dependence and independence, but emphasized the latter largely for politico-philosophical reasons. We, in spite of the fact that independence has been disproved only in the eyes of some fanatics like Ricker and Speransky, emphasize dependence. As this particular decision depends to such a high degree on general non-scientific convictions,* I doubt whether we are entitled to regard our own opinions as being any more objective than those of Virchow were.

Cellular pathology is limited in its possibilities to the same extent that pathological anatomy is.[19] Nobody has described more clearly the limitations of pathological anatomy than did Virchow throughout his life. Within these limits the cellular approach is still one of our most basic and useful biological and medical concepts.

Epidemiology and Public Health

IN THE MEMORY of men Virchow lives as the great pathologist. But this is only half of his medical accomplishments. Virchow was more than a medical scientist; he was also a great helper and saver of lives—a great doctor in the full sense of the word. It is true he made no outstanding direct contributions to in-

---

* In order to realize this fact, one has but to read carefully the wording of the following statement of Lubarsch (*BKW*, LVIII [1921], 1347): "The unit of the organism can be just as little derived from the sum of the cells, as a state from the sum of individuals composing it. They alone are but a mob, neither a nation nor a state." Lubarsch, who belonged to what Virchow once impolitely called the "dirty anti-Semitic Semites" (*BKW*, XXXI [1894], 129), was an extreme admirer of the old Prussian absolutistic system. It is very obvious how, in spite of his devotion to Virchow, this fact colored his outlook on the problem of independence of cells.

dividual therapy, but he was one of the greatest contributors to "mass therapy," to public health and preventive medicine which have preserved more lives during the past hundred years than all our spectacular progresses in individual therapeutics combined. It is significant that Virchow himself at the end of his life emphasized this aspect of his work more than any other. In view of the fact that Virchow was a reformer even before he became a scientist, his continual concern with practical medical accomplishments was quite natural. His training as a military surgeon probably did contribute to his orientation toward preventive medicine. The best of military surgeons have played a conspicuous role in the development of preventive medicine from Pringle and Desgenettes through Villemin and Laveran to R. Ross, Gorgas, Walter Reed, Loeffler, and Von Behring.[1] Virchow himself once emphasized these connections between military medicine and prevention.[2]

Virchow's activities in public health were based on an epidemiology of his own which he developed rather early in his career during his fateful trip to Upper Silesia in 1848 and which he incorporated into his famous report on the Upper Silesia typhus epidemic. He clearly saw that the "typhus" he was dealing with in Upper Silesia was not the customary "abdominal typhus" of Berlin and Paris (our typhoid), but the "British" (war, famine, etc.) typhus (our typhus). He called the latter "simple typhus." In 1848 he still believed in a genetic relationship between both forms. It is significant that he thought that the form of typhus which would appear depended on the "local social situation," the "simple" form being more frequent in proportion to poorer food supply and housing.[3] Under the influence of the discussions of the Paris Academy on the contagiosity of yellow fever and plague,[4] he developed a cautiously formulated anticontagionist attitude for typhus: "So far we have no facts that prove contagiosity [in Upper Silesia], while certain experiences are unfavorable to this assumption and almost all data in this direction can be explained by the endemicity of the disease cause."[5] He maintained, on the other hand, against Riecke that typhus and typhoid could be contagious under certain conditions.[6]

Famine alone obviously did not produce typhus directly. It might increase the predisposition. Both famine and typhus might be the product of certain climatic conditions, also producing above average humidity.[7] Bad housing, which Virchow described in detail in Upper Silesia, would enhance the effect of the climatic factor, as it would also in the case of cholera and plague. Under these combined conditions a "miasma" (a chemical poison) would develop, enter the body, and produce the disease.

So far Virchow's interpretation was more or less traditional, in the sense of the "physico-chemical" or "geographic" school of epidemiology.[8] His new attitude, his "socio-logical" epidemiology, becomes clearly apparent only when in his famous report he follows a short chapter on "Treatment of Cases" with the characteristic chapter on "Treatment of the Epidemic," where he asks for full democracy, education, liberty, and prosperity (here again consciously following the Paris Academy report on plague in Egypt), national autonomy, communal self-government, new roads, improvements in agriculture and industry, co-operatives, etc. The underlying idea of his whole argument is that the unfavorable climatic conditions would never have produced this emergency if the population had been free, educated, and prosperous.[9] Again Egypt served as an example. Egypt became a focus of plague in historical times, not through climatic changes, but through a social deterioration comparable to that in Upper Silesia. Virchow was to elaborate during the next months this sociological theory, which recognized the complex nature of the genesis of an epidemic, but regarded the social factor as the most significant one. Virchow maintained this point of view up to the end of his long life.

The second large epidemic that Virchow witnessed in 1848–49 was a cholera epidemic. Although his interest centered here on pathological anatomy especially of organs other than the intestine, he also emphasized the social implications.[10] Though in general a cholera anticontagionist, he found many data very suggestive of contagion.[11] That he was not dogmatic in his localism is evidenced by the fact that he upheld the general toxic nature of cholera against his two closest friends, Reinhardt and Leubuscher, who both regarded it as a local affection of the intestine.[12]

In 1849 Virchow also observed an epidemic-like outbreak of different forms of tuberculosis in Berlin. This, in his mind, gave some credit to the old theory of a "genius epidemicus," the epidemic constitution to which he also alluded several times in the 1850's.[13]

Virchow summarized his new epidemiological approach in 1848 and 1849 in the following passages:

Epidemics resemble great warning signs on which the true states-man is able to read that the evolution of his nation has been disturbed to a point which even a careless policy is no longer allowed to overlook.[14]

Don't crowd diseases point everywhere to deficiencies of society? One may adduce atmospheric or cosmic conditions or similar factors. But never do they alone make epidemics. They produce them only there where due to bad social conditions people have lived for some time in abnormal situations.

Why otherwise would individual diseases as well as epidemics be of a milder nature today than in the middle ages? Only because classes do now participate in living conditions from which they were then almost totally excluded. Only because the upper classes are now used to live in hygienic conditions while they then spent their lives in dirt, gluttony, and discomfort.[15]

Abnormal conditions always produce abnormal situations. War, plague and famine condition each other, and we don't know any period in world history, where they did not appear in a more or less large measure either simultaneously or following each other.[16]

Virchow even developed the idea that certain epidemic diseases might be specific for certain social crises,[17] like leprosy for the Middle Ages, the English sweat for the Reformation, cholera for the revolutions of the nineteenth century.

Epidemics of a character unknown so far appear, and often disappear without traces when a new culture period has started. Thus did leprosy and the English sweat. The history of artificial epidemics is therefore the history of disturbances of human culture.

Their changes announce to us in gigantic signs the turning points of culture into new directions. Each true culture revolution is followed by epidemics because a large sector of the population is only slowly absorbed by the new cultural movement and only slowly participates in its blessings.[18]

Virchow adopted the notion of "natural" and "artificial" diseases from his friend S. Neumann. Dysentery, malaria, pneumonia were "natural" diseases—that is, due primarily to natural conditions. Typhus, scurvy, tuberculosis, and mental diseases were "artificial"—that is, primarily due to social conditions. Virchow regarded certain large-scale mental aberrations just as much "epidemics" as bodily diseases appearing in great numbers.

The artificial epidemics are attributes of society, products of a false culture, that is not distributed to all classes. They point toward deficiencies produced by the structure of state or society, and strike therefore primarily those classes which do not enjoy the advantages of the culture.[19]

Being artificial, they could be overcome by social change. Tuberculosis had now to be conquered like scurvy, which had been overcome already. Typhus, malaria, and cholera should and could be limited to the same extent that gout, syphilis, and smallpox had been limited already. "The improvement of medicine would eventually prolong human life, *but improvement of social conditions could achieve this result now more rapidly and more successfully.*" [20]

If diseases were primarily social phenomena, then medicine was, of course, a "social science." This grandiose medical program implied the obligation of political activity for the true doctor.

Virchow's epidemiology was primarily a historical epidemiology. It was to a large extent inspired by his teachers Schoenlein and Hecker; in both men this interest was part of their romantic heritage. Temkin in 1929 showed the strong stimulus of romanticism in the development of historical epidemiology. [21] That the sociological theory was foreshadowed in this historical epidemiology is shown by the significant quotation from Hecker, given by Virchow himself: "The cultural level of nations that is their standard of living and their methods of treatment plays a decisive role in all crowd diseases, and crowd diseases in turn influence both." [22]

The sociological theory of disease had actually been fully developed in post-Revolutionary France by men like Virey, Villermé, Mélier, and Aubert-Roche ever since Cabanis wrote the famous aphorism, "Les maladies dépendent des erreurs de la société." [23] It had then been taken over by British authors in the 1840's. Virchow himself acknowledged, as usual, his French sources somewhat reluctantly, while he gave full credit to the influence of men like Alison, Corrigan, or Davidson and to the importance of Friedrich Engels' *Lage der arbeitenden Klassen in England.*[24]

Virchow was thus not original in embracing a sociological epidemiology that appeared in the nineteenth century between the climatic and the bacteriological concepts of epidemics. But he was instrumental in introducing it into Germany, proclaiming it with great clarity, strength, and in a language with a beauty and vigor akin to that of a Georg Buechner or a Freiligrath. And what is more, he was the one to preserve the concept, which is now an important element of our more complex present-day approach, through the period when the overwhelming concern with bacteriology threatened to extinguish the search for any other causative factor.

Virchow continued his epidemiological endeavors in Wuerzburg through his studies on cretinism in Franconia in 1851 and the following years. As late as 1840 a Bavarian official physician had reported that cretinism was the work of the devil! [25] How fast, on the other hand, the sociological concept spread is evidenced by the fact that Virchow was obliged to discuss the question whether cretinism is a social disease.[26] Although through proper education most of the cretins could be raised to higher mental levels, Virchow felt that cretinism was essentially a "product of the region." Its cause seemed to be the same endemic factor that also produced goiter, probably a miasma that was adversely affected by iodine. Virchow observed periodical oscillations in the occurrence of cretinism.

On his mission into the famine region of The Spessart in 1852, so similar to Upper Silesia in many respects, Virchow did not find typhus. He explained this by timely governmental action to relieve the famine and the absence of "typhus weather." [27] He felt again that education, freedom, and prosperity were the only effective preventives against the recurrence of such emergencies.

Although Virchow clearly realized the limitations of statistics in medicine,[28] he regarded its cultivation as early as 1848 as "one of the most urgent demands of our time." [29] In Wuerzburg he devoted himself to the vital and morbidity statistics of that city and began his studies on tumor statistics.[30] His interest in medical statistics is also illustrated by his participation in international statistical congresses (Paris, 1855; Berlin, 1863).

In the 1850's Virchow became first involved in a polemic with Von Pettenkofer on account of the latter's "ground water" theory of cholera, which was not recognized by Virchow because it was too dogmatic.[31] This discussion had periodical exacerbations in the 1860's and 1870's.[32] Virchow was strongly inclined since the 1860's toward the germ theory of cholera on the basis of experiences with infection through laundry and drinking water. He immediately hailed Koch's discovery in 1884 and organized its public dissemination.[33] He was still puzzled by the periodicity of cholera, which he tried to explain by changes in the virulence of the organism. During his 1892 sojourn in Russia he studied outbreaks and preventive methods there.[34]

The reappearance of typhus in Berlin and Eastern Prussia in 1868 led to renewed occupation with the subject. Virchow had become by now more and more a contagionist.[35] Yet his basic approach was little affected by this change, as basic social defects would play their role in any case. He reaffirmed his stand in Upper Silesia in 1848.[36] He advocated an approach that studies a multiplicity of factors: soil, air, nutrition, social customs, family life, housing, and occupation.[37] He showed the connection between famine condition and typhus outbreaks in Berlin and Eastern Prussia [38] and strongly emphasized the social element in the genesis of typhus: "The weather alone does not produce typhus." [39] Now a contagionist, he pointed toward the fact that the Slavonic countries became more and more the focus from which, under certain conditions, typhus could spread in Europe.[40]

In the late sixties Virchow was preparing a new sewerage system for Berlin. This and the experiences of the 1870/71 war brought about intensive studies in the epidemiology of typhoid fever. Any remnants of the unitary doctrine of typhoid and typhus were now completely overcome.[41] English and German health statistics were studied in all their complexity, especially as to the effect of improved canalization on typhoid frequency. In the case of typhoid frequency Virchow found positive correlations with ground water changes in Berlin. But his recognition of the role of contagion in typhoid again separated him from Pettenkofer.[42] As usual, Virchow warned against premature generalizations on the basis of contradictory data. Virchow made epidemiological studies of typhoid as late as 1893 in order to clear up doubts as to the healthfulness of his new sewerage installations.[43]

Intensive analyses of Berlin health statistics around 1870 revealed that the continuous mortality increase in Berlin was due primarily to an appallingly excessive infant mortality (38.3 per cent of the total mortality). The Berlin statistical pattern differed considerably from that of other big cities in Germany, but showed surprising similarity to that of large North American cities. Virchow felt that this might be due to similar social situations (like rapid growth).[44] In the 1870's Virchow forcefully re-emphasized the man-made character of epidemics.[45]

Virchow's concepts of public health corresponded to his epidemiology insofar as they were very broad, basic, sociopolitical rather than narrowly technical. As politics had become a question of social changes, medicine, on the other hand, was now involved in politics. Its progress too depended on social change.[46] Therefore, any political action of Virchow during his fifty years of political activity would in a way be "public health measures" and should logically be reported under this heading.

It is easy to see that for technical reasons I had to forego such an attempt, and to limit myself here to his public health accomplishments in the narrower sense. It remains true, nevertheless, that it was primarily his political position and power that enabled Virchow to obtain more realizations even in the narrower, technical field of public health than any "professional" German public health man of his time.[47]

In 1848 Virchow proclaimed the constitutional right of the individual citizen to live a healthful existence.[48] During his whole life he had to lead a two-front battle for public health against old-time reactionaries and "laissez-faire" liberals, who, for different reasons, wanted to leave the field in the hands of private philanthropy. But the crisis had reached a magnitude where private philanthropy was no longer adequate.[49] The state had to step in and had to practice public health, though Virchow wished that in the long run such intervention would be decentralized as much as possible.[50] Even in England, where private philanthropy was much more highly developed than elsewhere, it had become inadequate. Community intervention there had, on the other hand, proved that epidemics were preventable. How critical the health situation in Prussia * had become by 1848 was evidenced by the fact that the mortality in Prussia was higher than in England, in spite of the ravages of the industrial revolution in the latter country![51] A thorough reform of the housing, clothing, and nutrition of the masses was needed.

Virchow claimed furthermore in 1848 that public health should be concerned with such problems as working hours, work for the unemployed, free treatment for the indigent, insurance against invalidity, and health on emigrant ships where 20 per cent died during the voyage.[52] Large drainage works should be initiated in country districts.[53] The unhealthy barracks of the army should be improved.[54] In 1860 Virchow asked even the abolition of these sacred Prussian institutions.[55] School hygiene should be introduced. The whole penitentiary system was, according to Virchow, actually a public health

* Up to 1867 the political unit to which Virchow belonged and with which he could deal was only Prussia, not Germany.

problem. Punishment should be replaced by psychiatric education.[56] (This idea seems to have originated with Cabanis and Gall.) A thorough prison reform was necessary.[57]

In the 1860's Virchow passed from the stage of theorizing on public health into the stage of realizations, especially in the fields of sewerage, hospital construction, meat inspection, and school hygiene. As a "technician" he showed the same abilities —thoroughness, effectiveness, poise, and superior intelligence— that had characterized him as a scientist and "theoretician." The need to "sell" a technical procedure like sewerage might occasionally induce him to reverse his original, generalized position—for instance, in claiming "First health [through sewerage], then education." [58] But he would always remain aware of the fact that public health dealt in the last instance with human individuals and should therefore rather remain in the hands of doctors than pass into the hands of chemists and engineers.[59]

Health considerations should always prevail over merely financial ones.[60] In the last instance a good sanitary policy would also be economically the soundest. "City and state obtain their value only through men and their work." [61] Like the English sanitary reformers, to whom he referred in this respect since 1848,[62] Virchow showed in an actuarial way that the considerable investments in sanitary reforms would be more than balanced by avoiding financial losses from death, widows' pensions, medical expenses, and by avoiding loss in wages.*

Between 1862 and 1872 Virchow was much concerned with the problems of sewage disposal, especially in Berlin. His three lengthy studies on the subject—the Report of 1868 (*OM*, II, 203 ff.), the article "Canalization or Night Cart System?" (*OM*, II, 235 ff.), and the General Report of 1874 (*OM*, II, 287 ff.)—still make worthwhile reading on a subject (by no means easy) which we try to ignore because of its unaesthetic

* The same "sales" method that goes back to the Abbé St. Pierre was used abundantly by the English reformers (for a characteristic example, see "The Economy of Sanitary Improvements," *Liverpool Health of Towns Advocate*, No. 8, April, 1846), by J. C. Simonds of New Orleans (in *Southern Medical Reports*, II [1850], 207), and later by Pettenkofer (translation of 1873 paper in *Bull. Hist. Med.*, X [1941], 473 ff.).

character or whose solution we take for granted. The situation has not always been so fortunate, and it might not always remain so. That at present the subject does no longer intrude itself upon us is mainly the merit of the French and English sanitary reformers and people like Virchow and Pettenkofer.

A description of the sanitary situation that prevailed in Berlin, the new capital of the New Reich around 1870, sounds today rather fantastic. In a city of almost one million inhabitants the cesspool and the good old outdoor privy till dominated the scene. Only one-fourth of the houses had water closets. These emptied into the deep gutters that carried also all liquid domestic and industrial offal and the rain water. The gutters in turn ended in the sluggish Spree River and the canals of the city. The problem of crossing streets after heavy rainfalls and the effect on the nose are easily imaginable. And this was not the worst. Virchow, unlike many other sanitary reformers, always emphasized that stench is no reliable criterion for dangers to health. Nonodorous material might be just as detrimental.[63]

This unaesthetic situation became so alarming because of the fact that the majority of Berliners had no central water supply either. Nine hundred forty public and 14,000 private wells provided them with drinking water. And the rising mortality rates announced that something worse than stench was seeping and creeping into the wells. The initial attack against this situation had resulted rather from the desire for cleanliness and the economic motif of having agriculture benefit from this large excrement production. Virchow made the health motif the dominating factor in a campaign that had to wrestle millions of dollars from the taxpayers and landlords. (He was a landlord himself.) He made it clear that after decades of empty talk a decision would have to be reached and action would have to be taken.

It was obvious that cesspools and wells would have to be abolished. It was equally clear that an extensive sewer drainage system for rainwater, liquid offals, and excrements had to be built anyhow. Therefore, since 1861 the Geheime Oberbaurat Wiebe, following the example of English experiences, had also recommended the inclusion of solid excrements into this drainage system. But a strong party favored a separate night cart system for the latter in the interest of agriculture. The city council submitted the problem to a committe headed by Virchow. Virchow warned against hasty decisions and started a thorough examination of the situation and all possible solutions. He studied installations in Paris (1867) and in other European and German cities.[64] He scrutinized the whole literature, consulted experts, and set up special committees for studying and experimenting on detail problems. He examined the financial, technical, and scientific aspects of the problem. Only then did he give his expert opinion. He warned against any schematism. The night cart system might be a perfectly satisfactory solution in certain situations, especially smaller places. But for Berlin the general introduction of water closets connected with one great canalization system would be the best solution from a hygienic and financial point of view.

While emphasizing the sanitary and other advantages of canalization, Virchow made it clear that it was no panacea.[65] Water supply and housing would still have to be watched. While underlining the favorable results obtained in England and certain German cities with canalization, he showed in a thorough, critical, statistical analysis that typhus, typhoid, and cholera had not always been avoided through canalization. Paradoxically enough, the statistical correlations between canalization and decrease of mortality were stronger in the case of pulmonary tuberculosis and infant mortality than in the afore-mentioned diseases.[66] Virchow nevertheless felt confident that canalization would immediately reduce typhoid and the catastrophic infant mortality in Berlin.[67] In pushing city sanitation, Virchow warned not to forget the country, where in Prussia the situation was even worse than in the cities. While in England city mortality was higher than country mortality, the reverse was true in Prussia.

There was one more problem to solve in regard to the prospective Berlin canalization: where to empty its contents. It was clear to Virchow that the Spree River could not be used as an outlet. Sewage farms had been used in England with good success. After conducting extensive experiments in the different climate and on the different soil of Berlin as to the proper functioning of such farms and the innocuousness of their products,[68] Virchow recommended this system.

His General Report was adopted in 1874, and in 1877 the first sector of the new system was finished. Virchow continued to supervise closely the sewage farms.[69] He installed a special health service for the workers on the farms. It is told that for many years before retiring at night he read a special daily report on the health situation on the farms.

Virchow's successful cleaning up of the biggest German city was important enough in itself. It reached importance far beyond these limits, as it provided clarity on many of the issues involved and set a pattern for similar actions within and beyond the German borders.

Virchow had always been keenly interested in hospitals and hospital reform, as evidenced by his addresses on the subject in the 1860's. Already in 1848 he had clearly defined the triple task of the hospital as a center for treatment, for medical education, and for research.[70] The wars of 1866 and 1870 provided him with an opportunity for practical action. The slowness and inadequacy of the military administration and the semiofficial aristocratic order of St. John of Jerusalem[71] in the health field provoked the foundation of voluntary citizens' organizations (Hilfsvereine) that were, on account of their "bourgeois" membership, well provided with money, materials, and organizational talent. As the president of the Berlin Hilfsvereine, Virchow directed the installation of provisory military hospitals (Uhlanen barracks, Tempelhof, Moabit) and hospital trains.

Virchow here largely followed the procedures developed in the United States during the Civil War. He did not tire of praising the democratic spirit of initiative developed in the United States at the occasion and the excellence of the American methods and reports.[72] He had clearly realized the dangers of the old hospitals, and in the case of tuberculosis advised the creation of "xenodochia" (sanitaria) in the South, as hospitalization in this case in northern latitudes was useless or worse.[73]

He felt that the pavillon system, developed in the Civil War, solved a great many of his problems. Yet again he warned against one-sided schematism and panaceas. Under favorable conditions the old block system might also give satisfactory results. Virchow reported extensively on these war experiences, including the very drastic letters he received from soldiers to whom he had sent printed "health rules." [74]

After the war Virchow had an opportunity to supervise the construction of two big new Berlin city hospitals, Friedrichshain and Moabit. He also initiated the erection of the Children's Hospital in Berlin. Prague and Leipzig asked for his expert advice when building new hospitals.

Hospital reform and proper care of wounded soldiers was, of course, inseparable from the problem of training and obtaining adequate nursing personnel. Virchow, acquainted with the problem through the 1848 medical reform movement,[75] followed here the path broken by Florence Nightingale in the Crimean War. Neither religious orders nor the hiring of the dregs of humanity, the two traditional methods, could be continued. Nursing was a human, not a confessional task.[76] The training of adequate personnel had to start in peacetime, not only during war emergencies. Women also had to take over the nursing in men's wards. Nursing schools had to be founded in connection with hospitals. Voluntary associations should finance pioneer efforts in the field. Selection, pension funds, and improved general health education should help in the recruiting of qualified personnel.[77] Virchow began to practice what he preached by opening a nursing school in connection with the new Friedrichshain Hospital.[78]

We have already discussed Virchow's activities on behalf of obligatory meat inspection in the 1860's and 1870's (p. 110). Virchow continued these efforts into the 1890's.[79]

Virchow had already in 1848 and 1860 asked for hygienic improvements in schools. After 1869 he became more specific. He examined the deleterious effect of schools on eyesight in the genesis of skoliosis and tuberculosis.[80] He worked out better systems of ventilation and heating in schools. He was instrumental in the proper construction of many public schools in

Berlin. He discussed overwork in the schools and the employment of school children.[81]

Legal medicine has been so long a part of public health (or vice versa) that this might be the best place to mention Virchow's not inconsiderable activities in this field to which he was doubly related—as a pathological anatomist and as a public health man. Legal medicine was already a well-established field in Prussia, its promoter Casper an international authority, and the many full-time legal physicians a powerful influence, when Virchow appeared on the scene and tried to establish the more basic pathological anatomy as an independent discipline.[82] Frictions were thus unavoidable and lasted well into the 1870's.[83] It is probably due partly to these frictions, partly to Virchow's liberalism and horror of any bureaucracy that in 1848 he asked for the abolition of salaried forensic doctors, a useful institution as comparison with other countries shows.[84] Virchow gave numerous expert opinions in court in Wuerzburg and Berlin. He collaborated actively as a medical expert in the formulation of the new penal code in 1869. He himself contributed valuable tests for determination of death causes in infants (see p. 67) and determination of blood spots.[85]

Virchow's work in public health was so extensive and many sided that one might fairly state that the average German of 1900 had benefited from it in almost every phase of his life from the cradle to the grave, whether eating or drinking, going to school or working, whether healthy or sick in a hospital.

Medical Reform

"MEDICAL REFORM" was the catchword of Virchow's generation, and his whole lifework was in a certain sense dedicated to medical reform. We have already dealt with Virchow's efforts to reform medical science, to make exact sciences the basis of medical practice instead of romantic speculation or crude empiricism. We have already seen how in 1848 the reform of science fused for Virchow with the reform of society, how medicine became to him a social science. We have examined the sociological treatment he prescribed for Upper Silesia and the new epidemiology he developed on the basis of his Upper Silesian experience. We have studied the concept of public health conceived by the "natural attorney of the poor" in the same year of 1848, his claim for the right of each citizen to a healthful existence, for the obligation of the state to provide for medical supervision of working conditions, prisons, etc., and to provide for the unemployed.

It thus remains for us to deal more specifically, under the heading of "Medical Reform," with the 1848 movement for an improvement of the professional status of the medical personnel in which Virchow participated so conspicuously, and with Virchow's ideas and efforts in this direction.* Through publishing the weekly *Die medizinische Reform* together with Leubuscher and with the active participation of S. Neumann, L. Traube, and other friends, Virchow became the mouthpiece of the movement in Berlin where one-fifth of Prussia's doctors were concentrated. *Die medizinische Reform* claimed that "a radical reform of medicine could be no longer postponed." The reform had to follow the lines of "radical progress." A "social medicine" [1] was needed as it had been proclaimed in France.[2]

Virchow was also, together with C. Mayer, Remak, and Schuetz, the leading spirit in the so-called "General Assembly" (*Generalversammlung*), the reform society in Berlin that in the beginning united three-fourths of the Berlin profession. Continual struggle with a second, more moderate reform society— the Association of Physicians and Surgeons (*Verein der Aerzte und Wundaerzte*) led by Berend and Graevell—and the political

---

* Although I have re-examined the available sources, the following is based mostly on my extensive study, *Beitraege zur Geschichte der Medizinalreform von 1848* (Leipzig, 1932). I was preceded in this field by K. Finkenrath's *Die Medizinalreform* (Leipzig, 1929). Since then a number of valuable publications have appeared that deal with the 1848 movement in a larger context: Alfons Fischer's monumental *Geschichte des deutschen Gesundheitswesens* (2 vols.; Berlin, 1933), G. Kroeger's *The Concept of Social Medicine in Germany, 1779–1932* (Chicago, 1937), and George Rosen's "What is Social Medicine?," *Bull. Hist. Med.*, XXI (1947), 674–733.

regression reduced both groups to minority representations.*

The professional medical reform movement of 1848 was the product of a deep social and economic crisis, the so-called Industrial Revolution. In its beginnings modern industry was more of a curse than a blessing to most people. Modern industry upset the whole social structure: catapulting a few individuals into great wealth, it destroyed the large middle class of small artisans, shopkeepers, and tradesmen and profoundly changed rural conditions. The propertyless fragments of the old social structure were compressed into the factories and slums of the mushroomlike, growing cities as "proletarians," and tremendous health problems arose from these changes. But the new situation called not only for help for the majority of the public, for the patients; it also called for help for the doctors.

The new times had profoundly affected the social situation of the doctor, a typical member of the old middle class. While the number of doctors increased, the number of patients who were able to pay adequately decreased even more rapidly through the proletarization of the old middle classes. Doctors thus became materially very insecure, and this was admittedly an important stimulus for their reform movement.[3]

This material crisis was closely interwoven with a moral crisis. The doctor was humiliated not only by poverty and ruthless competition, but by the continual incompetent interference of the bureaucracy of the absolutist state, which meddled with all his activities to the point where in some regions it even told him when he was allowed to marry. The anachronism of this situation in the middle of the nineteenth century did not make it any more sympathetic.

The public reacted to these humiliations of the doctor by losing respect for and confidence in him. The public was by now educated enough to realize the ineptness of most older medical systems, and the new medical science that struggled

* For interesting details on both societies, see Posner's "Zur Geschichte des aerztlichen Vereinswesens in Berlin," BKW, XXX (1893), 1230, 1257, 1271. The moderate Verein was mostly composed of surgeons. It seems that here as elsewhere (see Fischer's "Geheimpolizeiberichte ueber Wiener Aerzte, 1855–57," Janus, XLIII [1939], 220) the surgeons tried to make up for their lower social status through "good behavior."

in the chaos of the scientific crisis had not yet been able to give the proofs of its usefulness that were later to reconquer public confidence for the profession.

Under these blows a great many German doctors of 1848 became materialists, democrats, and social reformers. They echoed the cry "freedom," one of the basic slogans of the political revolution, feeling that freedom for the people would also bring their freedom. Most of them, therefore, refused to conceive their professional movement in a narrow, egotistic "guild spirit." [4] This attitude was wholly supported by Virchow and his friends.[5] "Medical reform shall pass not so much for the doctors' but for the patients' sake." [6] "Medical instruction does not exist to provide individuals with an opportunity of learning how to earn a living, but in order to make possible the protection of the health of the public." [7] The three points Virchow wanted to have inserted in the constitution in the interest of medical reform illustrate this amalgamation of general and professional goals in the medical reform movement: the right of each citizen to a healthful existence, a special assembly of the medical personnel (Kongress), constitutional self-government for the communities that should regulate public health and the professional situation.[8]

The other basic slogan of the German revolution of 1848, "National Unity," was no less meaningful to the reformers. Dr. A. Pagenstecher, the father of Virchow's pupil and friend, submitted to the Frankfurt parliament bills that were the logical application of this general theme to medical reform and found general approval. Pagenstecher asked for a unified German examination system, the right to practice in all German states, and a German pharmacopoeia.[9] Virchow proposed the same changes in Die medizinische Reform, adding the claim for a German Ministry of Health.[10]

One of the most important demands of the medical reform movement was a unique and united medical profession and degree, and the abolition of the medieval subdivision of the medical profession into different classes and castes with different rights and privileges. Prussia had, for instance, at the time still three classes of physicians and two classes of surgeons. Even France and England had similar problems with their *officiers de santé* and apothecaries. Furthermore, there was a caste separation between military and civilian physicians. Within the army the latter were treated abominably, while the graduates of special military medical schools enjoyed certain privileges.

Virchow wrote little about the question of the united profession, the problem being too obvious. He devoted considerable attention to the problems of the medical privileges of the army, having acquired a firsthand knowledge of this situation. Part of a minimum program that Virchow submitted to the first reunion of the *Generalversammlung* on June 9, 1848,[11] included abolition of the cumulation of medical positions, elevation of rank of company surgeons, and opening of hospitals belonging to the army (especially the famous Charité in Berlin) for civilian medical instruction. The monopolization of the Charité by the army was considered the reason for the absence of a clinical school in Prussia, and its opening to civilian students was asked from all sides.[12] Equally popular was the cry for the abolition of special military medical schools, especially the Friedrich-Wilhelms Institute or *pépinière*. The famous radical, Dr. Johann Jacoby from Koenigberg, had launched his political career in 1831 on this claim.[13] Alumnus Dr. Virchow agreed with this demand, demonstrating *ad oculos* that the special institution did not prevent the formation of radicals.[14]

Just as the general rights of the citizen were to be codified in a constitution, thus the doctors asked for a charter that should fix their rights and duties, so that they would be no longer exposed to arbitrary handling by the bureaucracy.[15] According to Virchow the bureaucracy had completely failed in all fields: in promoting medical science, education, and professional standing, as well as in protecting the health of the public.[16] Therefore bureaucratic power should be restricted as much as possible by democratic procedures. An elected medical congress should work out the new medical constitution.[17] District and city physicians should be elected from then on. The old bureaucratic medical collegia should be abolished. Their scientific functions should be taken over by an Academy of

Medicine, their administrative functions by an elected medical council.[18] Teaching and assistant positions should be distributed after a *concours* (public competitive examination). Self-government and self-administration should also enter the administrative regions of medicine.

It was hoped that self-government and self-administration would help to overcome the evils arising out of the free, all too often too free, competition of doctors and the necessity of selling their services on the open market. The serious crisis made doctors very sensitive to these aspects of their profession.[19] On the one hand, they felt crushed and humiliated by this situation; on the other hand, "freedom" seemed to harbor the best chance of success for them and most of them (Virchow included) therefore repudiated the idea of doctors' becoming state employees.[20] (A large percentage of them still were civil servants and were not too happy in this position.) Like all "petty bourgeois," doctors had an ambivalent and contradictory attitude toward competition. On the one hand, they cursed and despised it (Virchow and Leubuscher included); on the other hand, they wanted it. The problem was therefore to "counterbalance" its excesses.[21] The counterweight was to be the local or regional voluntary medical association warmly recommended by Virchow and others.[22] This would be self-government, the happy mean between the guild and unlimited competition. The association would judge offenders of the medical code, locally supervise public health, take care of widows, orphans, and incapacitated colleagues.

The association would also help against one of the most bemoaned evils of the period—quackery.[23] Virchow belonged to those medical reformers who, although sworn enemies of quackery, asked as consistent liberals for the abolition of the antiquackery laws. Virchow and G. F. Loeffler (the well-known father of the bacteriologist) defended this point of view in *Die medizinische Reform,* while Leubuscher wrote in favor of prohibitive laws.[24]

Virchow on this occasion defined quackery as "the practice of medicine by the ignorant." [25] But with the continuous progress of science could not even a duly licensed physician be ignorant twenty years after graduation? Virchow therefore suggested the re-examination of physicians. The laws against quackery had been conspicuously unsuccessful throughout the centuries. The state should limit itself to periodical publications of lists of recognized physicians and to prosecution for bodily damage done by quacks. On the other hand, the state should strengthen the medical profession by raising the standards of medical education and examination.[26]

The essential preventive against quackery was better education of the masses inside and outside of schools, especially instruction in the natural sciences. The doctors should give up their aloof position. They should turn to the masses, help to educate them, like Tissot, Haller, Unzer, Zimmermann, and Carl Vogt had done. Then the masses would not run to the quacks. "Those, who are replaced by quacks, are often themselves the cause of their own misfortune." [27]

We know that Virchow practiced what he preached. He participated in educational reforms in public schools, high schools, and universities and worked most actively in popular adult education. He was later strongly attacked when (with the consensus of the Berlin profession) he, as a deputy in the Landtag, obtained the abolition of quackery laws in 1868.[28] But his point of view in this question remained unchanged throughout the years. In a late article, "The New Century" (A, CLIX [1900], 1 ff.), he complained of the spread of "nature healers" as a revival of shamanism. But he maintained that prohibitive laws were useless. Only education could help.

The medical reformers of 1848, like all reformers, saw in improved education one of the most important and useful agents of change ("the main weapon of democracy is education") and produced an enormous number of suggestions in this direction.[29] We already know Virchow's ideas on mass education and improvements in secondary schools. In the university field he was among those who asked for free medical education,[30] a year of internship,[31] abolition of the doctor examination,[32] and better instructional methods to replace mere lecture courses.[33]

Virchow asked for total secularization in the medical as

well as in the educational fields. From the Ministry for Education, Medical Matters, and Public Worship, the latter should be eliminated. The theological faculties should be separated from the universities, just as hospitals should become nonconfessional.[34]

The reformers were very much concerned with the problem of medical care for the indigent, so far mostly in the hands of a few underpaid, state-employed "pauper-doctors" (Armenaerzte). The present system had been unfair to both physicians and patients. Here again a great number of different suggestions was brought forward.[35] Virchow, supported by Remak,[36] proposed the following solutions: "Pauper-doctors" should not be state employed. The whole institution of "pauper-doctors" should be abolished.[37] The pauper should enjoy his right of free choice of a doctor like everybody else. (The liberal Virchow was a strong advocate of this right.[38]) The remuneration of those treating paupers should be settled by the association.[39] Virchow violently opposed at the same time the much decried "obligation to treat" (Behandlungszwang) by which a doctor could be forced to accept an unwanted patient. The doctor should be just as free to choose his patient as the patient should be free to choose his doctor.[40]

The triumph of political reaction in 1849 and the following years frustrated the medical reform movement in the professional sphere completely. Only very gradually, mostly by others than the old protagonists of medical reform and in different ways, were the demands of the reformers realized. Never again did Virchow become so deeply involved in professional reforms as in 1848, yet occasionally he was called again to take up the old problems.

In his expert opinion on the new malpractice laws of 1869 Virchow remarked: "The public and sometimes also the State's Attorney presuppose all too easily that the doctor is never ill, never tired, never exhausted." [41] He wanted the law to be amended by the provision that the doctor was liable only when, through lack of proper attention or caution, he violated *generally recognized* rules of the medical art.[42]

In 1872 Virchow became involved in a long polemic with

VIRCHOW ON FEBRUARY 2, 1849

This sketch was made several months before Virchow's engagement
to Rose Mayer. *Photo:* Courtesy of Dr. Med. Habil. Rudolf Rabl,
Landeskrankenhaus Neustadt in Holstein, Virchow's grandson.

the Frankfurt sanitarian Varrentrapp, who asked for a central health authority in the New Reich. Virchow, who had once in 1848 demanded a German ministry of health, opposed this new suggestion. He explained this formal contradiction of his own past suggestion by the fact that his 1848 plan made sense only in the framework of the democratic constitution of a really unified Reich. The Bismarck Reich was so built that Varrentrapp's suggestion would only produce a new bureaucratic structure. Under these conditions he preferred to be realistic and to leave health government to the states, where it would have at least some elements of democracy.[43]

Virchow always remained a defender and promoter of common action and organization of the medical profession in defense of its interests. When elected honorary president of the Berlin Medical Society in 1893, he made the following characteristic remarks:

Yes, my dear colleagues, we have a difficult position in life. The doctors are more attacked than ever. We have every reason to stick together, and to unite in the fight for existence where the whole profession is menaced and which will be won only through our own united strength. . . .

. . . .

If during the period when I had the honor to administer this society [as a regular officer] we have gained in several directions more and more recognition, as we all know, this is due to the cohesion of the many.[44]

Virchow's continual influence on the shaping of the professional situation nationally and internationally cannot be overestimated. It went far beyond those measures he was called to bring into realization himself. His many thoughts on the subject remained known and alive (especially through the republication of his 1848 articles in 1879*) and many took form in the work of others. Many are still worthy of consideration and application.

* It is most probably due to this fact that a casual idea like that of the re-examination of doctors could appear again, more than fifty years after its conception, in the book of W. Weressaiew, *Beichten eines praktischen Arztes* (Leipzig, 1902), p. 60.

Medical History

AMONG VIRCHOW's many contributions to various fields of medicine that deserve mention and analysis are those made in medical history. As Virchow had started his career as a writer with some perfectly competent pieces of original research on the history of his home town, it is not surprising that throughout his life his writings were full of remarks emphasizing the value of medical history.

Medicine needs historical knowledge more than any other science.[1]

The history of medicine is an integral part of culture history, and can be understood only in connection with the general history of mankind.[2]

The neglect of the history of medicine has produced that desolating circulatory movement in medical science which, almost without any metabolic changes, again and again produces the same material.[3]

The history of wars is only the external history of nations. Their internal history starts from two very different sources: the progress of human insight, culture history; on the other hand, the memory of painful suffering of humanity, the history of medicine, known only to few, but therefore a no less instructive part of general history.[4]

Historical and geographical inquiries have been very important for scientific as well as practical medicine. . . . One of the worst aspects of the present stage of medicine is the fact that historical knowledge decreases with each generation of students.* We see therefore the same problems discussed again and again, with few new materials. . . .[5]

It is a great progress that the men of peace have started during the last years to use medicohistorical materials, [a progress] that is to open this rich and carefully guarded treasure house of humanity.[6]

* Virchow obviously did not realize the causal relation between this state of things and the general educational reform away from classical education which he had himself sponsored so consistently.

Only historical knowledge is true knowledge.[7]

Virchow furthered medicohistorical work in publishing numerous medicohistorical contributions of others in his *Archives*. He encouraged Hirsch to write his monumental *Historical and Geographical Pathology* that appeared first as a kind of companion volume to his *Handbook*.[8] He seems to have given numerous historical details in his lectures.[9] Bartlett reports that he liked particularly to refer to the work of "John Hunter,* Boerhaave, Rokitansky and Johannes Mueller." [10] He thus stimulated some of his pupils to do their own medicohistorical research (for example, Walsh [11]).

To think historically was an absolutely natural approach for Virchow, as his thought started so often as an antithesis. His salutory critical skepticism, that was based in later years on the direct experience of a long life where he had seen so many theories, methods, and fashions come and go, rested in his earlier years largely on his great familiarity with medical history, the collective memory and experience of the medical profession. Virchow possessed not only an extensive knowledge of medical history, but he thought also in a truly historical fashion—insofar as he did not regard all previous history of medicine as a collection of nonsensical errors, like many of his "modernist" contemporaries did, but freely confessed to the "fault" that he regarded the ancients as able observers and considered many of their formulations meaningful for the present.[12] Virchow thought historically (genetically) even when he did not use specifically historical materials. Although in Virchow historical interest and knowledge were uncommonly well developed, other pioneers of the German medical renaissance of the 1840's—like Wunderlich, Griesinger, and Henle—were not much inferior to him in this respect. That this was, on the other hand, not necessarily so in this generation and not simply a reflection of the higher educational levels of the period can easily be seen from Rokitansky's historical introduction to his

* W. H. Welch (in *Boston Medical and Surgical Journal*, CXXV [1891], 453) draws an interesting parallel between Hunter and Virchow that might partly explain the somewhat strange cult of the latter for the former.

Handbook, which exhibits a very limited knowledge and even less understanding of medical history.*

Numerous original contributions to medical history are interspersed through Virchow's work in the form of historical introductions or excursions in articles devoted otherwise to actual pathological description and discussion. We mention here only his discussions of older medical opinions on rickets,[13] abdominal affections,[14] skull formation,[15] syphilis,[16] tuberculosis,[17] glanders,[18] and hemophilia.[19] Sometimes Virchow also published short notes on some old source he had run into—as on lupus,[20] which term he succeeded in tracing back to the Salernitan school, or on hemophilia,[21] of which he found a first modern description in the seventeenth century (treated, by the way, by bloodletting!). Virchow cultivated in the same way the history of diseases, for example, of typhus,[22] syphilis,[23] and arthritis deformans.[24] His Huxley lecture contains an interesting excursion on the effect of their activities as ship surgeons on Hunter, Darwin, and Huxley.[25]

But Virchow's importance as a medical historian goes far beyond these more or less accidental detailed studies. He must be credited with some basic concepts developed through systematic research. His most concentrated effort lies in the field of the history of hospitals and leprosoria, especially those in Germany. His trip to Norway in 1859 aroused his interest in the latter. In 1860–61 he published a series of articles on the history of leprosoria in Germany which all together covers over 220 pages.[26] In 1861 he also pioneered in the field of using works of art as documentation in medical history by drawing attention to a painting of the younger Holbein showing leprosy.[27] (In this field he was soon joined and surpassed by K. F. H. Marx and Charcot.) For years the *Archives* published data on the geography of leprosy outside Europe that reached Virchow as a response to his first leprosy article. He sum-

---

* It seems possible that historical leanings in Germany are, like the whole "genetic approach," connected with the romantic legacy. In France the anhistorical attitude was strong in, for example, Laennec or Louis, while Andral, Cruveilhier, and P. Rayer showed extensive historical knowledge.

marized these data in *Die krankhaften Geschwuelste*, II, 484–531.

In 1866 Virchow drew the general conclusions from his detailed studies on hospital history. He showed the roots of our hospitals to be in the Christian tradition, to which he gave full credit.* He showed, on the other hand, that these early hospitals and leprosoria, usually located *extra muros*, were not *medical* hospitals, but hostels for pilgrims or asylums for the needy and infirm.[28] A change came about through the so-called hospital orders. In the Holy Land they grew out of foundations of Italian and German merchants. To the most important European hospital order, that of the Holy Ghost founded by Guy of Montpellier in the twelfth century, Virchow devoted a special monographic study in 1877, which he reported in the Prussian Academy.[29] In this second stage of hospital history, hospitals were founded *intra muros* and had some medical characteristics. Virchow traced more than one hundred fifty hospitals of the Holy Ghost in Germany. From the beginning many were under the control of city administrations. Insofar as the Roman Church tried to centralize and hierarchize the movement, she ruined it. The full change from hostel to medical hospital came only when, as a third stage, the secular city administrations (which Virchow praised as "the standard bearers of freedom and science"[30]) took the hospitals over. As Virchow, on the other hand, regarded the *hospitals as the points of departure of modern medicine*,[31] it becomes clear that the essential result of his studies on the history of hospitals was that *modern medicine is the child of the "bourgeoisie," the citizenry, the middle class, and not of a feudal institution like the Church*. Virchow opposed the Roman Catholic Church throughout his life (beginning already in his Upper Silesia

---

* He emphasized, on the other hand, that other high religions (e.g., Buddhism) had hospital traditions too. Attacked because he had omitted the ancient Jews, he showed that they like the Greeks and Romans had no such traditions (*OM*, II, 83 ff.). This attack, nourished by "national liberals," the liberals who had joined Bismarck, was actually more of a foul political maneuver of these turncoats to brand their leftist neighbor as a "reactionary" than anything else.

report) as a feudal organization as well as a non-national, foreign influence.[32]

It is quite regrettable that no historian has so far followed up Virchow's ingenious idea of the hospital origin of modern medicine, which might explain many of the accomplishments as well as the shortcomings of the latter. As much suspicion as the results of Virchow's hospital studies concerning the bourgeois roots of their medical transformation might provoke at first, since they fit almost too well into his general political world picture, it must be noticed that they have been confirmed by numerous, less partial historians, Catholics included (for example, Haeser, Bensen, Kuester, and Sudhoff[33]).

The roots and principal stages of modern medical science, especially pathology, were the main theme of several of Virchow's historical writings that culminated in his "Hundred Years of General Pathology" of 1895, his contribution to the *Festschrift* of the Friedrich-Wilhelms Institute. Virchow's story started with Vesalius and Paracelsus, the latter of whom had, according to Virchow, in spite of his Arabist confusion done even more for the demolition of Galenism than the former. It went on through Harvey, whose work reduced the old humoral pathology to blood pathology, and Malpighi. Boerhaave and his school were to him the fathers of the modern physiological disease concept, Morgagni and John Hunter of pathological anatomy and physiology. The merits of the Paris School, especially Bichat and Magendie, were duly recognized. The embryologists C. F. Wolff, Doellinger, and J. F. Meckel were described as forerunners of a German development that came into its own with Rokitansky, Schoenlein, Johannes Mueller, and their pupils. The main trends of this essay are not very different from those of an editorial of the *Archives* in 1858 (Vol. 13) in which Hunter and Magendie occupy a prominent position.

Between these two historical essays, which both are essentially fair as far as the participation of different nationalities in the building of modern medicine and pathology is concerned, lies a not very glorious, but interesting outbreak of historical chauvinism in Virchow, when he tried to ignore foreign, and especially French, contributions.

Up to this time Virchow had often spoken with respect of French medical science.[34] He had published in French (for example, on cholera, statistics, and trichinosis).* He had freely recognized the indebtedness of German medicine to French revolutionary medicine.[35] We know of the particularly strong influence of Bichat, Broussais, Andral, and Cruveilhier on Virchow's work and of his rather close personal relations with Bernard, Broca, Velpeau, and Kuess. In 1865 at the Hannover *Naturforscherversammlung* he all of a sudden celebrated the "liberation" of German medicine from French medicine, its "superiority," its higher "moral seriousness," [36] drawing thus a justified and dignified censure from Charcot for this unscientific boasting.[37] In Innsbruck in 1869 Virchow repeated the superiority myth.[38] Up to 1865 he had held with his teacher Johannes Mueller that "a German, French, English school of scientific medicine is a barbarism." [39] Now, in 1865, he discovered the national as opposed to the cosmopolitan character of science. He showed how German science had grown together with and through nationalism.[40]

This episode can be understood only from the general political situation in Germany—the mounting war hysteria, the desire of the Bismarckian opposition to show that they were "good Germans too," and the supposedly pro-French policy of Bismarck.[41] It fortunately did not last long. When Virchow saw the bitter fruits of this irresponsible howling, he reversed himself rather rapidly. Already during the first months of the Franco-German war of 1870 he wrote: "We know very well what we owe to this nation, and Germany has been certainly most frank in this recognition." [42]

From then on Virchow made it a point to emphasize the historical accomplishments of French medicine. And he maintained this attitude in spite of the stupid attacks by French

* That Virchow and many of his German contemporaries still felt the urge to announce new, important discoveries to the Paris Academy of Science is symptomatic of the apprentice position of German science and of the fact that its independence was not yet fully gained.

chauvinists to which he was exposed. "At the time of the first *Naturforscherversammlung* German science was completely overshadowed by the brilliant French, these magnificent minds who, children of the great revolution, have opened new ways and roads in all fields of scientific research." [43] He poked fun at nationalism in science.[44] Science was again "human in essence, national only in form." "Politics separates, science unites the nations." "For many years we have imported French science and are still very grateful for what we received." [45] The French Revolution had stimulated the rebirth of science and medicine.[46] In 1800, under the impression of the French Revolution, the Paris School was formed, and "one must leave it to the genius of our neighbors that they are able to find the bases of a totally new science at one stroke." [47] There were occasional fluctuations in regard to the national versus the cosmopolitan character of science.[48] It must be admitted that the latter problem is actually far more complex than the question of the undeniable pioneer work of French scientists. In spite of its international "essence," modern science has actually grown up in close connection with nationalism. As a whole, nevertheless, Virchow's utterances as to the nature of science after 1870 followed the line: "Let us doctors not forget that our science is primarily a cosmopolitan one." [49]

Virchow was not blind to certain general shortcomings of German medicine (quite apart from the errors in detail of the romantic period or of later individuals). The regrettable separation of practice and theory was recent and German.[50] German medicine lacked continuity. It developed by sudden spurts.[51]

It was but natural that Virchow should devote particular attention to Glisson,[52] the father of "irritability," a concept that had assumed such an important place in his work, and to Morgagni, the promoter of localism, the "anatomic concept." [53] It is in his study on Morgagni that Virchow reaffirms the general theory which he had already proposed in the first chapter of his *Cellular Pathology*—that medicine always gains its freedom through progress in anatomy.[54] We know how much light this concept has thrown on medicohistorical problems in the hands of Sigerist, although much can also be said in favor of the older theory of Daremberg that the significant changes occur in physiology.

Two important medicohistorical contributions are Virchow's studies of his teachers Schoenlein (1865) [55] and Johannes Mueller (1858), the pioneers of modern scientific medicine in Germany. The Schoenlein study is an attempt to trace the important medical developments in Bamberg, Landshut, and Wuerzburg in the second and third decades of the nineteenth century when the three universities were centers of "romantic medicine" with Marcus, Roeschlaub, and Ringseis, but centers also of the "German science" of embryology through Doellinger and his school (Von Baer, Pander),[56] and centers of a more objective attitude through Tiedemann, Heusinger, and Phillip von Walther, the teacher of Mueller and Schoenlein. It is in this milieu that Schoenlein was formed and became great.

The other purpose of the Schoenlein study is evidently to present the latter as a consistent bourgeois liberal: he is shown as being born a roper's son, for a while himself a roper, and always proud of it; a fugitive from reaction in Zurich in the 1830's; a friend of the prisoner Eisenmann and the radical poet Herwegh; and, even though he was a court physician, an implacable enemy of reactionaries like Ringseis. Mueller again is presented as a cobbler's son, spiritually formed by the French Revolution, a revolutionary student (Burschenschaftler), etc. Both essays clearly intend to illustrate Virchow's thesis that contemporary scientific medicine in Germany as elsewhere was the creation of the middle class, his own class. "Our medicine has put on the simple bourgeois cloth, and will never take it off!" [57]

Virchow was not only a historian; he might also well qualify as a philologist. His continual concern with scientific terminology is well known. His articles and addresses are full of philological excursions.[58] He repeatedly devoted articles to the question of how to derive and spell a particular term,[59] how to create new terms.[60] His tremendous success in coining new terms—nine out of the ten he mentions in his Preface to Cellular Pathology are still used—was, of course, primarily due to the quality of the underlying concepts. But his philological skill might have been an additional asset. As a matter of fact, even the political terms like *Kulturkampf* and *Daemmerungsliberale* which he coined used to stick.

Virchow shared this bent for philology with most educated Germans. An equal trend toward microscopy was noticeable in Germans of his generation. One might argue that psychologically both inclinations have a common root and certain similarities. And one might explain psychologically the absence of outstanding microscopical discoveries in France through the absence of these traits in the French. The trouble with this theory is that it does not correspond to the facts. The French of the period did indeed produce no great philologists in the German sense. But they produced a whole galaxy of very able microscopists—to mention here only Dutrochet (1776–1847), Raspail (1794–1878), Fel. Dujardin (1801–1860), Alfr. Donné (1801–1878), Natali Guillot (1804–1866), Lereboullet (1804–1865), Charles Robin (1821–1885), and Follin (1823–1867). If, nevertheless, the French were outdistanced by German microscopists, this was less due to the lack of microscopical talent in France than to the very different reception microscopy received in Germany and France. The radical empiricism of the Paris clinical school had been detrimental to the development of microscopy within medicine in France,[61] while on the contrary the romantic embryologists had cultivated microscopy early and extensively in German medical schools.[62] Henle, Koelliker, and Virchow were full professors at the ages of thirty-one, thirty, and twenty-eight respectively, while Dujardin reached this position at thirty-eight, Donné at forty-seven, Guillot at fifty-four, Lereboullet at thirty-nine, Robin at forty-one, and Dutrochet, Raspail, and Follin never.

Virchow's little book on Goethe and the natural sciences (Berlin 1861) is of great interest beyond the fact that it is a pioneer study on Goethe's prominent role as a forerunner of the new biological science, and on the role of science in Goethe's life. It reveals how far Virchow's notion of science had developed from his mechanistic concepts during the 1840's. It suddenly shows him—though perhaps only momentarily—

bending toward a Goethean concept of man, frequent among German intellectuals, but foreign to most scientists of his generation: "Localism and Realism, Philosophy and Science they find their happy conciliation in the aesthetic development of the individual." "The sensual and the rational urge are synthesized *(heben sich auf)* in the aesthetic state of being." [63]

Virchow's contributions to medical history show him again basically consistent in all his many-sidedness. They round out the picture of the great doctor and demonstrate again that in his own personality he realized his goal of medical humanism.

The Statesman

Revolutionary Beginnings

T HE EARLIEST political remarks of Virchow transmitted to us are contained in a letter to his father dated December 21, 1840.[1] They are comments on the new king, Frederick William IV, who had just succeeded his father, Frederick William III, the notorious partner of the Holy Alliance. The nineteen-year-old student manifests here already his critical political insight. While liberals in general saw in some acts of the new monarch (like an amnesty) the beginnings of a new era, Virchow, criticizing the king's empty oratory, his inclination for pietist bigots, and his impotent foreign policy, showed a much clearer understanding of the true character of the glittering weakling who would live up fully to the reactionary standards of the house of Hohenzollern.

Virchow's early historical publications of 1842 reveal him as an adversary of feudal institutions and privileges and of their modern counterparts, monopolies. In 1842 he manifests his "urge, not to remain inactive in the great events of our days," and in 1844 he reports participation in "magnificent student meetings" of the political opposition.[2] The attempts of the king to introduce clerical control via the *Diakonissen* order into the Charité in 1843 were particularly provocative to the young Charité intern.[3]

One of the basic traits of Virchow's political creed, his concern with economic abuses, shows up first in a remark written in 1845:

159

At a railroad a young man of my age earns as much during a day as I do during a month. Of course, I wouldn't change with them, as I love medicine now more than ever. But you will realize that this extraordinary proletarization makes me examine the causes of such a situation. A carpenter earns daily 16 sgr. [*Silbergroschen*] and I 5 sgr. It is obvious that under these conditions I couldn't change my social opinions, even if I would not have reached the same conclusions by mere reasoning.[4]

In his letters Virchow appears very satisfied with the growth of the opposition in 1845 and with the moral defeat of the monarchy in the assembly of the United Estates (Vereinigter Landtag) of 1847.[5] He greets the revolutionary events in Switzerland, Italy, Denmark, France, and Hungary in February of 1848.[6] Then comes his mission to Upper Silesia, discussed already in more detail at previous occasions, and March 18 finds him on the barricades in Berlin. He continues his radical activities as a member of electoral colleges and democratic and labor associations, till the victory of the reaction drives him into temporary exile and political inactivity. But his political convictions remain unshaken.

Virchow's outstanding personal contributions to the revolution of 1848 were undoubtedly his report on Upper Silesia and his fight for public health (see pp. 124 ff.) and medical reforms (pp. 17 ff. and 137 ff.). Because of his youth he was a political activist, not yet a leader. He was only one of many thousands of devoted "soldiers of the revolution" who expended their time and energy more or less anonymously in the unspectacular tasks of daily propaganda and agitation for a policy worked out by older leaders. Yet in view of the leading role Virchow was to play later in Prussian and German politics, it seems worthwhile to reconstruct the basic ideas he entertained during the revolution, as they are reflected in his letters and his articles in the *Medical Reform*.

The revolution of 1848 had arisen in Germany under the slogans of "Unity and Freedom." While the great English or French Revolution would concentrate on "freedom," the question of unity having been solved previously, the German revolution was greatly complicated through this dual task.

Germany was politically still divided into thirty-nine states. "Unity" meant welding the thirty-nine anachronisms into one state. The only ones to profit from the national division were the thirty-nine princes and their military and civilian bureaucracy, recruited from the ranks of the nobility, who regarded and treated these states as their property by divine right. "Freedom" meant to substitute the rights of man for those allegedly divine prerogatives. All classes of the population opposed the old absolutism except the direct beneficiaries of the old system; little differentiation was noticeable in this opposition because of the almost total absence of political life and discussion. After the armed uprisings in March of 1848 had forced the monarchs to accept some ministers from the ranks of the opposition and to grant some rights—like freedom of the press, constitutional assemblies for the states and the whole of Germany, etc.—the situation changed rapidly. The opposition was split into two camps: the so-called liberals and the so-called democrats.

The liberals, led by bankers, manufacturers, and high bureaucrats (who now became ministers of the state), felt that the revolution was finished. In their almost pathological fear and hatred of the masses, the "mob" who had made the revolution (the lower middle class and the proletarians), they did not dare to touch the old bureaucratic and militaristic structure. They hoped to reach their goal of a constitutional monarchy through compromising with the monarchs. Their model was the English constitution. Unfortunately they lacked the energy and pride of the English middle class and forgot that the way toward the English constitution was marked by a king's head. They hoped to obtain the unity of Germany by making the Prussian king emperor of Germany, which would, of course, imply the loss of Austria. Even before the revolution they had claimed that when faced by the choice between unity and liberty they would prefer the former without the latter. The liberals were very proud of their "realism" and controlled the majority in the German constitutional assembly in the *Paulskirche* of Frankfurt and in the state assemblies. After having served as a smoke screen behind which the monarchs could regroup their armies, the constitutional assemblies were dispersed by armed force, the liberal ministers were kicked out, sham constitutions were given by decree of the monarch, and everything went back to normal—that is, to a Germany without either unity or freedom.

The minority of the former opposition—the "left" or "democrats" or "radicals," representing mainly the lower middle class —was striving for the destruction of the old bureaucratic structure and for a German republic, after the French or North American model, which should not be submitted to Prussian leadership and should include the German parts of Austria, while its Slavonic and Hungarian parts should regain their freedom. A "constitutional monarchy" in Germany would be nothing but a sham. The democrats sought to rally the middle class alongside plebeian journeymen and quasi-proletarian strata against the feudal forces. They provided the fighters and martyrs in the uprisings in the spring of 1849 that tried to stem the tide of reaction, and from their ranks came the "forty-eighters," the political refugees to the United States—like Carl Schurz, Sigel, Willich, and Hecker—who were to play an important role in the fight for liberty in this country, especially during the Civil War.

The liberals, representatives of the wealthiest part of the middle class, concentrated exclusively on political reforms and lacked all understanding or interest in the problems of the poor. Even many of the democrats were totally absorbed in political problems. Only a minority of the democrats developed clear insight into the fact that the basic problems of the revolution were economic ones, that—important as political changes were—they made sense only as steps toward large reforms of those social abuses that had actually caused the revolution.[7] They were called socialists, but their "socialism" had little in common with "Marxism," whose author was playing only a secondary role during the 1848 revolution and acquired fame and large-scale influence only as an exile in England in the 1860's.

Virchow saw the split in the oppositional camp clearly and as early as March 24.

For the time being there is no power here: neither the government nor the people or as one should say instead of the latter: neither the bourgeois nor the workers really hold the power. It would be our good luck if this division of powers would last. But this is unlikely. Already we see a reaction among the bourgeoisie against the people (workers). Already one talks of the "mob" again; already one plans to distribute rights unequally among various members of the community. . . . But the people's party is vigilant and powerful. She will see to it that the people who have shed their blood, will not be denied what has been promised to them, and that only the bourgeoisie enjoys the fruits of a battle which she did not fight. . . .[8]

He continued to emphasize the role of the workers in the victory of the revolution, their political virtues, and the political necessity for the middle class to side with them instead of siding with the reactionaries. He warned the liberals in his home province [9] about the reactionary maneuver to incite them against Berlin, the capital, which was the center of the active revolutionary mass movement.[10]

Virchow saw clearly that the revolution could triumph only by bringing freedom to the oppressed national minorities, especially the Poles.[11] In this question, a touchstone of progressive thinking in German politics, he saw even more clearly than many leaders of the left in his and later times. His attitude in the Polish question was purely rational, equally free from the pro-Polish emotional fashion of the 1830's and the traditional anti-Polish feelings fostered in Virchow's home province, an old border region with Poland.

Virchow continually opposed the "moderates" who proposed a "deal" with the bureaucracy instead of elimination of this evil.[12] From the very beginning he therefore put little hope in the National Constitutional Assembly in Frankfurt dominated by the moderate constitutionalists.[13]

Virchow's political goal was a German republic. "Either Germany becomes a republic, or it ceases to exist and becomes Russian." [14] For him it was no question of principle whether the republic was to have an elected president or, like England, a "hereditary president." But the latter version could not be realized in Germany, and especially not in Prussia, given the character of the princes, and especially that of the Hohenzollerns. Virchow foresaw clearly:

Even in the most favorable case: when the king will be inclined now to take an oath on a democratic constitution, he will not be able to remain loyal. The now living Hohenzollerns are through their education accustomed to such an extent to regard themselves as something special, and their wishes as the wishes of the people that they involuntarily, and even when full of good will, will never agree to execute the will of the people.[15]

One must eventually realize that here [that is, in Prussia] constitutionalism [that is, the "constitutional monarchy"] is nothing but a sham.[16]

As mentioned, Virchow's republic was to be based on equal rights of all citizens and a maximum of self-government. He dreamt of the eventual abolition of the state.[17]

Virchow was one of the few who clearly saw and tirelessly repeated that social reform was the basic task of the period, that political reforms were only a means to this end, and that the social problem was the central problem of the revolution.[18] Almost brutally he wrote in the *Medical Reform:* "Don't be mistaken: the upheaval of our days is a purely material one." [19] Very few German political thinkers before Virchow had formulated the problem so clearly. The first to do so was perhaps another gifted doctor (and one of the greatest German writers), Georg Buechner, who in 1837 at the age of twenty-three had died an exile in Zurich.*

Virchow became most eloquent when discussing social inequalities:

Is it so difficult to understand that our movement is a social one, and that the task is not to write instructions [against cholera] that

---

* "The relation between the rich and the poor is the only revolutionary element on earth." "The material oppression in Germany is just as sad and ignominious as the spiritual; and it is in my mind far less depressing that some liberal can't have his ideas printed than that many thousands of families have no lard to mix with their potatoes."—*Georg Buechner: Werke und Briefe,* pp. 381 and 417.

pacify the . . . wealthy bourgeois? We must make provisions that pro-
tect through improvement of their conditions the poor who lack fine
bread, soft meat, warm clothes, and a bed, who can't work while living on broth and tea, the poor who are *hit hardest by the epidemic.*
Let the nice people remember, when they sit at the warm stove and
give Christmas sweets to their little ones, that the men who carried
coal and sweets, have died from cholera. Alas, how sad it is that
thousands have to die in misery so that a few hundred may live
well. And when it is the turn of another hecatomb all that the hundreds do is write another regulation.[20]

The goal of the 1848 revolution was to Virchow the liberation of the working man. "Christianity liberated the slaves, the
reformation the burgher, the [French] revolution the peasant.
We try to incorporate the worker, the have-not, into the great
stream of culture. This is the long fight of the human against
the inhuman, the natural against the unnatural, of right against
privilege." [21]

Virchow gave the simplest, but not perhaps the least impressive, form to his politico-social creed in a letter of May 2, 1848,
in which he tried to explain to his politically uneducated
mother the sense of the revolution:

We want that the poor . . . should enjoy on earth a happier life and
not have to wait for the joys of paradise. This improvement of
the situation of the poor, or the working classes was impossible in
the old monarchy because only the will of the king was law, and the
working classes had no means to formulate their demands. . . . Therefore we have reversed the old state. No longer shall the king have
his will; no longer shall there be privileged classes . . . everybody shall
have the same rights. This is corresponding to nature. Our new constitution shall guarantee these rights. Once we have this constitution
the people will be better educated so that everybody respects the
law, and the rights of his fellow citizens, and can develop the gifts
given to him by nature. . . . In order to keep the new constitution the
people must be armed. . . . When the people are educated and free,
everybody will understand best and be able to obtain what he
needs, and everybody will be as happy as possible.[22]

At least in the field of health "everybody should receive
according to his needs." [23] This should be the leading principle

of public health. With these opinions Virchow called himself a socialist.[24] He interpreted this term in the following way:

As I told you before, I regard communism as madness, if one wants to realize it directly. Yet socialism is to me the only goal of our efforts; not this or that system as it is now formulated in France, but the endeavor to build society on reasonable foundations, or in other words to create institutions that guarantee the liquidation of pauperism.[25]

Virchow had a dim view of the future of a society that continued to resist social reform:

The fear of the wealthy, which now is a mental epidemic in Europe, is insane, and just like ordinary insanity, it uses such means of defense . . . as will serve to realize in the end what it fears. . . . Our society, like blind Oedipus, stumbles deeper and deeper into its regrettable madness, and in producing and strengthening its enemies and pushing them eventually towards extreme measures, that again are insane, it creates its own destruction. Thus it fulfills the prophecy of the oracle.[26]

Virchow regarded himself as being on the extreme left of the political movement.[27] His social theories actually placed him to the left of Waldeck, whom he admired as the political leader of the left in Prussia,[28] or of Arnold Ruge, the neo-Hegelian and later leader of the extreme left in the *Paulskirche*. Virchow met Ruge through his friend and later father-in-law, Carl Mayer. (Ruge's brother Louis had married another daughter of Carl Mayer.) Virchow took over from A. Ruge such ideas as international arbitration, disarmament, and abolition of the death penalty.[29]

Virchow seems to have known the writings of Frederick Engels, Proudhon, and Louis Blanc,[30] but seems to have been particularly influenced by Julius Froebel [31]—the nephew of the famous educator, another leftist leader in the *Paulskirche*—and Gustav von Struve,[32] both of whom emphasized the slogan of "Education, Freedom, and Prosperity for all." Froebel had, like Ruge, started as a neo-Hegelian, but turned socialist in Zurich in 1843 under the influence of Weitling and Bakunin. (This was not the last metamorphosis in his eventful career.) Unlike another neo-Hegelian turning socialist at about the same period, Karl Marx, Froebel tried to combine individualism with social justice.[33] Struve, leader of two insurrections in Badenia, saw that "the fanatics of keeping quiet are always simultaneously the fanatics of mammon." He was not blind to the faults of the working class, and her "little Napoleons." But he knew that the future of liberty depended on an alliance of the third and the fourth estates, and he sincerely strove to overcome a system that always made the rich only richer, the poor poorer.[34] Through Struve [35] and Ruge [36] Virchow also acquired early a deep admiration for the political structure of the United States.

Virchow's political orientation is partly, of course, an expression of his temperament. That it is more than a personal accident is evident from the fact that he held his political convictions in common with a large number of outstanding young German scientists of the period. There was no place for either them as persons or for their goal and god, science, in the old feudal-bureaucratic structure where the command posts were in the hands of noblemen and their obedient instruments, and especially where all forms of education were under the tutelage of the high functionaries of the official churches. Their strivings for a better future implied, therefore, a breaking down of the old structure.

The Constitutional Conflict

THE VOICE of the people had been silenced in Prussia in 1848 by army and police. The sham constitution that Frederick William IV imposed by decree in 1848 was neither apt nor intended to change this fact. When in 1849 the king reversed his brand new constitution by another decree and introduced a census vote that Bismarck in one of his moments of cynical frankness called "the most nonsensical and most miserable electoral law ever invented," [1] the democrats decided to boycott the election.* The new vote gave the king eventually an obedient parliament that up to 1857 went on changing the constitution in a reactionary sense. This caricature of a constitution was valid in Prussia up to 1918. There was no public political life worth the name in Prussia between 1849 and 1858.

Change was again, as in 1840, brought about by a change in the person of the monarch. External events like the Franco-Austrian war in Italy stirred up political hopes. Another "new era" of liberalism seemed to dawn when Frederick William IV became so obviously insane that he had to be replaced in 1858 by his brother, William, as regent. William became king in 1861 after the death of his brother.

The hope to obtain liberal government from the hands of elderly William I—the *Kartaetschenprinz* of March, 1848, the reactionary civil war general of 1849—was one of the amazing illusions that characterize the history of German liberalism. To be sure, William personally resented and dismissed some of the most obnoxious policemen and bigots that had surrounded his brother and installed some ministers very faintly tainted with liberalism. But from the very beginning he made it perfectly clear that he was king "by divine right" and, as a professional soldier, primarily interested in strengthening the *Junker* army.

The illusion of the "new era" nevertheless caused masses of discouraged liberals and democrats to resume political activity. The election results for the Prussian diet (the lower house, House of Deputies, or *Abgeordnetenhaus;* the upper house, House of Lords, or *Herrenhaus* was nominated by the king) in November, 1858, illustrate this clearly. The conservatives (*Junker* party) went down from 220 to 60 seats; the moderate liberals went up from 57 to 204; the Catholics and Poles, who formed a kind of center, increased from 60 to 76 seats.

Virchow (like Lassalle) was one of the numerous "forty-eighters" who were brought back into politics by the popular awakening of the "new era." Virchow was elected into the city

* How this system worked may be seen, for example, from the fact that in 1908 the Social Democrats obtained six seats with 600,000 votes, while the conservatives held 212 with 418,000 votes.—Froelich, *Rosa Luxemburg,* p. 205.

council of Berlin in 1859 and participated in the same year in the foundation of the Deutscher National-Verein, an all-German league of liberal politicians taking up again the cause of German unity.

In his last article in the *Medical Reform* in 1849, Virchow had foreseen with great clarity what would be the political issues of a future in which he was to play such a conspicuous role. "Military reforms and constitutional guarantees against professional armies will form the contents of our political battles." [2] Control of the army is a decisive point in all those unfortunate countries where the army has become an independent political force.

The "new era" brought, in spite of the extreme tactfulness of the liberals ("Don't push" was their slogan), none of the hoped-for reforms. The one "reform" the new king presented forcefully through his defense minister Von Roon was an *army reform*. Von Roon was a conservative *Junker* and had helped to crush by force of arms the Badenian movement of 1849. The bill which Von Roon submitted in 1860 proposed to annually draft 63,000 instead of 40,000 men, to double the infantry battalions, to extend active service to three years from the two years in force since 1834, and to practically eliminate the Landwehr, a kind of militia created by the reformers of 1813. The reform was to cost 9,500,000 talers per year; the military budget would thus increase by one-third and form one-fourth of the total budget. The liberal majority was opposed to this bill, which would tremendously strengthen the power of king and *Junkers* who held a monopoly of officers' positions in the army. Of 119 infantry colonels, for instance, only eight were commoners. The common people, however, were to pay the bill, as the *Junkers* were tax-exempt. The liberals were ready to compromise on certain points, but were rather determined on the question of the three years' service and the elimination of the militia. The reform made no sense with regard to foreign politics, as the king and his conservative advisers had no conception of an active foreign policy.

As no compromise could be reached, the government withdrew its bill but asked for a special credit "to make some army reforms within the framework of the existing laws." The liberals were soft and shortsighted enough to grant this credit, which, of course, was used to effectuate the very reorganization that the parliament had refused to endorse.

The results of the first three years of the "new era" and the spineless attitude of liberal ministers and deputies were so disappointing that on the eve of new elections in 1861 a new party, the German Progressive Party, was formed in Prussia to carry on the battle for constitutional reforms and German unity on the basis of a definite program. This party was to lead the opposition during the constitutional conflict (*Verfassungskonflikt*) of 1862–66. Virchow was instrumental in establishing this party. He presided in the deliberations of the program, signed the program of June 9, 1861,[3] and in December, 1861, was elected as a member of this party into the lower house. He soon became one of the representative leaders and spokesmen of the new party alongside Von Hoverbeck, Schultze-Delitzsch, and Waldeck.

The new party undoubtedly expressed the feelings of the electorate. It obtained 109 seats in the elections of December, 1861. The left liberals obtained 52 seats, while the right liberals declined to 94, and the conservatives to only 15 seats.[4] The German Progressive Party was certainly far from being revolutionary and could be considered thus only by the reactionary officer clique and their king. The program of the Progressives[5] shows that they subscribed to the constitutional Prussian monarchy and to the unification of Germany under Prussian leadership. Their demands were only for responsibility of the cabinet to parliament instead of to the king, abolition of some *Junker* privileges, retention of the Landwehr and two years' service. The Progressive Party attracted former democrats like Virchow and Waldeck, and former moderates like Von Unruh and Von Forckenbeck. The former revolutionaries in this combination apparently had changed their policy because a revolutionary movement seemed objectively impossible. Even Lassalle had no more radical or practical suggestions than "abstention" from parliament. The results of these tactics had not been very satisfactory in 1849.

The former moderates had been taught by their 1848–49 experiences that the sacrifice of "freedom" still had not brought them "unity." They had therefore been converted to a policy of "Unity through Freedom." More freedom in Prussia, it was hoped, would make Prussia more attractive to the rest of the German people and produce a popular demand for unification, which the other governments would find irresistible in the long run. The Progressives could not hope to gain new freedoms in the immediate future. They concentrated on the active defense of the one little parcel of freedom left to them by the pseudo constitution: the constitutionally required consent of the lower house to the budget together with that of the king and of the upper house. *For the first time since 1849 a parliamentary opposition dared to assert its rights.* It was in this fight that Virchow acquired political fame.

It is almost paradoxical, but significant, that Virchow's political activity (very much like that of his erstwhile mentor, Julius Froebel, in 1848 [6]) should focus on a constitutional not a social problem, in spite of his continual insight into the social background of political problems (pp. 164 ff.). This is partly due to the fact that much of his social policy found practical expression elsewhere (pp. 133 ff.). To a larger degree this paradox seems due to the fact that he succumbed to the social blindness of his party, which, under the influence of its following of manufacturers, limited itself to pure "Manchesterism" and became unable to incorporate the oppositional forces of the rapidly increasing proletariat. The laboring classes had to create their own political parties, and at the time of the Bismarck-Lassalle alliance the Progressives found themselves menaced by a pincer movement of *Junkers* and proletarians. Their isolation from the impoverished masses that had manned the barricades in 1848 deprived the Progressives of one of their most impressive arguments, reduced their opposition to a purely parliamentary one, and was one of the main elements of their failure.

The "liberal" king reacted to the liberal elections of 1861 in characteristic fashion. After seeing the impossibility of legalizing his army reform with this chamber, he dissolved it after only two months of deliberations in the hope of obtaining a "better" parliament through extensive pressure on the electorate. The last liberal ministers were dismissed and replaced by conservatives. The "new era" was formally closed. The elections of March, 1862, were a bitter disappointment for the king. The Progressives and the left center (liberals) emerged for the first time with an absolute majority (135 plus 96 out of 363 deputies). Conservatives, Catholics, and right center were further reduced to 13, 54, and 65 seats respectively.

In August, 1862, the deliberations of the new house and its commissions on the budget of 1862, especially that of the army, started. For a while it seemed as if ministers as well as deputies were willing and able to reach a compromise by which the budget would pass in exchange for the two years' military service. But the king remained adamant.[7] Under these conditions the army budget was turned down by the house in September with 308 against 11 votes.

Virchow showed the constitutional alternatives of the situation:

> The constitution leaves two possibilities when such a conflict arises that a bill which has to be passed cannot be passed by a given administration. One possibility is to dissolve the house and appeal to the electorate, the other . . . the resignation of the cabinet and the formation of one able to obtain a budget. If the ministry wants neither to dissolve nor to resign it has either to present another budget . . . or army bill . . . or to ask for indemnity and a short credit with definite guarantees. It would try thus to follow regular constitutional procedure, a course which the house will always support.[8]

There existed, besides resignation or compromise (dissolution had just been tried in vain), a third possibility—that is, *unconstitutional rule without a budget act,* in the hope that the house would eventually give in and swallow the army reform integrally. This was the one the king chose, the course of the so-called "constitutional conflict." In order to execute this policy, the king nominated for prime minister and minister of foreign affairs a man whom he feared somewhat himself—the Prussian ambassador in Paris, *Otto von Bismarck.*

Bismarck had been a deputy from 1848 to 1851 and had been notorious for the brutal way in which he represented the extreme conservative point of view: a *Junker* monarchy in internal politics, the defense of princely prerogative (that is, German disunity) in external politics. Like all *Junkers* he had opposed unity for fear it might bring freedom.

Bismarck remained a Prussian *Junker* up to the end of his days, probably the most brutal and cynical, and certainly one of the few truly intelligent, men this caste ever produced. But in one respect he had changed profoundly between 1851 and 1862. He was no longer a simple conservative, a sterile defender of the *status quo;* he had become a reactionary "revolutionary." He had made the great discovery that unity could be obtained, after all, without freedom, that therefore Prussia could and should eliminate Austria, conquer the rest of Germany, and put an end to the "anhistorical, godless, and rightless swindle of the sovereignty of German princes" [9] (with the exception, of course, of that of his own of king). Bismarck could not, however, make his plans public for a long time; he had to hide them from his own king and his conservative friends, as well as from his prospective victims and the surrounding great powers: France, Russia, and England. By breaking the constitution he would obtain the new army for his king (the only thing the old man seemed to care for), gradually gain the king's assent for his plans, and eventually make himself dictator of Germany by making the king his tool. In pursuit of this end Bismarck would win and exploit allies wherever he found them, change and cheat them when necessary—his own caste, obedient liberals, socialist revolutionaries, the Russian Tsar, revolutionary Italians and Hungarians, the French dictator Napoleon III, etc. Bismarck embarked on a gamble for high stakes in September, 1862, which was the less transparent to the opposition as it did not realize that it no longer dealt simply with the conservative deputy of 1849 but with a reactionary revolutionary, a new phenomenon to become familiar only during the twentieth century.

Bismarck started his regime, which was to last twenty-eight

years, by sending the deputies home for a recess without having obtained a budget law for either 1862 or 1863. In a committee meeting he made the memorable declaration that gave the country an inkling of the basic principles of his reign:

Germany does not look to Prussia's liberalism but to her power. The South German States would like to indulge in liberalism, and therefore nobody will assign Prussia's role to them! Prussia must collect her forces and hold them in reserve for a favorable moment which has already come and gone several times. Since the treaties of Vienna, our frontiers have been ill-designed for a healthy body politic. The great questions of the time will be decided, not by speeches and resolutions of majorities (that was the mistake of 1848 and 1849) but by iron and blood.[10]

It is characteristic of Bismarck's policy that, while he announced brutally to the bourgeoisie her political disfranchise, he furthered her desire for material gain in concluding favorable trade agreements with France. Here again he was far more elastic than his *Junker* peers, who had nothing to offer to the middle class but oppression. Bismarck was not averse to using force extensively in order to soften parliament. The press and many Progressive deputies, who were at the same time civil servants (especially county judges), were submitted to all sorts of chicanery and sanctions. Yet Bismarck never lost sight of the fact that sometimes a political adversary who cannot be broken can be bought.

The session of 1863 started in January with deliberations of an address to the king, submitted by Virchow, which appealed to the king against the unconstitutional attitude of the government and the persecution of the opposition which disabled Prussia's promotion of German unity.[11] In this discussion Bismarck declared coldly to the house that such conflicts were questions of power, "and the one who has the power, uses it in his sense." [12] The king, of course, backed his government. No agreement was reached on the budget of 1863 and an army law.

When in January of 1863 a rebellion broke out in the Russian parts of Poland, Prussia entered a secret military alliance with Russia against the Poles.* The majority of the house, who had to learn about the treaty from foreign newspapers, was opposed to a policy which would bring no advantage to Prussia, but would make Prussia unpopular in the whole world. Virchow showed that this treaty was unconstitutional, as it had never been submitted for ratification to the house.[13] Subsequent events confirmed the predictions of the opposition—one more reason for Bismarck to be more arrogant than ever. The discussion became very heated. While Bismarck accused Virchow of spreading rumors with more effrontery than factualness, the latter retorted that the prime minister's speeches were on a sophomoric level.

Bismarck and the opposition debated no less acrimoniously another foreign policy issue, the Schleswig-Holstein question. These two German lands of the Danish crown were by new edicts of the Danish government in danger of being absorbed by Denmark. Bismarck, though secretly planning to annex Schleswig-Holstein, gave none but ambiguous statements and the opposition had every reason to believe that he maintained his 1848 stand for the Prussian betrayal of the provinces in their attempt to secede from Danish suzerainty. Virchow submitted a motion that all German states should jointly intervene on behalf of Schleswig-Holstein and the rights of the Prince of Augustenburg as Duke of Schleswig-Holstein, an independent German state. As to Bismarck's policy he said:

> The king must be informed of the imminent danger. The minister president has within a comparatively short time adopted so many different standpoints . . . that nobody can define his policy. He is speeding without a compass into the sea of foreign complications . . . ; he has no guiding principle; . . . that is his weakness that he has . . . no understanding for the essence of our nation, for what issues from the heart of the people. . . . He is given over to the evil one from those whose clutches he will never escape. . . .[14]

Bismarck retorted with the doctrine of the incompetence of

* Bismarck's true feelings concerning the Poles are given with rare frankness in a letter of 1861 to his sister: "I have plenty of sympathy for their situation, but if we want to survive we have to exterminate them" (as printed in Eyck, *Bismarck*, I, 464).

the parliament in foreign affairs, which through his later successes unfortunately became a dogma in Germany.

An assembly of three hundred and fifty members cannot, nowadays, in the last resort direct the policy of a great power, prescribing to the government a program which must be followed out to the end. . . . The politician who is not a specialist at the work regards every move on the chessboard as the end of the game. Hence his illusion that the goal is continually changing. . . . Politics is not an exact science.[15]

As far as Virchow personally was concerned, Bismarck became even more specific, asserting that he might be a famous anatomist, but:

The honorable member charges me with a lack of understanding of national politics. I can throw back the charge while suppressing the adjective. To me it seems that the honorable member has no understanding of politics of any kind.[16]

It is not surprising that under these circumstances the house refused a loan asked by the government for a possible war with Denmark.

Bismarck and his ministers continued systematically to provoke parliament. In May, 1863, they denied to the president of the house the right to call them to order; and when through their arrogant behavior they forced him to do so, they ceased to appear before the house until this "injustice" was removed. In these days Bismarck started his meetings with Lassalle. The house was closed, and an unconstitutional decree against the press was given that provoked the crown prince to disavow publicly the policy of his father's minister.

It was hoped that this decree and other repressive measures would help the government in the fall elections of 1863. But for the third time the elections confirmed the stand of the opposition. Progressives and left liberals again had the majority (235 seats). Small gains of the conservatives (36) were made at the expense of their Catholic (26) and rightist liberal allies (9).

The session of 1864 was only a repetition of the old sterile discussion of a military law and a budget which, in view of the persistency of both partners, could not be settled. The government could again point to advantageous new commercial treaties. It could point to a short and successful war against Denmark, together with Austria, for the "liberation" of Schleswig-Holstein.

It is remarkable that, nevertheless, the position of the house on the budget and military law remained unchanged in 1865. In this year falls the "duel affair" between Bismarck and Virchow. Bismarck interpreted a remark of Virchow during the discussion of the navy budget as an aspersion on his truthfulness. Although Bismarck had in private very definite opinions on the political necessity of lying [17] and was undoubtedly one of the most adroit liars of all times, he chose Virchow's remark as a welcome pretext to give this impudent commoner a radical lesson in "good behavior." As previously reported, Virchow did not fall into the trap.

This challenge formed only part of Bismarck's mounting campaign to intimidate the opposition. Deputies received summonses for remarks made in parliament and were even (like J. Jacoby) jailed for "treasonable" public utterances.[18] It was certainly no overstatement when Virchow wrote in the report of the budget commission of 1866:

It is clear that absolutism has been re-established in Prussia, and without the limitations it imposed upon itself before March, 1848. There is no control of public finances, no budget law any more; instead of laws we have decrees; the control court is without subject; treasury and property of the state are at the free disposal of the government.[19]

In June, 1866, Prussia declared war on the rest of Germany and Austria. That Bismarck was able to engineer this war in spite of the fact that practically everybody—not only the house and the people, but even the king and the *Junkers*—was opposed to it shows the full extent of his evil genius. It was a desperate gamble, but he won it most intelligently and with it the future.

In a war of nerves lasting four years Bismarck had worn out the opposition. The conflict had meant economic losses for what was, after all, a middle-class movement. Certainly not all followers of the Progressive Party had agreed with Virchow when he in 1866 turned down economically advantageous railroad laws of the government in declaring that "one could not sacrifice the constitution to material gains." [20] It had been increasingly difficult for the opposition to refuse military credits, as they themselves were afraid of foreign intervention. Bismarck had physically persecuted the opposition, which still had remained compact. But what Bismarck had failed to obtain by force, or wear, he eventually obtained through his tremendous success in foreign policy. He brought back from the battlefields of Bohemia the "North German Union"—that is, the unification of northern Germany—and an alliance with the south German states which promised eventual unification of all Germany, except Austria, under the leadership of the Prussian king and his prime minister. Bismarck now had proved that he could bring unity (and new markets) by his "blood and iron" method, and thus the majority of the German bourgeoisie decided for the second time to forgo freedom for the sake of national unity.

The change of popular feeling had become obvious already in the elections of July, 1866, taking place on the day of the battle at Sadowa and after the Prussian victories in Saxonia, Hanover, and Bavaria. The Progressives obtained only 83, the left liberals 65 seats, a most precarious majority. The conservatives came back with 142 and the right liberals with 26 seats.

Bismarck did even better. He split the Progressives. A new liberal party, which supported Bismarck blindly till his turn in economic policy in 1878, the so-called "National Liberal Party," was founded by the left liberals and those who abandoned the Progressive Party. This party symbolizes the profound change in German mentality around 1870. It tried to play the role of the "loyal opposition," a notion which makes sense only in a democracy and which was absurd under the pseudoconstitutional absolutism of the New Reich. It consoled itself for its continual capitulations with the material gains of its adherents and with confidence in the "historical tendencies" that would accomplish what it did not dare to do itself. The government, which remained free of legal responsibility to the parliament, could become "constitutional" now, as every one of its wishes was fulfilled by a "loyal opposition." Robert von Mohl had written unwittingly the motto for the new Bismarckean era in 1860, when stating:

The only possible means to obtain constant unity in the constitutional state are: either corruption or government responsible to the parliament.[21]

The constitutional conflict was closed formally in September, 1866, by the action of the house giving "indemnity" to the government (with 230 against 75 votes) for the four years it had governed against the constitution.

Virchow, who had been unsuccessful with his admonition, "Beware of the fetishism of success," [22] remained faithful to his party and his past in voting against the indemnity and the army budget for 1867. But his political role had profoundly changed. While from 1862 to 1866 he had represented the majority of the people against Bismarck and his *Junker* monarchy, now and for the rest of his life he was to represent only a small group of nonconformist bourgeois against a coalition of *Junkers* and bourgeoisie under the absolute leadership of Bismarck. Even as an opposition party, his Progressives would be overshadowed in importance not too far in the future by the new labor party, the Social Democrats.

It is easy to see the limitations of the Progressive, and therewith Virchow's attitude in the constitutional conflict. Even granted that conditions were unfavorable for extraparliamentary actions—and they certainly were—we see no attempts of the Progressives in this direction as the democrats had made in 1848–49. Their monarchism, which in the beginning might have been a smart electoral maneuver, involved them increasingly in difficulties when the monarch proved to be the most stubborn violator of the constitution. They had cut themselves off from the impoverished masses. They acted as if politics was a kind of educational campaign for realizing "ideas" and not a conflict of powers. Eyck has praised the constitutional conflict as "a fight for the right,* perhaps the only large-scale fight for the right known in German history." [23] Quite apart from the fact that this assertion is only formally correct, it shows the weakness of the movement. The fight for freedom was reduced to a formal legalistic discussion—it is no accident that so many Progressive leaders were jurists or professors—which was sterile and hopeless because the fight had started precisely on account of the refusal of the partner to transact on this level.† Our admiration for the moral values of the Progressives (especially those who, like Virchow, did not capitulate in 1866), for their courage, steadfastness, and uprightness, tends to be greater than our admiration for their political realism and inventiveness.

Yet the formalism and the pettiness of the constitutional conflict should not deceive us into underestimating its historical importance. *It was the last large-scale attempt of the German middle class to play an independent political role.* The defeat of the Progressives was full of unfortunate consequences for Germany's further political evolution. The victory of the reaction made it possible to maintain to a large extent the old political structure, in spite of some liberal window dressings and in spite of an economic development going in the opposite direction. "Historical tendencies," unfortunately, do not realize themselves automatically. The army remained a decisive political factor, while its political strength was broken in other Western countries and while it had never been one so far in the United States. The conquest of Germany by Prussia can perhaps be best visualized to Americans when they imagine what would have happened in the United States after a victory of the Confederacy in the Civil War.

Ranke called the conflict period the most brilliant period in

* Bismarck admitted in 1876 after one of Virchow's speeches in the lower house that the right had been with the opposition (see *K-H*, I, 282).

† I have nevertheless avoided using the expression "doctrinaire" in regard to the Progressives, as it was invented by the National Liberals who differed from the Progressives, not in having a more practical program to reach the same goal, but in embracing a "realism" which consisted mainly in giving up the goal, praising Bismarck, and making money.

Bismarck's long political career.[24] The same holds true for
Virchow. A conservative polemist stated ironically seventy
years ago that "it was good that Mr. Virchow had gained a
title to immortality in other fields. We believe that as an
opponent of Bismarck little will be left of Virchow, only a
name without resonance, touching the ears of posterity unap-
preciated." [25] It seems quite possible that—once the Germans
have fully realized the consequences of Bismarck's victory [26]
and the Western world has reached a full understanding of the
impact of the miscarriage of Germany democracy on its own
fate—posterity might, in spite of our conservative prophet and
in spite of the shortcomings of the Progressives, respect Virchow for his consistent opposition to Bismarck in a decisive
moment of history as deeply as it now respects him for his
scientific achievements.

In the New Reich

ALTHOUGH the new German Reich (Empire) was established
only in 1871, its constitution actually dated from 1867. The
New Reich simply took over (with very slight changes) the
constitution that had been worked out in the North German
Reichstag (Parliament) by Bismarck and his National Liberals
for the new North German Federation after the war of 1866.

At first sight the new constitution looked like a tremendous
progress. Instead of the Prussian electoral "census" system it
provided for equal and universal suffrage. Bismarck introduced
this, not because he had suddenly been converted to liberalism, but because the Prussian electoral system had never provided the reactionary majorities which his political model, the
emperor-dictator Napoleon III, had obtained from plebiscites.
Only universal suffrage utilized the reactionary votes of the
multitude of ignorant and dependent peasants. In the second
place, Bismarck had taken good care that, should this electoral

system ever turn against him, it was practically irrelevant, as this new constitution vested final decisions in the "Bundesrat." The Bundesrat was a kind of upper house, not of popularly elected, but of governmentally nominated and instructed representatives of the German princes. The German government, presided over by a chancellor who was nominated by the Prussian king in his role of German Emperor, was ultimately responsible to nobody but the latter.

Virchow felt that "this new federation bears the stigma of impotence as already its first paragraph gives only advisory powers to the Reichstag." "Thus the parliament, which is supposed to be the larger one, is under the control of the Prussian parliament." "This is a very poor substitute for what the German people had hoped for when the government waved the banner of parliamentarism." "This will be no more than a new machine for granting money." [1] Virchow, therefore, not only voted against this constitution, but for twelve years he refused to accept a seat in the Reichstag, which he regarded as a sham. Only in 1880 he gave way to the pressure of his party and stayed in the Reichstag till 1893.

While thus little or nothing was accomplished after 1866 in the way of political liberties, the new Reichstag, dominated by the National Liberals, furthered tremendously the economic development of the middle classes in creating unified currency, measurements, and law code, the freedom of trade and settlement all over Germany, and a federal bank (*Reichsbank*).

When in 1869 Bismarck asked the Prussian lower house to grant him the free disposal of the annual interest of the confiscated property of the ex-king of Hanover (some 400,000 talers), Virchow distinguished himself by being one of the very few, even among the opposition leaders, to foresee the consequences of this move and to oppose it. Unfortunately, Virchow's prophecy that this so-called *Welfenfund* or Reptile Fund would serve the ends of political corruption was more than fulfilled. Bismarck used it for bribing, not only the "free" press, but also public officials and even kings, like Ludwig II of Bavaria.[2]

In the mid-sixties, as mentioned above (pp. 151 ff.), Virchow had become infected with the chauvinistic, anti-French phraseology of the period. Yet after 1866 he realized more or less clearly that, far from combating Bismarck's foreign policy by this means, he unwittingly had helped the dictator to prepare his next war. He therefore warned against new wars.[3] Stating that there had been more than enough blood and iron on the road to German unity, he suggested in 1869 in the Landtag European *disarmament* instead of new armament as a practical guarantee of further peaceful developments.[4] None of Virchow's political stands has been used more frequently against him by political adversaries than this unsuccessful and almost desperate step on the eve of the Franco-German war of 1870–71. Yet Virchow never disavowed it, and the experience of the two World Wars which have grown out of the 1870 conflict has transformed his "shame" into a title of honor.

During the war Virchow concentrated on medical, humanitarian work. In the general excitement he publicly expressed a deep longing for peace, and tried to make scientists aware of their moral obligation to facilitate a reconciliation of the warring nations.[5] Virchow continued these endeavors after the war in full consciousness of their difficulty.

Let us not forget that we are the victors, and that it behooves the victor to build the roads of reconciliation, and to keep them open, even if the vanquished for a long time should disdain to enter these roads. Let the German nation show that in its glory it will be able to avoid the great danger of complacency that has ruined France.[6]

It is true that the decisive step for a Franco-German reconciliation, the disavowal of the annexation of Alsace-Lorraine, was dared by Bebel and his party but not by Virchow and his Progressive friends. In his programmatic speech at the *Naturforscherversammlung* in Rostock in 1871 ("The Tasks of the Sciences in Germany's New National Existence") Virchow expressed the hope that the unification of Germany would be a step toward the unification of humanity.[7] His orientation toward peace and his belief in the special role that scientists and doctors were destined to play in the peace movement caused Virchow to pay great attention to the International Medical

Congresses.[8] He considered such personal contacts as indeed serving international conciliation; he regretted the absence of such contacts, especially between Germany and Russia, and tried to exploit his own trips in this direction.[9]

In the Turko-Russian war of 1877 Virchow wanted to overcome the indifference of the German people toward an event which affected them economically and threatened to bring about even more dangerous involvements. As a remedy he recommended a European intervention via arbitration.[10] Through the Berlin Congress of 1878 Bismarck brought about to a certain extent these suggestions.

Virchow's concern with the peaceful development of Germany made him oppose the policy of colonial expansion which Bismarck's Germany started in 1884–85. A trip to Africa confirmed Virchow in the opinion that colonial expansion was a costly, risky, and eventually useless enterprise for Germany.[11] His "testament" of 1902 still contains a passage against colonialism.[12] Virchow's competence and interest in foreign affairs, his personal relations, and his linguistic abilities made him a possible candidate for foreign minister during the years when the imminent succession of Frederick William, the liberal son of William I, still made a liberal cabinet a not unlikely prospect.

Bismarck had thoroughly domesticated the majority of conservatives and liberals even before the Reich was officially founded. Yet there remained the *Catholic party*, now constituting itself as "Center Party" in the Reich and strengthened by the incorporation of Catholic states like Bavaria. This party retained a large degree of independence in spite of its conservatism. The declaration of infallibility of Pope Pius IX in 1870 provided Bismarck with a welcome occasion to attack the Center as an "enemy of Germany" (every adversary of Bismarck being an "enemy of Germany") in an attempt to break it. From 1871 on, beginning with the so-called "pulpit paragraph" to the 1875 laws against religious orders, Reichstag and Landtag passed a series of laws reducing the right of the Church in the state (supervision of schools, civil marriage) as well as in its own affairs and submitting the resistant clergy to incarceration and expatriation. As far as the Center Party was concerned, Bismarck never reached his goal. When Bismarck was forced by failure to give up the fight in 1878, the Center was stronger than ever before. The anti-Catholic laws had served, nevertheless, to corrupt and sidetrack Bismarck's conservative and liberal followers, who both denied their basic principles in supporting Bismarck in this enterprise.

It must be regretfully stated that Bismarck was followed this time, not only by the National Liberals, but also by the majority of the Progressives under the leadership of Virchow. Virchow entered the battle early in 1872 immediately after Bismarck [13] and even coined the name under which the conflict has entered history, "Kulturkampf" (fight for culture). Virchow drew much of the fire from the enemies of the Kulturkampf. It was during the Kulturkampf that the unreconstructed *Junker,* H. von Kleist–Retzow, wanted to nail him down in the Reichstag "as one nails certain animals at the barn door." [14]

Virchow had been provoked by the Pope's dogma of infallibility and announced a counterattack in his programmatic Rostock speech of 1871.[15] It is regrettable, but characteristic, that Virchow concentrated on this point of his Rostock program, while another important point of it—improvement of the situation and rights of the laboring class—played no practical role in his political activities during the 1870's. As a consistent liberal, Virchow stood for the separation of church and state. He saw in Bismarck's fight an important step in this direction. He overlooked the fact that Bismarck's goal was an entirely different one: the submission of the church and its party to *"the state"* (that is, his personal dictatorship) and that the unsavory means used in the fight were consistent with Bismarck's, but not with any liberal, goals. Virchow's fight has been often compared with that led at about the same time by the great physiologist Paul Bert against the Catholic Church in France.[16] The comparison is legitimate as far as the goals are concerned. But while Bert fought Church and reaction, Virchow, while fighting the Church, became the ally of an even worse reactionary. In the Kulturkampf Virchow again

became a leader of large masses. But at what price! Virchow
later (in 1881) realized and freely admitted his mistake,[17] undoubtedly the greatest error of his political career. But it was
too late. While the liberals had fought for Bismarck against
the Catholics, Bismarck had prepared a situation which allowed him to govern from then on even without National Liberal approval.

It is no accident that after the Kulturkampf Virchow's star
as a leader of the Progressives was largely outshone by that
of the seventeen-year-younger Eugen Richter, the son of the
well-known reformer of military medicine, Adolf Leopold
Richter. Richter was one of the few Progressives who had been
unwilling to participate in Bismarck's persecution of Catholics.

After the incorporation of provinces with a better and freer
administrative system into Prussia in 1866, it became necessary
to introduce some reforms into the feudal administrative organization of the old provinces. The first attempts in this direction were undertaken in 1868, at which time Virchow made
the following important programmatic remarks:

> We do not try to reach decentralization through federalism which
> is more or less feudally oriented. . . . We have the precise, clear
> formula of self-government, where decentralization is based on the
> freedom of local communities. The conservatives want the freedom
> of provinces, federalism, in favor of a few privileged classes; we
> want the freedom of the communities for everybody.[18]

Actual legislation in this field was obtained only between
1872 and 1876, not without bitter fights against the *Junkers*
who did not want to surrender any of their local privileges.
In these discussions Virchow again played a great role.[19] The
laws that were eventually obtained were unsatisfactory, but
even Virchow voted for them in the hope that they constituted
a first step. The fact that it was unwise at this moment to
shock the government with which he was then allied in the
Kulturkampf might also have influenced his decision, although
—unlike the National Liberals—Virchow remained adamant on
the question of the military budget even during this period.

The alliance between Bismarck and the National Liberals concluded in 1866 had been based on their common interest in free trade. In the 1870's the problem for the *Junkers* changed as, with the appearance of cheaper grain on the world market, their main problem was no longer that of free exportation but became that of a protective tariff. Their interest in protective tariffs was shared by big business, and thus in the 1870's a ruling economic coalition was born that lasted up to Hitler's time. With these changes in *Junker* interests Bismarck decided on a basic change in economic policy. He started to eliminate the representatives of free trade in government (for example, Delbrueck in 1876), but he had to hide his plans because he could not forgo the help of the National Liberals as long as he was still involved in his fight with the Pope. Two "lucky" accidents in 1878 allowed Bismarck to end his "liberal" era in the political and economic field: the death of Pius IX in February, which made a peace with the (pro-tariff) Center possible, and the two attempts against William I by insane individuals—not Social Democrats—which obscured the issues by a tremendous "red scare" and forced the National Liberals into another antiliberal legislative adventure, the notorious *Anti-Socialist Law*.

Bismarck proposed to outlaw the Socialists right after the first attempt in May, but was turned down even by his National Liberals. After the second attempt in June, Bismarck dissolved the Reichstag; and in October after elections in an atmosphere of artificial hysteria the National Liberals were sufficiently softened up to pass the Anti-Socialist Law. As far as the Social Democrats were concerned, the law proved abortive and contributed heavily to Bismarck's downfall in 1890. Twelve years of outlawry and persecution had not in the least affected the growth of the Social Democrats. On the contrary, between 1877 and 1890 (the year the law expired) they had tripled their vote to one and a half million, and had over 35 instead of 12 members in the Reichstag.

Virchow, despite his aversion to the Social Democrats, vigorously fought Bismarck's bill and the act when it was on the books. The Social Democrats might be "good revolutionaries" (how shocked were his contemporaries by this combination of adjective and noun!); that did not make them regicides yet.[20] And who else, according to Virchow, had nursed the Social Democrats in their beginnings but Lassalle's friend Bismarck? When it was shown that the government had used *agents provocateurs* against the Social Democrats, Virchow made the unparliamentary appeal to the Secretary of the Interior, "Liberate us from these scoundrels, Mr. von Puttkammer!" Virchow confessed in these discussions that he himself was no longer a democratic revolutionary, but that—if one could now follow the way of legal and constitutional progress—it was due to a revolution, that of 1848, without which there would be no constitution in Prussia or Germany.[21]

In this year of reactionary attacks, 1878, anti-Semitism, always a political weapon of the *Junkers,* began to play a larger political role in Germany with the foundation of the Christian-Social Party by the court preacher (!) Stoecker. This so-called Christian, a forerunner of Hitler, tried with the blessings of Bismarck to bring the laboring masses into the fold of reaction through a demagogic mixture of social protest and anti-Semitism. Virchow courageously fought this fatal superstition.[22] He defeated Stoecker personally in Berlin in the 1881 elections.[23]

After thus having prepared the field, Bismarck presented his high tariffs in 1879 and carried them through with the Center Party and the conservatives against the majority of the National Liberals. The left wing of the National Liberals (Lasker, Bamberger, Forckenbeck) split in 1880 from the right wing, who wanted to follow Bismarck even under these circumstances, and founded with the Progressives in 1884 the Deutschfreisinnige Partei. It was an uneasy marriage that dissolved again in 1893 on the question of military credits, Richter, Virchow, and their friends carrying on under the label of Freisinnige Volkspartei.

Virchow played a minor role in the discussions of the 1880's concerning Bismarck's tariffs and social legislation when Richter had become the main speaker of the party. He would undoubtedly have come into the limelight again under Frederick III, with whom he was on close personal terms (see p. 29), but Frederick III succumbed to cancer in 1888 after a reign of only one hundred days.

A field in which Virchow continued to play a role was that of budget control. His meticulousness and industry made him an ideal chairman of the accounting commission of the Prussian Landtag Diet from 1872 to 1902.[24] Virchow had always been particularly interested in this problem. It was his contention that, not the mere granting of expenses, but control of the actual expenses should be the central concern of the representative body. In this field it was more often possible to gain the support of the National Liberals, whose devotion to Prince Bismarck was most likely to find certain limits when questions concerning their pocketbooks were raised.

Quantitatively Virchow's political contribution is no less extensive than his scientific contribution. (Therefore, argued his friend L. Traube, future generations would be unable to believe that deputy Virchow and Dr. Virchow were the same person.) I have nevertheless given less space to Virchow's political thought because, unlike some of his scientific problems, many parliamentary issues of the time strike us as dated and devoid of contemporary interest.* We might also have succumbed to the emotional dissatisfaction that any examination of the life of a German liberal of the second half of the nineteenth century must produce. The story of Virchow's political life is essentially a story of courage, insight, and devoted industry. And yet it came to nought—primarily not through the errors of the hero, considerable as they were sometimes, but through his being chained to a class and a nation involved in insoluble contradictions and paralyzed by traditions of submis-

---

* I have for the same reasons disregarded the incessant smear campaigns to which Virchow was exposed—from the calumnies of the *Kreuzzeitung* in 1849 (*Briefe*, p. 169) down to such pamphlets as Carl Pansch's series "Geheimes Judentum, Nebenregierung, und Juedische Weltherrschaft," the second number of which was *Geheimrat Prof. Dr. Rud. Virchow aus Schivelbein, unser grosser Gelehrter* (Leipzig, 1892). Almost none of his political adversaries was above exploiting the emotional repulsion that Virchow's professional occupation with death and cadavers would produce in the average person.

sion. It is easy to see how different Virchow's political career would have been, had he lived in France, England, or the United States.

Virchow was spared much of the suffering—for example, exile or the long prison terms—to which most progressives of the generation preceding him (like Ruge, Auerbach, Reuter, Eisenmann, etc.) had been submitted. He enjoyed the acclaim of large sectors of the population as a reward for his political activities. But to witness the desired and stupendous growth of one's country and at the same time to observe helplessly the growth of those elements that eventually would bring about catastrophe must have been a continual source of frustration to him. What was the use even of witnessing eventually the fall of his old antipode Bismarck in 1890, if this event was not and could not be brought about in Germany by the will of the people but must be brought about by the whims of a young monarch whose character promised the worst adventures for Germany's future?

We have no evidence that Virchow suffered with the same intensity from this state of affairs as Mommsen did.[25] But by what else than a feeling of utter futility can one explain the following strange remark of Virchow on the relative value of political and scientific activities?

> I can say to quiet my friends that the silent and often unnoticed work of the researcher demands more force and concentration than the activity of the politician, by nature more noisy and therefore more rewarding. I at least have often found the latter to be a kind of recreation.[26]

Under these conditions it is surprising that Virchow remained politically active up to the end of his life, when a man of his make-up would appear more and more as a "fossil" in the new imperialistic Germany. Obviously the impulse received in 1848 was strong enough to outlast all disappointments. The positive function that Virchow attributed to criticism might also make his kind of political career acceptable to him. It is significant that his testament-like "To My Friends" of 1902 refers in a positive vein to his 1848 activities.[27] His untiring and active sense of civic responsibility elevates Virchow above most great scientists and gives meaning to his political contribution, even though final realization was denied to it.*

* Virchow's most attractive political trait was probably this courageous faithfulness to his own past, so rare among his contemporaries. I know of only one lapse of his. When rector of the University of Berlin in 1893—in an official speech on "The Foundation of the University of Berlin and the Transition from the Philosophical to the Scientific Age"—he obviously felt morally obliged to say a few laudatory words on the intelligence of the university's founder, Frederick William III. These he could not possibly have believed, having contributed some documentary evidence years before (A, XXXIII [1865], 170 ff.) as to the true mental horizon of the king. Frederick William's reign is characterized by the large-scale persecutions of students, professors, and writers, many of whom spent their best years in the prisons of this culture hero.

The Anthropologist

Dynamics of Skull Growth

I N CONSIDERATION of the fact previously explained that Virchow was basically a great biologist, it is not surprising that sooner or later he should come in contact with anthropological problems. As he was a professional pathologist, it was quite natural that his first contacts with anthropology should come by way of pathology.

One of the local pathological problems facing Virchow in Wuerzburg was cretinism. In 1851 Virchow published an extensive study, "On Cretinism, Especially in Franconia, and on Pathological Conformations of the Skull." [1] Skull deformation is one of the most striking characteristics of cretinism. Virchow found that none of the possible deformations of the skull—up to that time studied primarily by psychiatrists, since mental disease was so often accompanied by skull deformation—was specific for cretinism. [2] He therefore carefully surveyed them all, measuring the twenty-nine deformed skulls of the Wuerzburg collection and arriving at the following still valid classification: (1) macrocephaly, (2) microcephaly, (3) pathological dolichocephaly (subgroups: spheno-, lepto-, clinocephaly), (4) pathological brachycephaly (subgroups: pachy-, oxy-, platy-, trocho-, plagiocephaly).

However, his great contribution to the field of skull deformation was not of a classificatory nature: it was his emphasis on the causal connection between deformation and the premature synostosis (closure) of certain of the sutures of the skull. From his microscopical work on osseous growth (see p. 77) he knew them to be the growth zones of the cranial bones. Inflammatory processes might provoke such synostoses. The use of the notions of dolicho- and brachycephaly shows that Virchow was familiar with the contemporary work of Anders Retzius on racial craniology. In the case of racial dolicho- and brachycephaly, no "premature" synostosis could be involved, but according to Virchow the growth rhythm of the marginal zones might be different in different races.

In 1856 Virchow made another communication, "On the Development of Cretinism and Skull Deformations." [3] He then assumed that of all synostoses those of the base of the skull would be the most consequential ones and that the specific physiognomy of cretins was due to premature synostosis of the skull base. In the skull of a newborn cretin he was able to confirm this hypothesis.

Virchow's interest in the skull base culminated in his masterly book of 1857, *Researches on the Development of the Skull Base in the Healthy and Diseased and Its Influence on the Form of the Skull, the Formation of the Face and the Structure of the Brain*. He showed that phrenology had brought about an undue neglect of the base of the skull. His own interest in the base was stimulated by Froriep. (As a matter of fact, interest in the skull base was a romantic legacy from Oken, Goethe, C. G. Carus, etc. Malacarne and the Wenzel brothers had connected the skull base with cretinism.) He felt that quantitative studies of the skull base were more relevant than Retzius' measuring of the skull length and skull breadth. The base of the skull expressed the connections between configuration of the cranium, the face, and the brain.

Virchow followed Soemmering in regarding the sphenoid and the occipital in the adult as one bone (os tribasilare). Embryological research had shown that the part between the foramen magnum and the os ethmoidale grows out of the preformation of three vertebral bodies. The synchondrosis spheno-occipitalis might be ossified at 13–14 years, usually would be ossified at 18–20 years. The two "vertebrae" forming the sphenoid could occur united at birth, and usually would be united by 13 years. (All of Virchow's statements were supported by thirteen plates of sagittal skull sections of rare excellence.) Virchow discussed in detail the prenatal and postnatal growth of the "basilar bone," including microscopy and sinus formation. The angle formed between sphenoid and occipital bone (called "saddle angle" by Virchow, "basal angle" by L. Fick) increases from the third fetal month to birth and decreases between birth and puberty. Its smallness in man characteristically differentiates men from apes. The nasal angle, according to Virchow, is in inverse proportion to the saddle angle. He discussed the disturbances produced by premature synostosis and the compensations through growth in other directions which make it possible for even severe deformation of the skull not to imply necessarily disorders of brain functions.

Virchow came to the following conclusions:

1. All original impairments of the base produce a deficiency in the cranium. They are accompanied by a disturbance in the development of the brain and in the position and growth of facial bones. The latter depend in turn on the deficient growth of the brain, yet mostly on the mechanical effect of the bones of the base.

2. All original impairments of the cranium, especially of its anterior and median parts, affect, besides brain growth, the growth of the base and can affect the position of facial bones.

3. Original impairments of brain growth have little effect on the basilar bone, but have important consequences for the growth of the cranium. Aside from asymmetry, they affect the formation of the face only in isolated, rather teratological cases.

4. All typical and more extensive differences in facial formation depend primarily on differences in the formation of the skull base.[4]

Virchow felt that in spite of all its defects his study "has opened a path hardly trod hitherto, and leading closer toward the desired goal. It has replaced instinctive feelings and intuitive contemplation by the secure insight of measurable quantities. It has dissolved relationships, so far only crudely indicated, into a series of mutually dependent numerical values."[5]

However much opinions may have changed on details of these studies, the basic importance of such discoveries as the role of synostoses of sutures and the role of the cranial base and the saddle angle for anatomy and anthropology is so obvious as to make any further elaboration superfluous.* Many of these morphological results have been confirmed, and few have been extended by modern experimental studies.

In 1858 Virchow rediscussed some of his findings in opposition to Ludwig Fick,[6] who was experimenting at that time on bone growth in young animals by removing parts of the musculature and who felt able to explain bone formation exclusively on mechanical grounds (muscle pressure and traction). Fick felt that his results alone had validity, since only results obtained by experiment were "exact acquisitions of physiology." Virchow upheld the rights of morphology in answering that "experiment is superfluous in certain experiences, impossible in others." [7] Fick reproached Virchow with "mixing of physiological and pathological facts," only to draw the justified rebuke: did he feel that his experiments were less pathological because they had the purpose of physiological research?

In this same article Virchow closes a splendid historical survey of the skull formation and deformation problem from Herodotus and Hippocrates to Malgaigne and Larrey with the melancholy statement: "If the acquisitions of our predecessors had been better preserved and developed in medical science, it probably would not have been my privilege to create on these bases a theory of abnormal skulls and of typical skull formation." Things have not improved since in this direction. The extreme scarcity of Virchow's great book even in his lifetime is but a partial excuse for the neglect of his findings and consequent re-"discoveries" in following generations.

Virchow dealt once more with problems of the skull base in his 1876 academy paper on the anthropology of the Germans.

* This is very obvious, for example, from the work of the late F. Weidenreich, who—though modifying many of Virchow's findings—frequently emphasized his indebtedness to Virchow's basic concepts in personal conversations with me.

He discussed the possible etiology of J. B. Davis' "plastic deformation" (called "basilary impressions" by Virchow) and of ankylosis of the atlas.

The Origin of Man

DARWINISM or transformism acted as an extremely powerful stimulus in the rise of European anthropology during the 1860's, even more powerful than the famous prehistoric discoveries of the period in Scandinavia, Switzerland, and France. In the eyes of many, Darwinism at last had given anthropology meaning and orientation. It is no accident that the formation of the German Anthropological Association in 1869 was due to one of the outstanding German transformists, Karl Vogt. If the nontransformist Virchow nevertheless became shortly afterwards the leader of the association and retained this role to the end of his life, it must be credited to his powerful personality and his indefatigable propaganda for his point of view on the question of the origin of man.

Virchow's position in the discussion of tranformism tends to become more and more oversimplified and misrepresented as a stubborn, reactionary, absolute opposition—very much in the vein in which his attitude toward bacteriology has been misrepresented. As a matter of fact, this legend seems about all students know of Virchow's accomplishments in anthropology. The truth, as in the case of bacteriology (see the chapter of this book entitled "Parasites and Bacteria"), is far more complex.

Actually, Virchow—as he liked to remind people in later years [1]—had proclaimed transformistic hypotheses years before the publication of Darwin's *Origin of Species*.

At the *Naturforscherversammlung* in Karlsruhe in 1858 he said:

Our experiences give us no title whatsoever to regard as an eternal rule the immutability of species which at present appears so certain. Geology teaches us a certain succession of stages where the species follow each other, higher to lower ones. As much as the experience of our time seems to contradict such an idea, I must confess that to me it seems to be a need of science to re-examine the possibility of changes of species into species. Only thus will the mechanical theory of life be firmly established in this direction.[2]

Two years earlier Virchow had in a similar vein spoken of the fact that geology teaches the existence of progress in nature and that the laws, but not the forms of nature, are eternal.[3] Anybody who had been under the influence of Goethe and the "genetic idea" of the German romantics was bound to have some understanding of transformistic ideas. Virchow's notion of metaplasia, in particular, would give him a sympathetic attitude toward transformism, although he always emphasized the limitations of metaplasia.[4] He realized that the biologist's "daily bread" variability was partial transformism.[5] In spite of their persistence, he did not think races to be permanent or unalterable.[6]

Virchow, therefore, continually showed respect and sympathy for Darwinism as a hypothesis. In 1870 he found the so-called "theory of descent" (of man from a simian ancestor) excellent from a logical and speculative standpoint. He also found the evolutionary theory to be an ethical postulate. Not as a dogma, but as a "beacon of science," Darwinism would bring a rich harvest.[7] In 1887 his attitude was just as sympathetic:

Although facts are still lacking to prove generic variation experimentally or by direct observation, the experiences of embryology, zoology, and pathology are in excellent accord with the hypothesis of descent. It is evident even that all these disciplines have made important progress in the knowledge of actual processes, under the rule of the descent hypothesis. Darwinism has proved to be a most fertile idea, and will act as an energetic ferment for a long time.[8]

On the other hand, this sympathy held only so far as Darwinism appeared as a hypothesis. Those who wanted to go further were warned again and again by Virchow that direct evidence for the transformation of species, and especially simians into man, was still lacking. It had to be kept clear what were facts and what were opinions. Although the amount of indirect evidence has so tremendously increased during the last sixty years as to make Darwinism one of the most plausible hypotheses ever propounded, Virchow's statement remains basically correct. His attitude can hardly shock anybody today, but appeared reactionary ninety years ago. It brought him a somewhat unusual applause from Catholic quarters.[9]

It is evident that, apart from his objective reservations concerning Darwinism, Virchow was very disturbed by the fact that a mere hypothesis should all of a sudden exert such a tremendous, almost monopolistic influence on all divisions of biology. He was sincerely afraid of a relapse into romantic "nature philosophy," [10] into that speculative and dogmatic biology which had, in his opinion, paralyzed German science in his youth.[11] His erstwhile pupil Ernst Haeckel—who regarded not only evolution as a fact, but also such products of his fertile imagination as the "plastidul soul," the "original creation" (Urzeugung), etc., and who practically made Darwinism a new religion—certainly justified such fears. Virchow opposed to this kind of Darwinism his "cold-blooded anthropology." [12] It is significant that, just as in bacteriology Virchow was forced to contend against Klebs, not Pasteur, so in transformism his polemic had to be directed primarily against Haeckel, not Darwin. And in the case of Klebs as well as of Haeckel, the reader of 1950 who is not obliged to be "modern" in the sense of 1880 feels that Virchow's arguments have stood the test of time much better than those of his opponents. Virchow, by the way, is by no means the only great anthropologist of his time who maintained reservations with regard to Darwinism. De Quatrefages and Von Baer, for instance, revealed a similar attitude.

Virchow's famous address of 1879 ("The Freedom of Science in the Modern State"), [13] which was directed partly against Haeckel, did not even discuss primarily a problem of natural science, but one of political expediency. Virchow's argument was very clear: the situation after the unification of Germany and during the conflict between Bismarck and the Catholic

Church seemed very favorable to the realization of an old dream of all friends of natural science and liberal progress, the dream of large-scale introduction of the teaching of the natural sciences into the public schools. At this moment some tact and self-restraint seemed necessary in order not to jeopardize the whole project. One could ask the schools only to teach definite facts. One could not ask them to teach Darwinism or Haeckelism, which were hypothetical. The state should freely sponsor research in these problems, but not as yet the teaching of them in public schools.

As Darwinism was to Virchow a problem of evidence, he admitted that "one single fresh discovery can give a new turn to the whole question." [14] The best expression of his position seems to be the following statement:

> I have spoken as *a friend, not an adversary* of transformism, and at all times I have approached the immortal Darwin in a friendly, not a hostile way. But I have always differentiated between friend and partisan. I can salute and even support a scientific hypothesis, before it is proven by facts. But I *cannot become its partisan* as long as sufficient proof is lacking.[15]

While Virchow was right for a long time in claiming that no "missing links" were known, he certainly did not facilitate their recognition when they eventually turned up. He felt, for instance, that in the so-called Neanderthaler so many pathological stigmata could be found that it was impossible to state whether the material was a prehistorical variation or just a recent pathological specimen. He was inclined to regard it as a recent pathological specimen. In the few fragments from the Neander Valley he found evidence of senile atrophy, traumatism, caries, hyperostosis, premature synostosis, rickets, and arthritis deformans.[16] While this burying of the Neanderthaler under pathological diagnosis is not far from the ludicrous, another of Virchow's principles—*not to establish new prehistoric races on the basis of one single specimen*—deserves more respect, especially when viewed against the background of the practice by such of Virchow's contemporaries as De Quatrefages. Unfortunately, Virchow maintained his opinion on the

Neanderthaler up to the time of his death.[17] By similar "pathological" explanations he tried to interpret away a later Neanderthaler finding, the Shipka mandible.[18]

The discovery of Pithecanthropus excited Virchow greatly,
as can easily be seen from the number of papers he devoted to
the subject within one year.[19] He went immediately to visit
E. Dubois, the Dutch discoverer, and had him come to speak
in Berlin. It was impossible to deny the hominid character of
the femur. Thus femur and skullcap had to be attributed to two
individuals. The femur was pathological, the owner of the
skullcap a *giant gibbon,* according to Virchow—an opinion to
which he apparently eventually converted even the discoverer
of Pithecanthropus. Virchow's summary of the Pithecanthropus
case has nevertheless a remarkably evolutionist ring: "Whether
man or ape, he is in any case a new link in the series of forms
which make the whole realm of vertebrates appear to us as
one that belongs together in an evolutionary sense." [20]

If Germany had been contributing very little to human
paleontology as compared to France, England, and South
Africa (the work of F. Weidenreich was mostly done in exile),
this is partly due to the extreme scarcity of relevant findings
in Germany. But it is difficult also not to blame part of this
situation on Virchow, who for thirty years discouraged in a
practical way all interest in this field.

Though Virchow became only a "friend," not a "partisan" of
Darwinism, the new hypothesis stimulated him to undertake
a large series of original studies starting with his Academy
memoir of 1875, "On Some Characteristics of Lower Races."
Here, as at many other occasions, he warned against the unjustified expression "lower races." Probably none of the living
races is "lower" than another one. In isolation, races of "high"
organization might live on a very low level of culture.[21]

In his academy memoir [22] Virchow studied first the frontal
extension of the temporal bone which debars the normal union
of the great wing of the sphenoid with the anterior inferior
prolongation of the parietal. This trait is pithecoid indeed and
is, according to Virchow, found more frequently among Australians, Melanesians, and Polynesians than among other races.

Catarrhinia is also pithecoid, while the so-called "os Incae" (Inca bone), most frequent among Peruvians and Malays, has nothing to do with pithecoidism. In another Academy paper of 1881 Virchow dealt with the pithecoid os malare bipartum, found most frequently among Japanese and Ainus. The more frequent observations of pithecoid traits in southeast Asia, a region actually to yield later so many relevant fossils, induced Virchow to ask for intensified prehistoric research in this region [23] and to send Vaughan Stevens in 1891 to Malaya in order to search for evidence of the missing link. (All Stevens actually found were the Malayan pigmies.[24])

Virchow also studied extensively and repeatedly the problem of the tail in humans.[25] In his *Trojan Graves and Skulls* (Berlin, 1882) he dealt at length with platycnemia, regarded as pithecoid by Broca, as rachitic by Pruner, as due to sitting habits by Busk. Virchow sided with Busk. Virchow's pioneer work on the anatomy of the young gorilla (Academy paper of 1880), and on the greater similarity of the young human and anthropoid as compared to the adults also belongs to the group of studies stimulated by Darwinism.

On the basis of such detailed studies he tried to bring some order and light into the problem of atavism, which was then much discussed. Atavism in man—that is, the relapse into ancestral conformation—is, according to Virchow, an odd notion to begin with, as man's detailed ancestry and genealogy are unknown.[26] There are traits that can qualify as pithecoid atavism, like the frontal extension of the temporal bone. Others like microcephaly, which were also regarded by some as "atavisms," are actually pathological pithecoidism. Microcephalics resemble apes only accidentally. Since microcephalics were unable to propagate and survive, it is certain that neither man nor ape had ever passed through this stage. Theromorphy (similarity with animals) can therefore be either atavistic or acquired.[27] It is interesting to see that on this occasion Virchow showed great familiarity and sympathy with the early experimental work in embryology (beginning with Gerlach in 1850) and that he believed the cause of twin formation to be an irritation (chemical) rather than a purely mechanical division of the egg.[28]

The problem of the origin of man is inseparable from the problem of the origin of races. For the polygenist—and Virchow had polygenist inclinations [29]—both tend to coincide. Virchow stated repeatedly that the problem of the origin of races is even farther from solution than that of the origin of man, a statement in which we would probably still concur. This may make us more indulgent toward Virchow's failure to contribute much to the solution of this problem.

He called every deviation from the parent type a pathological process.[30] As any new race had to start with a deviation from the parent type, in this nomenclature the beginning of each race was pathological. In order to justify this arbitrary use of the term "pathological," Virchow had to deprive it of its customary meaning, and use for what is in general called pathological the term "nosological"—an innovation which he occasionally forgot, speaking of "pathological races" and giving the word "pathological" its generally accepted meaning. He was contradictory as to whether or not pathological human races do exist.[31]

It is not surprising that, in spite of ceaseless repetition and his authority and influence, Virchow could not find adherents for his "pathological" theory of the origin of race. It is difficult to find objective reasons for his adopting this nomenclature, which only confused an already unclear situation. Was it in order to show that the discussion of this problem by the leading pathologist was legitimate within the hierarchy of the sciences? Was it in order to emphasize again the role of pathology as a biological science? Was he succumbing to the same trend that in his time made the new "degeneration" concept of the psychiatrist-anthropologist Morel, for whom degeneration was no longer simple variation but deterioration, so universally popular?

Virchow defined race as a hereditary variation.[32] He thought it to be very unlikely that racial types were permanent.[33] He doubted the preponderant influence of climate in race differentiation. His remarks on the possible role of the adrenals in the

genesis of colored races [34] show that neither he nor Keith nor
Bolk was the first to formulate endocrinological theories of race
formation.

Like practically all his contemporaries Virchow was handi-
capped by the lack of knowledge concerning heredity. Mendel's great discovery had passed unnoticed. Virchow's cell
theory *(Omnis cellula a cellula)* always led him to stress the
"continuity of life" in a period when environment was emphasized. In 1897 he went so far as to claim that "the doctrine of
heredity dominates the whole of biology." [35] His experience
in medicine, on the other hand, provided him with a wealth
of examples of misplaced applications of the principle of
heredity.

If one surveys the almost immeasurable number of diseases,
which have been held to be hereditary, it soon becomes obvious that
the habit of doctors of recognizing the hereditary character of certain diseases has changed almost according to fashion. An inclination in this direction has always existed, as the assumption of
heredity protects against any further mental efforts concerning the
cause of the condition.[36]

He reminded his contemporaries how many traditionally "hereditary" diseases (scabies, favus, leprosy, tuberculosis, etc.)
had during the nineteenth century been shown to be the effects
of parasitic infestation.[37]

Virchow made no great contributions to the science of
heredity. Still, it took anthropologists about thirty years to
catch up with the statement in his Huxley lecture of 1898, that
heredity rests in the cell not in the blood; [38] indeed, assimilation of this insight by the general public is not yet even in
sight. His discussion of the problems involved created a favorable atmosphere for progress. He struggled with the problem
of the inheritance of acquired characteristics, completely denied by such neo-Darwinians as August Weismann. Virchow
showed that Darwin, on the contrary, had assumed this possibility and that it still remained a logical necessity despite lack
of evidence.[39] The history of skull deformation, which Virchow
had studied in other contexts, certainly showed no evidence for
the inheritance of acquired characteristics. Nor did circum-

cision or other artificial deformations which he now studied. (See his report at the *Naturforscherversammlung* in Cologne, 1888.) He saw that heredity is a partial phenomenon and that each individual carries two sets of hereditary characters.[40] But the full exploitation of such insights was possible only to later researchers armed with Mendel's rediscovered results, the knowledge of the existence of chromosomes and the gene theory.

Races, Especially in Germany

VIRCHOW was a most devoted patriot and one of Germany's greatest sons. But his name (which could just as well be spelled Virchoff) was Slavonic beyond any doubt.* His external appearance—short, dark-eyed, of yellowish complexion which tanned very deeply after exposure—was not exactly an illustration of what Germans are supposed to look like. Most of his countrymen and contemporaries completely overlooked this obvious contradiction, but not Virchow himself. The problem must have occupied him very early, because as a student he corresponded about it with his father. He wrote to the latter:

> Our ancestors are that Polish tribe that under the name of Pomeranians branched off, and inhabited originally the region between Oder and Vistula, the Baltic and the Warthe.[1]

Walsh reports on the following conversation he had with Virchow around 1895 concerning this problem:

> I once discussed with him the question that his fathers were probably Slav in blood though they had been two hundred years or more on German soil. He said he must therefore be considered at least as

---

* It is also evidence of the fact that the Germans who invaded Pomerania in the eleventh century subscribed neither to the slogan that the only good Slav was a dead Slav, nor to the methods of total evacuation of the Communist Polish-Russian "liberators" of 1945.

much German as Americans who have been two hundred years in our country think themselves Americans. I reminded him that the older countries never quite gave up their claim on their children who came to America, and that even after many generations, the best that we could hope for from European writers with regard to them, was some such compound term as German-American, Irish-American or the like. He smilingly assented and said that under those circumstances the best he could say of himself was that he was a Slav-German.[2]

I am inclined to think that Virchow's wonder over the contradiction between his biological ancestry and his cultural loyalties acted as a most important stimulus for him to work in the fields of history, physical anthropology, and prehistory, and within these fields to work especially on Central European material. Much of his best and most significant work in anthropology can be directly referred to this stimulus and this interest. While his earliest contributions in physical anthropology (for example, the studies on the skull base) were of a purely biological nature, most of his later work in physical anthropology was historically oriented—"Anthropology studies the whence and the whither of humanity." [3] This ties anthropology closely to his work in prehistory, archeology, and ethnology. A historical orientation dominated in Virchow's time, at least in Germany, in all three branches of anthropology—cultural anthropology, physical anthropology, and archeology—and gave anthropology a relatively greater spiritual unity than it has today.

A double myth has prevailed for a long time as to the physical characteristics of the Germans and their Teutonic ancestors. Descriptions of the latter by Greek and Roman authors as being tall, blond, blue-eyed, and of light complexion have been taken as absolute truth. This seems to be myth number one, and part of the romantic way that classic authors have looked at their primitives.[4] Secondly, it has been assumed that the modern descendants of these ancient Germans are also predominantly tall, blond, blue-eyed, and of light complexion. This is myth number two. While the persistence of myth number one is not surprising in view of the difficulties of evidence,

VIRCHOW AS A SEPTUAGENARIAN

This and the frontispiece, though they have never before been printed, were circulated among Virchow's students. It was the practice of German universities to arrange for portraits or photographs of favorite professors to be reproduced and sold to students. *Photo:* Courtesy of the New York Academy of Medicine.

it is amazing that, in spite of the most obvious *dementi* given daily by reality to myth number two, very few people down to Virchow's time seem to have realized that the majority of Germans were neither particularly tall nor particularly blond. What is worse, three hundred years after Conringius had published his perplexities about the darkness, shortness, and flatheadedness of many of the actual Germans and seventy years after Virchow's basic demonstrations of the same, the German racist myth could still be elevated to the rank of a cannibalistic state religion and defended by so-called respectable scientists.

Virchow started studying the Germanic problem in the late 1860's by measuring ancient Scandinavian skulls.[5] He found those from five paleolithic sites (Borreby, etc.) to be mesocephalic with a tendency toward brachycephaly, and those from the Scandinavian Bronze and Iron Ages to be dolichocephalic. In spite of brachycephaly, the paleolithic Danish skulls differed very definitely from brachycephalic Finnish or Lapp skulls. They rather resembled modern Danish skulls. In this paper Virchow put much emphasis on his maxillary index (*Oberkieferindex*)—that is, the relation of the spina-foramen magnum distance to the root-of-nose–foramen magnum distance.

These quiet studies were all of a sudden transformed into an extremely controversial subject through Armand de Quatrefages' book of 1871, *La Race prussienne*. Justifiable bitterness over the defeat of his country and the bombardment of Paris and the Musée in the Jardin des Plantes by the Germans in 1871 induced De Quatrefages to bring out an unjustifiable, pseudoscientific pamphlet, *The Prussian Race*. De Quatrefages claimed that German unity was due to an anthropological error. The Prussians were racially Finns—that is, a dark Mongoloid race—and different from the rest of the Germans, a rather blond group. These Finns were supposedly once very widespread in Europe. Their descendants, the dark Finno-Prussians, were the perpetrators of the late "war crimes."

Virchow answered De Quatrefages' emotional political onslaught with an equally vehement text.[6] But to refute De Quatrefages' scientific inventions he suppressed emotion and started on three very important series of extensive studies that went far beyond a mere refutation of De Quatrefages and occupied him for several years: a study of "the Finnish race" (Virchow actually found three racial types among Finns); craniological studies of ancient and modern Germans, culminating in his "Contributions to the Physical Anthropology of the Germans, Especially the Frisians" (Berlin Academy, 1876); and the gigantic 1876 survey of German school children for color of hair, eyes, and skin, the final results of which were published in 1886.[7] It is not without interest that, in spite of the lively polemics between De Quatrefages and Virchow in the 1870's,[8] the latter wrote a very friendly necrology for the former twenty years later.[9]

Virchow started the refutation of De Quatrefages' Finnish hypothesis by comparing Finnish, Estonian, and northeast German skulls.[10] In 1874 he undertook a trip to Finland, greatly extending the scope of his measurements and completing them by observation of the living. He found four morphological types: eastern Finns (Karelians), "Savolaks," western Finns, and Lapps. Furthermore, he found gypsies, whose presence in Finland had so far been unknown even to Finnish scientists.[11] All three Finnish groups had a high percentage of blonds. The Lapps were hyperbrachycephalic but not as dark as the gypsies, rather "brown" than "black." Virchow was guarded with his statements on the Lapps, as he regarded them as a "pathological race"—that is, a group changed through unfavorable environmental conditions.[12] He regarded it as a confirmation of this hypothesis when considerable increase in stature was reported from settled (that is, better-fed) Lapps.[13] Estonians and Lithuanians too, located between Prussians and Finns, proved to be predominantly blond groups.[14]

De Quatrefages' "Finnish" theory had grown out of general speculations on "the primary population" of Europe. Estonians, Finns, Basques, etc., were candidates for this honor. Virchow examined all these hypotheses in 1874 without committing himself to any. One of the main difficulties seemed to him that it was by no means clear whether such traits as the cranial index and perhaps even the hair color would remain stable during the very long period that must have passed since the settling of Europe.[15]

The skulls in the so-called *Reihengraeber* (row graves) of Western Germany, described by Lindenschmit and Alex. Ecker and known to be those of ancient Franks and Alamanni, were mostly dolichocephalic. It had therefore been generally assumed that dolichocephaly was a specific characteristic of the ancient Germans. When Virchow and Lissauer found *Reihengraeber* in Eastern Germany containing dolichocephals, they automatically assumed that they were dealing with Germans. It was quite a surprise when archeological evidence showed these people to be Slavs (supposedly always brachycephalic).[16] *Dolichocephaly was thus obviously not a specific anatomical trait of the ancient Germans.* It was also found among Romans, Greeks, Basques, Galatians, and the blond variety of Finns. Far from being a trait announcing "high" development, as some romantic racists still assume, it was particularly frequent amongst paleolithic populations, as Virchow knew firsthand from his work on Belgian cave dwellers.[17] It was quite inappropriate to attribute early dolichocephalic skulls in Germany automatically to Germanic individuals. Virchow called it "loose talk." [18] This was all the more true as, because of cremation between 600 B.C. and 600 A.D., there was a tremendous gap in the bone record and no evidence whatsoever existed to show that the dolichocephals of 600 A.D. were descendants of the dolichocephals of 600 B.C. Noble dolichocephaly was not even limited to whites. It was quite common among Negroes and African pygmies.[19]

Brachycephaly, on the other hand, could be found among Germans since the earliest times and in groups reputed to be very "pure," like the Frisians. This was one of the results of a research trip of 1873 into northwest Germany and Holland reported in the 1876 Academy paper on the physical anthropology of the Germans. Virchow found the Frisians to "correspond in the main traits to the classic picture of the Germans," which is putting it very diplomatically. He actually found them to be mesocephalic and chamecephalic with a tendency toward brachycephaly. On this occasion he stated his conviction that height-breadth index of skulls is more important than the length-breadth index—that is, chamecephaly and hypsicephaly are more important than dolicho- and brachycephaly.

The classic Greeks had also been a mixture of brachycephals and dolichocephals. Now the brachycephals prevailed. Virchow asked: How did this come about? Through brachycephalization of the original stock? Through elimination of the dolichocephals? Through a new influx and mixture with brachycephals? The same questions, of course, held good for the blond and brown stocks in Germany. The answer is still unknown.

One thing seemed certain. Even such relatively old peoples as the Germanic or Slavonic tribes were already mixtures as far as skull type was concerned.[20] The assumption of a single, simple, uniform, primitive German (urgermanisch) type was arbitrary and unfounded.[21]

In many ways Virchow was the typical anatomist-anthropologist of his period, measuring incessantly very small samples of skulls from all possible regions of the world, and his preeminence in anthropology often was more quantitative than qualitative. The accomplishment that perhaps made him most transcend the narrow limits of contemporary craniology was his gigantic *survey of German school children in 1876* made in the name of the German Anthropological Society.[22] Initiated to refute De Quatrefages' legends of the racial composition of the German nation and perhaps to show that Germany had outgrown French leadership in anthropology, it went far beyond the original purpose. At no time has anthropology been brought back from the bone house to observation of the living more radically and on a more grandiose scale. This survey at once outdistanced previous similar attempts by Broca and Beddoe. The results of this survey mark an epoch in anthropological knowledge and, within their limitations, maintain their validity.

Virchow was very conscious of certain of these limitations, such as the fact that about 15 per cent of the blonds darken in later life.[23] He therefore preferred to have the draftees examined, but the army refused. The ministry of education was less in a position to turn a cold shoulder on one of its strongest supporters in the Kulturkampf that was then raging. Thus 6,760,000 German school children were surveyed as to the color of their hair, eyes, and skin. The example was contagious; neighboring Austria, Switzerland, Holland, and Belgium undertook the same type of survey.

That color was identified and no measurements were made was dictated by the material as well as by the background of the examiners, the public school teachers. Although Virchow continued to ask for the collection and analysis of bone material, he did not regard this aspect of his survey as a disadvantage. He regarded color as far more important, because he thought it was a more permanent trait. He regarded skull proportions as not permanent, but more as plastic traits.[24] This was one of the reasons why he felt that far too much attention had been paid to the presence or absence of dolichocephaly, or of brachycephaly.[25]

The survey itself was unintelligible to the uneducated part of the population. Strange rumors originated, especially in the eastern provinces.

The report had spread far and wide that all Catholic children with black hair and blue eyes were to be sent out of the country, some said to Russia, while others declared that it was the King of Prussia, who had been playing cards with the Sultan of Turkey and had staked and lost 40,000 fair-haired, blue-eyed children, and there were Moors travelling about in covered carts to collect them; and the schoolmasters were helping for they were to have five dollars for every child they handed over. For a time popular excitement was quite serious. . . . One schoolmaster who evidently knew his people assured the terrified parents that it was only the children with blue hair and green eyes that were wanted—an explanation which sent them home quite comforted.[26]

In spite of such and a great many other difficulties the survey, whose proportions quite transcended anything hitherto known to biological research on man, was successfully carried through.

The survey, which we do not intend to analyze here in all its many regional details, showed Prussians to be blonder than

most other Germans, in spite of De Quatrefages. But it also
scientifically buried once and for all the German race myth by
showing that *nowhere were the Germans racially uniform and
least of all were they predominantly blond.*[27] Only 31.8 per
cent of the children surveyed were "blond" (that is, blond
haired, blue eyed, and white skinned). (With later darkening
this meant that not even two out of ten Germans were
"blond.") The number of blond children might in the blondest
regions increase to a maximum of 43.5 per cent, but might
diminish to 18.44 per cent in the darker provinces—as, for example, in Bavaria. True "browns" (dark hair and eyes, brown-
ish skin) formed 14.05 per cent of the total, ranging from 6.95
up to 25.21 per cent in different subdivisions. The majority of
the children surveyed (54.15 per cent) showed a mixture of
traits—dark eyes with blond hair, or blue eyes with dark hair,
etc. While this survey thus established definitely that by no
means all Germans were blond, Virchow could, on the other
hand, show that Slavs and Celts also contained a strong blond
and dolichocephalic element, especially in the northern regions.[28]

Virchow surveyed separately at the same time the Jewish
children in German schools; and, though this group as a whole
was darker than the German group (42 per cent "browns"), it
showed a surprising percentage of blonds (11.17 per cent).
Anti-Semites never forgave Virchow for his objective handling
of the Jewish problem. (See, for example, the pamphlet by
C. Pansch, *Geheimrat Prof. Dr. Rud. Virchow aus Schivelbein,
unser grosser Gelehrter,* the second in a series entitled "Geheimes Judentum, Nebenregierung, und Juedische Weltherrschaft.")

It was primarily his work on races in Germany that led Virchow to formulate some more general conclusions on races and
nations.

We know that every nationality, take for instance the German or
Slavonic, is of a composite character and no one can say, on the spur
of the moment, from what original stock either may have been developed.[29]

This mixing of different morphological types in the same group apparently went back through the "row graves" [30] to the "reindeer period" (our Upper Paleolithic).[31] That at least seemed to Virchow the result of an examination of Belgian cave material. There was no such thing as a La Tène race either.[32] To speak of different "races" in Europe was misleading. There were no such differences involved as between Negro, Mongol, and White. One should speak of different stocks or tribes. What, for instance, was erroneously called the "German Race" was actually a northwest German stock.[33] The problem was actually not only a German problem. Just as there were blond north and dark south Germans, so there were blond north Slavs (including the Wends in Germany) and dark south Slavs (Bohemians, Serbs), blond and dark Finns, Celts, and Jews.[34]

Virchow opposed continually and emphatically any attempt to prostitute anthropology for political purposes, be this under the flag of Celtism, Aryanism, or Germanism. He did not feel that there existed any proof for the superiority of any race or nation.[35] "If different races would recognize one another as independent co-laborers in the great field of humanity, if all possessed a modesty which would allow them to see merits in neighboring people, much of the strife now agitating the world would disappear." [36]

Racial and linguistic, cultural, or national traits do not coincide. Reality contradicts the naive assumptions of a De Quatrefages, a Lindenschmit, or a Retzius that those who belong to the same nation—that is, speak the same language—have also the same skull shape or skin color. Neither German nor French nor any other national unity is based on common race. Language and culture can pass and have passed continuously from one race to another.[37] Thus typically Aryan languages are spoken by people like Armenians, Persians, or Hindus, who are neither blond nor dolichocephalic nor sometimes even very white.[38] Products of different racial stocks can be assimilated into the same nation: "They [the Huguenot refugees in Germany] are Germanized, just like the numerous Jews, whom we accept from Poland or Russia, and of whom we have never denied that they too have become a powerful ferment of cultural progress for us." [39] In his insistence on the difference of racial and cultural relations Virchow, sensitized through his own experience and fortified through the results of his studies, was scientifically and culturally far ahead of most of his contemporaries and even many of his successors. Although a biologist by training, Virchow did not subscribe to a biological philosophy which, if consistently handled, would eliminate the freedom of will in man.

The physical anthropology of German and Slavonic stocks is probably the regional field to which Virchow devoted most time and energy. This is logical, since his work in archeology, especially in the 1860's and 1870's, also centered in this region. For the same reason, once he had become interested in Trojan archeology, he did a good deal of research in the 1880's on Trojan skulls (*BG,* 1879; Academy, 1882, etc.) and Greek skulls (*BG,* 1873; Academy, 1884, 1893, etc.).

In 1892, to commemorate the four hundredth anniversary of Columbus' discovery, Virchow published a large, most splendidly illustrated monograph, *Crania Ethnica Americana,* the contents of which he had submitted already to the Seventh International Congress of Americanists in Berlin in 1888. Thirty-six skulls of American aborigines from Patagonia to Labrador, representatives of the different cranial types of the Western Hemisphere, were described and discussed. Particular attention was given to natural and artificial skull deformation and to the two American centers of the latter, Peru and the northwest Pacific coast. Virchow had already written on Peruvian skulls in Reiss and Stuebel's *Necropolis of Ancon* (Berlin, 1887). In *Crania Ethnica,* an informant and provider of material concerning the northwest Pacific coast, Franz Boas, is often mentioned. Skull deformation might have been diffused or might have been invented repeatedly, derived from accidental deformations. Virchow inclined toward the latter hypothesis.

Virchow also discussed specimens of nonpathological over- and undersize of skulls in America. He called the former kephalones, the latter nannocephali. The Inca bone, Inca exostoses, processus frontalis, epipterica, stenocrotaphy, and the Lagoa Santa skulls were surveyed. He felt that America could not offer much to human paleontology. He asked for a study of the new white race mixture now taking shape in America.

A fourth region whose racial composition Virchow studied with particular interest was the Philippines. Between 1870 (*BG*, 1870, p. 151) and 1897 (a summary paper read in the Academy and translated in the *Annual Report of the Smithsonian Institution* of the same year), Virchow published many contributions on this subject. Virchow regarded the Negritos, closely related to the Andamans, as the original population of the islands. He then recognized a second pre-Malayan layer in what popularly was called "Alfuros." These proto-Malays (for example, the Igorots) were related to similar layers in other islands of southeastern Asia, like the Dayaks of Borneo. Then came the Malays. Virchow also thought he had found racial traces of the passage of Polynesians. His ideas on the raciology of the Philippines have become standard opinions.

Virchow's activity as a craniologist was by no means limited to the four above-mentioned regions. As a matter of fact, there is no region on earth from which he did not receive a certain number of skulls for measuring. He published, for example, on skulls from Bulgaria and New Guinea (*BG*, 1873), the Andaman Islands (*BG*, 1875), Siberia (*BG*, 1877), West Africa and Assam (*BG*, 1880), New Hebrides (*BG*, 1884), Southern Morocco (Academy, 1886), East Africa (Academy, 1889 and 1891), Illyria (Vienna Academy, 1877), and on skulls of Bushmen and Hottentots (*BG*, 1887). In addition, he measured whatever live exotic human specimen he could get hold of. This was the time of traveling shows; and whenever such a show was in town, Professor Virchow, mostly assisted by son Hans, showed up and measured. When he had satisfied himself that the specimens were authentic (which was by no means always the case), he published. He thus measured living Eskimos (*BG*, 1878 and 1880), Patagonians (1881), Australians (1883), Hottentots (1887), Dinka and Ceylonese (1889), and Samoans (1890). The show owners might not particularly like this interference, but it was not advisable to refuse a scientific service to such an extremely popular public figure.

That he had opposed the biased "applications" of anthropology in politics does not mean that he was opposed to proper practical applications of anthropology. On the contrary, we might regard him as one of the pioneers of *applied anthropology*. Typical in this respect is his suggestion of 1869 to base the construction of school benches on anatomical measurements from then on.[40]

Virchow had shown interest in health conditions of immigrants as far back as 1848.[41] The launching of colonial expansion by the New Reich, which he opposed for political reasons, induced him to examine also the biological premises of such an undertaking: the problem of acclimatization. In 1885 he submitted to the *Naturforscherversammlung* in Strasbourg the hypothesis that, while the white individual might be able to acclimatize in the tropics, the white race as such, especially its more northern varieties, seemed unable to do so.[42] No white group had so far survived by its own propagation for several generations in the tropics. Hence, biologically only a limited number of regions remained available for settlement by Germans. Virchow's intervention stimulated a large-scale discussion in and outside learned societies. A large amount of relevant material was produced. His friends Hirsch and Bastian were involved. Even Schliemann obliged with population statistics from Cuba, where he had large commercial interests.[43]

Virchow had recommended in 1849 that judges should be "practical anthropologists." [44] He was, on the other hand, disgusted with Lombroso's application of anthropology to the problem of the criminal, which he felt to be a relapse into the system of Gall and a "caricature of science." [45]

It is quite natural that Virchow should make numerous contributions to one particular subdivision of physical anthropology—paleopathology.[46] We already know Virchow's paleopathological analysis of the Neanderthaler. He studied arthritis deformans—or cave gout, as he named the disease—in a great number of prehistoric human and animal bones. He repeatedly analyzed such material from cave bears.[47] The fact that some of his cave bear material looked exactly like syphilitic periostitis inspired him with salutary caution against diagnosing syphilis in prehistoric bones.[48] In surveying the situation he did not feel that any unequivocal pre-Columbian syphilitic bone material, European or American, existed.[49] Other of his paleopathological findings, like the frequency of exostoses of the external auditory meatus in ancient Peruvians (Academy, 1885), have been mentioned already.

Virchow became involved in the 1890's in a very lively discussion as to the pathology underlying the strange mutilations represented in the impressive ancient Peruvian vases.[50] Ashmead of New York, who had called for his arbitration (only to attack him later), was very positive that no pre-Columbian leprosy did exist. The lesions might be syphilitic, tuberculous, or uta (a local disease, now found to be Leishmaniasis). Virchow left the question open; but, while he saw little evidence for pre-Columbian syphilis, he felt unable to deny the possibility of pre-Columbian leprosy. The discussion is still going on. Today most authorities assume the mutilations to be due to Leishmaniasis of the skin, a disease not yet known in the 1890's.

It will surprise nobody that from the very beginning Virchow, as a professional anatomist, was extremely interested in the technical aspects of physical anthropology: on what points and planes to base measurements and what instruments and techniques to use. His discussions of these matters commence in the 1850's [51] and continue throughout the years [52] up to the very end.[53] He was instrumental in establishing the "Frankfurt agreements" [54] of German anthropologists, and thereafter he championed vigorously the German *norma horizontalis* against the French *norma horizontalis*.[55]

Germanic and Slavonic Antiquities

OF VIRCHOW's 1180 anthropological publications, 523 deal with subjects pertaining to physical anthropology. An almost equal number (518) is devoted to archeological or prehistoric subjects. At the same time that Darwinism was stimulating physical anthropology, prehistoric discoveries in Scandinavia, France, and Switzerland gave a tremendous impetus to archeological research in Germany. Virchow, who too was seized by this wave, never disguised the fact that the stimulus had come from abroad.[1]

Virchow thus passed from historical to prehistorical work. His training in morphology and pathology prepared him ideally for successful archeological work, the comparative anatomy of cultures, as Honoré de Balzac called it; here too life processes had to be reconstructed from dead remnants. Here was a field of the humanities or social sciences which, better than any other, offered itself to the application of Virchow's beloved "method of the natural sciences."

As a historian, Virchow had dealt primarily with his home state, Pomerania. He was puzzled by the contradiction between innumerable Slavonic names of persons and places and a completely Germanized population. It was this region that occupied his first prehistoric research. The same quest for Germanic or for Slavonic origins, which had animated his historical research and which was simultaneously provoking his research in physical anthropology, was at the bottom of this new endeavor. One can but admire the objectivity and the detachment Virchow showed in these investigations in spite of his personal involvement.

The discovery of ancient pile dwellings in Swiss lakes had produced quite a sensation in the 1850's. Virchow's first archeological discovery was that of the existence of pile dwellings in northern Germany, especially at the site of Luebtow Lake in Pomerania in 1865.[2] Virchow showed that these pile dwellings were contemporary with the so-called *Burgwaelle* (walled mounds) frequently encountered in northeastern Germany. Through pottery findings (the characteristic wave ornament) he showed both types of structures to be Slavonic.[3] Virchow was one of the first prehistorians to devote particular attention to pottery as a clue for dating and correlation.[4] Pottery was an all the more valuable clue in this region, since for about 1000 years (500 B.C. to 500 A.D.) cremation had prevailed and bone material was absent. Archeological evidence showed that Slavonic tribes had once advanced as far as Braunschweig and Franconia.[5] The northeast European pile dwellings contained iron. They were therefore not only much younger than the "reindeer age" of paleolithic hunters, but also much younger than the agricultural neolithic Swiss pile dwellings.

Virchow started his excavations of walled mounds (hill forts) in 1870 in the Lausitz, where a number of so-called "burned" walled mounds were found.[6] Walled mounds were found to be overwhelmingly Slavonic and to belong to the Iron Age.

Virchow had started his archeological work in Pomerania, but he soon branched out all over Prussia's eastern provinces. And thus one morning in the month of May, 1875, he found himself digging a walled mound in Wollstein, province of Posen, together with the local physician, Kreisphysikus Dr. Robert Koch.[7] This first contact seems to have been pleasant. Dr. Koch published a paper on the Wollstein mound in the journal edited by Virchow.[8] Little did both men then foresee their future relations and rivalries in medicine. Their contacts in anthropology seem to have continued to be the more pleasant ones. In 1884 (*BG*, 1884, p. 273) Virchow proudly demonstrated photographs of human tails that Doctor Koch had brought him from India.

The third important type of prehistoric structure in northeastern Germany on which Virchow also worked—the *Graeberfelder* (grave fields) containing bronze—proved to be older and therefore pre-Slavonic. In some cases (for example, the Spreewald) where it was known that Germanic tribes had preceded the Slavs, the grave fields were obviously Germanic. But in other places they might be non-Germanic or pre-Germanic. Virchow thought little in this respect of the Finnish or Basque theories. But he sided with French scientists, like Bertrand and Salomon Reinach, in regarding the Celts as possible pre-Germanic dwellers in Germany.[9] This opinion was strengthened by the Etruscan-like bronze cars found in grave fields. Virchow regarded both the Austrian Bronze Hallstatt culture (*ca.* 800 B.C.) and the Swiss Iron La Tène culture (*ca.* 400 B.C.) as Celtic. Virchow found his first and one of his finest grave fields in 1870 in Wollin—a city on the Baltic island of the same name and an important prehistoric and early historic trade center, where Arabian silver had been found and where Virchow also demonstrated extensive pile dwellings.[10] Through the early identification and dating of the three basic prehistoric structures in northeastern Germany, Virchow made a fundamental contribution to German prehistory.

Bronze cars found in Germany, especially the small one of Burg on the Spree, occupied Virchow early and repeatedly. One of his earliest archeological papers was "Chariots de bronze," which was read at the first International Congress for Prehistory in Paris in 1867 (*Transactions,* pp. 251 ff.). The main interest of these bronze cars rested in their pointing toward Etruscan relationships. This impression was reinforced by bird and bull ornaments found with the cars which suggested Hallstatt and other southern connections.[11] But who had received these Etruscan influences in Germany between 1000 and 500 B.C.? Germanic tribes? Celtic tribes? The prevalence of cremation during this period made any determination even more difficult.[12] By what route had bronze traveled toward the northeast besides through the valley of the Vistula? [13]

Bronze objects were not the only ones suggesting Etruscan connections. In 1870 Virchow found, to his great surprise, urns decorated with human faces (face urns, *Gesichtsurnen*) in eastern Pomerania.[14] Such vessels had so far been seen only in Etruria and Egypt. The urns were pre-Slavonic, dating from about 400 B.C. Another Etruscan type of vessel to turn up in Germany was the house urn, an urn formed like a house.[15]

Virchow was very eager to explore the pathways of culture that often coincide with the pathways of trade and commerce. He traced the neolithic silex and amber trade, amber being exported from the Baltic into the Mediterannean basin. In approaching the nephrite and jadeite problem, on the other hand, he felt that local deposits much rather than fantastic trade relations over enormous distances, which it was then fashionable to assume, accounted for the occurrence of jadeite.

Arabic silver coins of the tenth to thirteenth centuries, found all over northeastern Germany, testified to the extensive trade relations of this period.[16] Arab trade was obviously restricted to the parts of Germany which were then Slavonic. It was well known that Arabs traveled north along the Volga. Did they use other north-south roads besides in order to reach a place located as far west as Wollin? Virchow was able to describe Slavonic pottery and silver, testifying to trade activities before 1138, at the site of Luebeck, later a center of Germanic commerce.[17] He spent a summer tracing the roads the Langobards had taken when migrating into Italy.[18]

Between 1887 and 1890 Virchow made extensive field studies of old German farmhouses and house types,[19] a kind of archeology above ground stimulated by his work on house urns. Virchow studied house types in northern Germany, central Germany (Franconia), and in the southern mountainous regions (Germany, Switzerland, Austria). In Switzerland he discovered the oldest standing wooden house in the German language area. It dated from 1346. This discovery involved him in an interesting discussion on the earliest use of Arabic numerals in Germany,[20] as the numerals on this old house were Arabic. Virchow hoped for, but was not able to find, a Slavonic house type. He felt that house types afforded valuable clues to the origins of an immigrant population. Virchow's research on house types had a very stimulating effect and was continued by others.

Virchow used, of course, the three-period classification (stone, bronze, iron), as introduced by Danish archeologists in the first half of the nineteenth century; but he was fully aware of the existence of transitional stages and of the necessity of avoiding schematism in the use of the period classification.[21] Virchow tried to claim priority of the period classification for German archeologists. This would have been valid if C. J. Thomsen had actually launched the idea in 1837, but in the ensuing interesting discussion the Dane, Vedel Simonsen, was discovered to have actually fathered the idea as early as 1813.[22]

Archeology in the Near East

VIRCHOW never stopped archeological work in northeastern Germany, his own bailiwick, where he made most of his original contributions to archeology. But toward the end of the 1870's he grew more and more interested in the archeology of the Near East. This was the logical outcome of his first decade of archeological research, which had convinced him that civilization in Europe was primarily not home-grown,* but had been imported from the East.[1]

Virchow's work in the Near East was above all the result of his friendship with Heinrich Schliemann. In 1874 W. E. Gladstone, Homeric scholar as well as statesman, advised Schliemann to consult Professor Virchow, the authority on face urns, concerning the strange specimens found in Hissarlik. Virchow and Schliemann never came to an agreement concerning these urns, but this consultation started a friendship which was to last for the remaining seventeen years of Schliemann's life. It was a decisive factor in Schliemann's recognition as a scientist and in the donation of his priceless collections to Germany. Today this friendship reflects as much glory on Virchow as at the time it reflected on Schliemann.

Schliemann, a poor German parson's son, had become a millionaire in Russia, an American citizen in California, a man of the world in Paris. At forty-one he had decided to fulfill the dream of his youth and, aided by his considerable private means, to dig out the cities described by his beloved Homer. In 1871 he started in the plain of Troy on a hill called Hissarlik. The enterprise seemed doubly ridiculous, as according to most philologists the *Iliad* was nothing but a legend and Ilion therefore nonexistent, while according to most archeologists

---

* Virchow is thus an early representative of the *ex oriente lux* tendency. On the *ex oriente lux* vs. *mirage oriental* controversy of the 1890's, see Daniel, *A Hundred Years of Archeology*, p. 180.

the ancient city had existed near a Turkish village called Bu-
narbaschi where nothing could then be found. But Schliemann
dug out on his hill no less than seven cities, one built upon the
ruins of the other. He regarded the third city, which had
perished by a large fire, as the city described by Homer. A
tremendous treasure of golden objects found in these ruins
made Schliemann world famous overnight. In 1874 he made
similar sensational discoveries at Mykene and Tiryns on the
basis of the same unorthodox mixture of intuition and interpretation of Homer. But the "experts," especially in Germany,
continued to regard him as little better than a fraud. To mis-
represent Schliemann publicly was not too difficult. He was
inexperienced and uninhibited as to the limits of the normal
in his ways of expressing himself. It is at this juncture that
Virchow joined Schliemann. Emil Ludwig has characterized
the event as follows:

> This distracted Orestes needed a Pylades who would steer him
> with a quiet hand out of the sea of his phantasies to a safe shore.
> He had need of a man who was a scholar, but without academic ar-
> rogance, an expert without prejudice, fond of him and yet possessed
> of sufficient authority to guide him gently on occasion. At the end
> of his fifties Schliemann in his struggle needed what he had never
> possessed. Once more the Gods were gracious to him. He needed a
> friend and he found him.[2]

Though Schliemann himself had learned a great deal from his
past errors and though it seems unlikely that in our society
a millionaire like Schliemann should not eventually have
achieved some kind of recognition, even as an archeologist,
there is no doubt that Virchow's intervention accelerated and
facilitated this progress considerably. It is certain that without
Virchow Schliemann's treasures would probably have gone to
England, never to Germany. The bitter resentment of certain
German philologists against the man who had befriended the
"dilettante" Schliemann came to the fore in the "Sophocles"
skull discussion of 1894.[3]

It seems at first sight unbelievable that Virchow the man
of the "coldest objectivity" [4] and the mad enthusiast Schlie-

mann should have become such close friends. Virchow's determination to obtain Schliemann's treasures for Germany is an insufficient explanation. Virchow was patient and objective, but no cad. When he called Schliemann his friend, he meant it. As much as Schliemann might at times have shocked Virchow, there was much in the background of both men to make them feel close to each other: of the same age, both had started as poor boys in the agrarian northeastern region of Germany, to become world famous. Both were blessed with boundless energy and industry. Both excellent linguists and worshippers of Homer, they were nevertheless outsiders in the German classical archeology of their time. They approached archeological objects not primarily as handmaidens of philology or as aesthetic art critics. Their primary goal was a historical one, and they were actually instrumental in introducing the prehistoric approach into German classical archeology. A technical offshoot of this approach was their early interest in pottery as a "chronometer" quite independent of aesthetic merits.

Virchow's first success in "regularizing" Schliemann and in reconciling him with the land of his birth was the latter's nomination as honorary member of the German Anthropological Society in 1877. Virchow spent the spring of 1879 excavating and surveying with Schliemann in Hissarlik.[5] He knew Schliemann's jealous and suspicious character too well to do any independent archeological work in Troy. He concentrated on studies less important to Schliemann—on the geology, geography, botany, zoology, and craniology of the region.[6] He was very positive that Hissarlik was Troy and felt that Schliemann had in this respect made even too many concessions to his critics. Virchow studied particularly the warm and cold sources mentioned in Homer, the courses of rivers (he felt that the Scamander had changed its course), and the coastal line. An extensive medical practice,[7] in the course of which he made valuable observations on the then forgotten malaria of infants and on "geophagy with anemia" (hookworm disease),[8] brought him into many native houses. He was struck by the fact that the house type was still the same as at the time of the burnt third city of Hissarlik.

In 1880 Schliemann donated his collections to the Berlin Museum of Ethnology. The grateful city of Berlin made him an honorary citizen in 1881, an honor so far bestowed only upon Bismarck and Moltke. In 1888 Schliemann and Virchow went together to Egypt. In 1890 Virchow made another trip to Hissarlik primarily to participate in a commission investigating the scurrilous attacks of a retired army captain, Boetticher, against Schliemann.[9] Virchow used the sojourn for more studies of the house type of the region and for a trip with Schliemann to the Ida Mountains. It was to be their last. Schliemann died on December 26, 1890, in Naples on his way home to Athens. At the official commemoration at Berlin Virchow surveyed once more the life and work of the man whom he had recaptured for Germany.[10]

Virchow made his first expedition to the Caucasus in 1881.[11] Since Blumenbach, the Caucasus had been regarded as the cradle of the white (therefore "Caucasian") race. It had also been regarded as the cradle of bronze culture. This archeological hypothesis appeared to Virchow as fallacious as the anthropological had been. (The "Caucasians" of the Caucasus had proved to be a far cry from blond and dolichocephalic.) At the grave field of Koban (excavated before by Chantre) Virchow found numerous bronze objects mixed with early iron objects. He assumed the site to date from 1000 B.C., thus being earlier than Hissarlik III. He also found early enamels and was puzzled by the absence of stone implements. The culture he found was nothing primary, just a variation of south Caspian culture. Virchow tried to identify the animals depicted on the ornaments in order to trace the origins and peregrinations of this culture. The fauna of the costume jewelry pointed toward Babylon.

Research done on a second trip to the Caucasus in 1894 produced similar results.[12] Realizing the fragmentary character of his own sporadic efforts in the Caucasus, Virchow vigorously supported the Lehmann-Belck expedition.

In 1888 Virchow and Schliemann made with Schweinfurth

an extensive trip into Egypt.[13] Their main concern was the existence of a predynastic Egyptian stone age, claimed against much resistance by Pitt-Rivers, Hamy, and others. The friends were able to confirm these observations fully.

From this trip of Virchow's grew a number of interesting studies located on the borderline between archeology and physical anthropology. Measuring the mummies of the Pharaohs at the Museum of Bulak and comparing the results with statues of the same men, Virchow found that old Egyptian statuary gave by no means correct anthropological information.[14] On the other hand, comparing measurements taken from mummies with those taken from modern Egyptians, Virchow came to the conclusion that Egyptian bodies had remained practically unchanged during the millennia.[15]

In Egypt Virchow became interested in a number of apparently minute detail problems, like the chemical composition of ancient Egyptian eye paints[16] and the osteological nature of the cats living in Third Dynasty temples.[17] (The latter proved, interestingly enough, to be either ichneumons or wild cats.)

Both excursions are extremely typical of a most characteristic trait of Virchow's archeology: *the enlistment, if possible, of every known and available science and scientific technique for the solution of archeological problems.* This accounts, therefore, for the frequent excursions into zoology and paleontology: study of remnants of hunted and of domestic animals in prehistoric dwellings, study of animals depicted, studies of Bos primigenus, the fossile horse, etc.[18] Hence also proceeds his energetic propagation of the chemical analysis of the different kinds of bronze[19] and of amber and his initiation of microscopic studies of the different types of nephrite and jadeite.[20] At seventy-four he was flexible enough to realize immediately the value of X rays for archeological purpose and to pioneer in their application.[21]

Yet even the indefatigable could not eternally remain active. His contributions became rarer and rarer. The last problem he tackled with his customary energy after the Pithecanthropus and pre-Columbian leprosy discussions was that of the red-painted bones in prehistoric graves.[22] Here again chemical analysis of the coloring material was used in the hope of tracing relations.

The Organizer of German Anthropology

ALTHOUGH VIRCHOW was extremely productive in physical anthropology and archeology, he almost never dealt with the third great subdivision of anthropology: cultural anthropology or ethnology. It was not that he lacked interest or knowledge in the field; he had obviously come in contact with it early through his friend and father-in-law, Carl Mayer, who was a friend of the ethnologist L. Dieffenbach, of the Schomburgk brothers, the famous explorers, and who was the owner of an ethnographic collection.[1] Remarks that show familiarity with ethnographic material appear early in Virchow's writings— for instance, those on extreme parasite infestation of primitives,[2] aimed at those who idealized savage life; or the remarks on the psychological advantages of animism.[3] In his great address on goals and means of modern anthropology at the *Naturforscherversammlung* in Hamburg in 1876 he put cultural anthropolgy in the center of his exposition, emphasizing here as elsewhere the pressing need of collecting material, as the traditions of natives were dying out even more rapidly than their human carriers.[4]

His basic insight into social factors might have guided Virchow into dealing with problems of cultural anthropology. His sociological attitude is typified, for instance, in his interpretation of stimulants as "conditioned by the situation of society"; [5] or in his refusal to explain "national character" through climate and food; [6] or in his remark about Troy, "The Troas is so desolate not on account of her poor soil or her lazy inhabitants but on account of the economic system." [7] Virchow continued to make impressive asides on problems of cultural anthropology like: "Magic outlives even religion," [8] or "The future belongs to nativism." [9] But the thirty-nine pages in his monograph on the Veddahs of Ceylon (Berlin Academy, 1881—the remaining one hundred four pages deal with the physical anthropology of the Veddah) are probably the most extensive excursion Virchow ever made into cultural anthropology. They contain interesting remarks (for example, on the history of silent trade in Ceylon, or the history of invasions into Ceylon); but as they had to be based on not too excellent primary sources, they have left no permanent imprint. Probably the explanation for Virchow's abstention in the field of cultural anthropology lies in the fact that, unable here to base any work upon "autopsy" (direct inspection) as he did in all his other endeavors, he preferred to stay out—all the more as he felt the field to be ably cultivated by his pupil and friend A. Bastian.

Virchow's strong belief in progress made him sympathetic toward social evolutionism. "The development of human [societies] largely follows everywhere the same laws of progressive formation." [10] When the discovery of Magdalenian art along with the subsequent lowering of artistic levels suggested to him (as it did to contemporary archeologists [11]) that perhaps evolution did not always progress in a straight line, he found the idea "painful." [12] But evidence was, of course, the supreme judge. And absence of evidence—for example, of cannibalism in Europe—rendered Virchow quite aggressive against those who, out of evolutionary dogmatism, claimed a "stage of cannibalism" for Europe too.[13]

The "naturalistic" anthropology that grew up under Virchow's leadership had to emancipate itself from German philologists who had developed a deplorable tendency of feeling competent to answer all the questions. In the midst of personal frictions between the "naturalistic" and "philological" tendencies in anthropology, Virchow emphasized the necessity for mutual interpenetration by the two; [14] nevertheless, during his lifetime this did not come about. Anthropology was to him the real "meeting ground between the natural sciences and history."

Among the motives behind Virchow's absorbing interest in anthropology we have already mentioned his concern with his

Slavonic background. It is rather obvious that Virchow's interest and the growth of anthropology in general coincide with the growth of imperialism. Some of Virchow's anthropological activities derive clearly from imperialistic activities (or rather his opposition to such activities), as, for instance, his work on acclimatization. German imperialistic expansion undoubtedly facilitated the acquisition of anthropological information and objects. Yet it might be advisable to abstain from too far-reaching conclusions as to the automatic influence of imperialism on the growth of anthropology, though we regretfully observe such connections occasionally even today. It was precisely the Germans who inaugurated geographical research, and especially the geography of diseases, long before the actively imperialistic British and French; they did this at a time when Germany, landlocked, disunited, and prostrate, could not even dream of colonial expansion.

Seen against the background of his time, Virchow's work in physical anthropology appears much more conventional than it would today. In those days it was obviously quite a normal thing for anatomists to be interested, to collect, and to work in the field of physical anthropology. K. E. von Baer, the famous embryologist, devoted himself almost entirely to anthropology during the later years of his life. Outstanding German anatomists of the period—like Welcker, K. E. R. Hartmann, Ecker, Wilhelm His, Sr., Waldeyer, and in Austria Hyrtl, Heschl, and Joseph Engel—spent a great deal of their time in anthropological research. Was this participation of anatomists in physical anthropology simply a matter of tradition? Though the tradition of the anatomist-anthropologist seems originally a British one, in Germany more than in any other country, from Blumenbach and Soemmering to F. Weidenreich and Eugen Fischer, physical anthropology has remained the concern of the anatomist. Or was it because physical anthropology was all that was left to do in the field of gross anatomy? *

* In the United States, where most anatomists have solved their problem by becoming physiologists, as far as research is concerned, it is, on the contrary, the physical anthropologist who has taken over much morphological research that normally should be taken care of by anatomists or other medical men.

It must have been a challenge to Virchow's patriotism that Germany, which had been so eminent in all branches of anthropology toward the end of the eighteenth century, which—partly under British influence—had produced men like Blumenbach, Soemmering, Meckel, Kant, Herder, and Georg Forster, had been outdistanced so badly, especially by France, during the first half of the nineteenth century. One might date the revival of German anthropology from the meeting of Von Baer, R. Wagner, Lucae, Schaaffhausen, and Vrolick in Goettingen in 1861; or from the meeting of the founders of the *Archiv fuer Anthropologie* (A. Ecker, Desor, W. His, Sr., Lindenschmit, Lucae, Schaaffhausen, C. Vogt, Welcker) in Frankfurt in 1865. Nonetheless, it so happens that things did not advance very much till 1869, when Virchow started participating in the organizational aspects of German anthropology.

Virchow's dominant role in German anthropology has often been commented upon.[15] It is amazing to what extent he influenced men who were outstanding scientists in their own right, whether they belonged to his own generation like Alexander Ecker, Hermann Welcker, Schaaffhausen, and Waldeyer, or whether they had been his pupils, like Joh. Ranke, Kollmann, and His, Sr. The few he could not convince he outlived. Due to the fact that most "explorers" (cultural anthropologists) of the period were medical men,[16] Virchow's pupils were numerous, not only among physical, but also among cultural anthropologists. Virchow himself proudly mentions as his old Wuerzburg pupils A. Bastian, Gerhard Rohlfs, Nachtigal, Karl Semper, and the archeologist A. Voss.[17]

Virchow owed his position in German anthropology even more to his organizational work than to his scientific contributions. His organizational work was so extensive that it warrants at least some short comments. It is also to be realized that for a "science in the making," as anthropology was around 1870, organizational work is often as important as or even more important than scientific contributions. The latter obtain value only if mediums for their diffusion and preservation like journals and associations are created.

Virchow was the founder of the Berlin Society and directed

its meetings for more than thirty years. The same holds true for the German Society, where his annual presidential addresses provided him with an opportunity to develop every year a program for research, general as well as local (for the region where the meeting took place). In addition he maintained international contacts by visiting meetings of foreign societies or international societies like the Americanists or the International Congresses for Prehistory and Anthropology. Between 1869 (Paris) and 1900 (Paris again) he hardly missed one of these congresses, which in the first decade met every one or two years, but which became rarer after 1880—according to Virchow, because of the chauvinistic attitude of French anthropologists like De Quatrefages and De Mortillet.[18] Virchow often visited four to five anthropological congresses in one year! Furthermore, he agitated for anthropology at other meetings (medical, *Naturforscherversammlung*, Academy) and in publications at his disposal.

Virchow was a collaborator of many anthropological publications. He edited (including proofreading) the *Zeitschrift fuer Ethnologie,* the *Transactions of the Berlin Society,* and after 1890 the *Nachrichten ueber deutsche Altertumsfunde.* His pupils, his assistants, his friends (Von Frantzius and Waldeyer), even his children were enlisted in archeological work. Adele, Hans, Marie, and son-in-law Rabl went digging with him. Son Carl (and the assistants of the Pathological Institute) had to make chemical analyses.

Virchow found money to finance expeditions like those of Ehrenreich, Von Steinen, J. M. Hildebrandt, Vaughan Stevens, Finsch, and Kubary. He procured collections (like those of Schliemann) for the museum; as a politician, he obtained credits for museum buildings. It is no accident that till 1945 the Berlin Museum of Ethnology was the biggest and finest anthropological museum on earth. It was Virchow's fame as a medical scientist and his energy that made respectable the young disciplines of prehistory and ethnology, which hitherto had been regarded with a not unjustified suspicion because of the frauds and crackpots that had infested them.

It is not surprising that under these circumstances Virchow's authority in German anthropology was eventually even far greater than in German medicine. He knew this and disliked it:

A long time has now passed since I was a pupil, and since I began to develop my own opinions. It took a very long time till those opinions were accepted. But now my opinions are so familiar, so generally accepted that I am scared of myself and am asking myself: surely it cannot be that so many of the things which occupy us, have already been perfectly ascertained? [19]

This authority sometimes stimulated, sometimes retarded. On the negative side, this retarding is all too well remembered in the case of paleonthropology. The positive side of this braking—which, for instance, kept racism out of German scientific anthropology during Virchow's lifetime and even much longer —is less clearly realized.

International relations, exchange of ideas, and personal contacts were very highly developed in those first decades of European anthropology, and techniques and approaches differed only slightly. Most representative of this period, which Muehlmann calls "elementaristic," was probably Paul Broca. Virchow's admiration and sympathy for Broca [20] and his naive disappointment that Broca did not help him in his fight against De Quatrefages in 1871 were equally sincere. Virchow was a typical child of the Broca epoch with all its limitations in displaying the fascination with craniology, with technical problems, etc. And yet, in some of his accomplishments—such as his work on the skull base, the German school survey, and his work on pile dwellings, walled mounds, and grave fields in northeastern Germany—he transcended these limitations and made lasting contributions.

His accomplishments in anthropology are nevertheless not comparable to his accomplishments in medicine. This is primarily due to the differences between the two fields: in medicine Virchow was heir to three hundred years of uninterrupted scientific progress and in medicine he dealt with a field which had matured sufficiently to produce true and spectacular practical advances. Anthropology seemed to Virchow ill defined.[21]

It is still. At best it was and is at the stage medicine had reached in the sixteenth century. To truly appreciate anthropological contributions will be possible only when and if anthropology bears fruits comparable to those of nineteenth-century medicine. A true assessment of this work, like the assessment of the work of Benivieni, Fracastorius, or Sylvius, has also become possible only in the light of nineteenth- and twentieth-century medical accomplishments.

Virchow's medical and anthropological contributions also differ widely in that *in medicine Virchow was the great synthesist, while his "cold-blooded" anthropology shied away from synthesis.* The same dichotomy is to be seen in the work of many of his contemporaries. K. E. von Baer, for instance, so prone to synthesis in his romantic youth, is absolutely "elementaristic" in his anthropological work. The Goettingen meeting of 1861 decided to leave "philosophy" out of anthropology. This attitude was certainly not unwise and avoided a number of "romantic" errors. But it also missed a readily imaginable contribution. That Virchow, diffuse enough as a medical writer, is even far worse as an anthropological author is a clear expression of this change in attitude from synthesis to "elementarism."

As an anthropologist Virchow could not have "pupils" in the formal sense in which he had them as a medical man. No chairs of anthropology existed in his lifetime, except that of Ranke in Munich. His personal influence was nevertheless deep and far reaching. One of those to come under his influence was the geographer Franz Boas, who was an assistant curator at the Berlin Ethnological Museum, 1883–86. Boas later came to the United States and occupied for forty years a position in American anthropology which was not without similarities to that of Virchow in German anthropology. Those who have read the above analysis of Virchow's work will admit that both men had more in common than merely certain aspects of character, such as great courage, industry, coldness, and versatility. Their mutual strong convictions on the equality of races could easily be coincidental. Yet it seems significant, in view of Boas' later work on change in cranial indices of descendants of immigrants, that he had been exposed to Virchow, perhaps the only man in his generation to uphold the plasticity of races and the possibility of change in cranial indices (see p. 210). Boas started work in physical anthropology much earlier than is usually assumed.[22] How strongly Boas was influenced by Virchow in this field is shown by his paper on the relative merits of the length-breadth and the length-height indices of the skull.[23] One cannot help feeling that Boas' arguments against social evolutionism are to a large extent transcriptions of Virchow's polemics against Haeckel in the question of biological transformism. Even their common interest in the art of the Northwest Coast Indians may have been mutually stimulated.[24] Since both men had the same basic concept of science when approaching anthropology, the expositions suffer equally from diffuseness. Surely their recognition of this relationship in no wise detracts from the greatness of Boas; to realize the relationship should, however, lead to a better understanding of Boas' contributions. To have inspired a Boas is perhaps not the least of Virchow's titles to glory as an anthropologist.

Epicrisis

Epicrisis

VIRCHOW STARTED OUT in medicine as an experimentalist (embolism) and biochemist (amyloid, haematoidin, myelin), but became more and more absorbed in microscopy. Microscopical pathology led him from the discovery of leukemia to a better understanding of connective tissue and inflammation. He became one of the great oncologists. Pathological studies made him an important biologist, because the battle cry of cellular pathology, *Omnis cellula a cellula,* is above all a biological law.

Cellular pathology had far-reaching consequences for therapeutics. A localist creed, it contributed to the tremendous growth of surgery. Asking for drugs with special affinities to special cells, it became a stimulus for modern chemotherapy.

Virchow made important discoveries in the field of parasitology. He was one of the pioneers of modern public health and of a social approach in medicine and epidemiology.

Virchow was one of the leaders against Bismarck in the constitutional conflict of 1862–66 (but also one of the leaders of the Kulturkampf in the 1870's). He fought against militarism, the Anti-Socialist Laws, and anti-Semitism.

Virchow made important discoveries concerning the growth of the skull, the racial composition of the German nation, and the nature of prehistoric structures in northeast Germany. He worked with Schliemann at Troy.

Condorcet, philosopher and mathematician, had prophesied

239

in 1794 that morphology was completed and that the future was with experimentalism. This was perfectly logical. But subsequent developments have shown the potentialities of morphology, have shown that despite the growth of experimentation morphology does not die so easily, probably will never die. Virchow was one of those to demonstrate that morphology has this future because true morphology is more than mere description and systematization.

Max Neuburger once very aptly called Rokitansky the "sun" of the second Vienna school.[1] Virchow played the same role for Germany, probably even for world medicine in his time. That pathologists occupied these central positions during this period is more than an accident. With the great clinicians of the first half of the nineteenth century, pathological anatomy had been an important aid of the clinician. In the second half of the nineteenth century pathology was the portal through which the future clinician had to pass. Some of the best-known clinicians of the second half of the nineteenth century—for example, Charcot, Frerichs, Friedreich, Osler—were pathologists before they became clinicians. What wonder that a pathologist was the "sun" of medicine during this half century.

Most great medical men became great, not only through their own inventions, but also by transmitting vitally important information and orientations from some more developed country. This is very clear, for example, in the case of William H. Welch. Although the situation is somewhat more complex in Germany around 1850, there seems little doubt that some of Virchow's greatness rests on his ability to absorb and develop French and British ideas.

This is not to detract from his stupendous creativeness which, among other things, is reflected in the number of terms he introduced into medicine—terms which were not empty phraseology, but which all had new and important meaning. I counted fifty, and this is probably not the total.

"I have regarded as the basic task of my life to clarify this biological nature of pathology in its single traits. . . . Albrecht Haller already said: *pathologia physiologiam illustrat.*"[2] Virchow succeeded in this attempt to make pathology a branch of biology.

At the same time he was one of the strongest protagonists of the sociological approach in medicine. As a matter of fact, this social approach pervades not only his medical work; it pervades all his many simultaneous activities. Virchow's first publications were in the field of social history. The social approach is the common denominator which made it possible for Virchow to do so many things at the same time and to remain sane. Because of this common approach all the many different and various activities eventually belonged together.

In order to explain Virchow's work, it was necessary to describe in sequence what was actually done simultaneously. Now that the reader is familiar with Virchow's work, he might appreciate the reminder that in 1848 Virchow simultaneously worked on the blood and on cholera, wrote the Upper Silesia Report, edited *Die medizinische Reform,* and was active in politics. In the 1860's he simultaneously engaged in the constitutional conflict, experimented with trichinae, wrote his book on tumors, fought for Berlin sewerage, started his archeological diggings, and did the routine work of a busy professor. In the 1870's he simultaneously did the anthropological school survey, counterattacked Haeckel and Klebs, worked for Troy, and fought the Kulturkampf.

Under these conditions one of these many activities would have had unforeseen consequences in other fields. Thus the Kulturkampf induced him to study the anthropology of Saint Cordula [3] and the history of medieval hospitals; it made him compromise on the administrative reorganization of communities; and, on the other hand, it helped him to obtain permission for his anthropological school survey.

It is almost certain that, had Virchow not lived, somebody else would have created cellular pathology, somebody else would have played his role in the constitutional conflict, somebody else would have done most of his work in anthropology. This does not make the fact any less remarkable that this one individual did all these things, and it does not change the fact that, because these things were done by one and the same person, they became related to each other and colored by the personality of the actor in ways that otherwise would never have developed. That is why Virchow's total work is more impressive than the simple sum of its elements.

It appeared phenomenal even to an age when doctors were in general less specialized (and therefore more proficient in general education), less affluent, and more liberal. It impressed people all the more as Virchow had been doubly an outsider, coming from the "backwoods" and having very modest social origins.

Into Virchow's later years, in the years after 1870, fall great changes in German life and mentality. Though Virchow was one of the last universalists and individualists in Germany, even he shows signs of the new times. After him a sort of highly specialized and efficient, obsequious anonymity would more and more hold the field. In trying to characterize Virchow I insist perhaps too much on his intellectual accomplishments and abilities, on his industry. His essential trait was perhaps his courage. This "civic courage," whose absence among Germans was bewailed by a Bismarck who had done more than anybody else to penalize "civic courage" in Germany, this "civic courage" had been by no means rare in Germany between 1815 and 1848. Virchow was one of its last representatives in the middle class; but it lived on in the workers' movement and reappeared in a small minority of martyrs of all classes in the dark ages of Nazism.

The story of Virchow is an important chapter in the history of medicine and science. It is more. It is the story of a rare man whose life mankind can be proud of.

Notes

Notes

LIFE HISTORY

1. Reprinted in *Briefe* and in a special publication of the Prussian Ministry of Culture, *Der Kleine Virchow*, in 1901.
2. *Briefe*, p. 47.
3. *BM*, p. 120.
4. As quoted by Waldeyer in *Gedaechtnisrede auf Rudolf Virchow*, p. 37.
5. *A*, IV (1852), 543.
6. Billroth, *The Medical Sciences in the German Universities*, pp. 218, 222, 225.
7. Virchow in *Baltische Studien*, IX (1844), No. 2, pp. 51–94. Reprinted in *Drei historische Arbeiten Virchows zur Geschichte seiner Vaterstadt Schivelbein*.
8. Waldeyer, *op. cit.*, p. 1.
9. *Briefe*, pp. 66, 75, 77.
10. *A*, XXVIII (1863), 273.
11. Reprinted in *GA*.
12. Reprinted in *GA*. Virchow on Traube in necrology in *BKW*, XIII (1876), 209.
13. Reprinted in *A*, CLXXXVIII (1907), 1 ff.
14. *Briefe*, p. 99.
15. *Ibid.*, pp. 96, 97.
16. Virchow in *Preussische Medicinal-Zeitung*, XV (1846), pp. 237 and 243; reprinted in Becher, *Rudolf Virchow*.
17. *Briefe*, p. 187. On liberal bureaucrats see Gerth, *Die Sozialgeschichtliche Lage der Buergerlichen Intelligenz um die Wende des 18. Jahrhunderts*, pp. 109 ff.
18. Virchow, *Gedaechtnisrede auf Carl Mayer*, p. 23.
19. See *OM*, I, 523, and *A*, XXXV (1866), 193. The recent publication of Virchow's letters to Meckel von Hemsbach by Gruber (*A*, CCCXXI [1952], 462–81) throws much light on Virchow's work and friendships during these years.
20. Reprinted in *A*, CLIX (1900), 24.
21. "De ossificatione pathologica"; reprinted in *A*, CLI (1898), 538.
22. Reprinted in *A*, IV (1852), 262 ff.
23. *Briefe*, p. 120.
24. Reprinted in *A*, IV (1852), 274.
25. *A*, CLXVII (1902), 3.
26. *A*, II (1849), 143–322; reprinted in *OM*, II, 214–334.
27. See Ackerknecht in *Bull. Hist. Med.*, XXII (1948), 117–155.
28. *A*, II (1849), 303.
29. *Ibid.*, p. 309.
30. *Ibid.*, pp. 310–22.
31. *Briefe*, p. 137.
32. Schleich, *Besonnte Vergangenheit*, p. 62.
33. *Briefe*, p. 141.
34. *Ibid.*, p. 145.
35. *OM*, I, 8.
36. See Finkenrath, *Die Medizinalreform*, and *BM* (especially the

245

chapter "Medical Reform," pp. 169 ff.). On its actuality see Sigerist, *Medicine and Human Welfare*, pp. 92 ff.

37. Ackerknecht in *Bull. Hist. Med.*, XXII (1948), 136.

38. Letter of March 19, 1849, to Bardeleben; reprinted in *A*, CCXXIII (1917), 3.

39. Reprinted in *OM*, I, 75.

40. *Briefe*, p. 181.

41. *Ibid.*, p. 201. See also *A*, III (1851), 195.

42. *OM*, I, 108.

43. *Ibid.*, p. vi.

44. Printed in *A*, CCXXIII (1917), 3.

45. In *A*, CCXXXV (1921), 47.

46. Mehring, *Karl Marx*, pp. 242, 244.

47. Haeckel, *The Story of the Development of a Youth: Letters to His Parents, 1852–1856*, p. 13.

48. *Briefe*, p. 189.

49. In a necrology of Beckmann (*A*, XIX [1860], 557) Virchow himself gives some data on his Wuerzburg pupils.

50. Klebs in *Deutsche medizinische Wochenschrift*, XVII (1891), 1166.

51. *OM*, I, 416.

52. Boerner in *Nord und Sued*, XXI (1882), 113.

53. Grote (ed.), *Die Medizin der Gegenwart in Selbstdarstellungen*.

54. In *A*, CCXXXV (1921), 27.

55. Bismarck, *Die gesammelten Werke*, XIV, Part II, 695.

56. Letter to an unidentified addressee in the Thor Jager collection.

57. Simpson in *Scottish Medical and Surgical Journal*, XI (1907).

58. Aschoff, *Rudolf Virchow*, p. 23.

59. Waldeyer, *Lebenserinnerungen*, p. 153.

60. *Ibid.*, pp. 323–34, 407–8. Virchow in *BKW*, XXIV (1887), 445, 519, 585, 877, and XXV (1888), 137.

61. *A*, CLXVII (1902), 1 ff.

62. Semon in *British Medical Journal*, II (1902), 802.

63. E.g., *BKW*, XXX (1893), 1127; *DN*, pp. 106–7, 245. For his reception speech in the Prussian Academy in 1874 see Becher, *op. cit.*, pp. 102 ff.

64. See *Autobiography of Samuel D. Gross*, I, 233, and Trendelenburg, *Aus Heiteren Jugendtagen*, p. 125.

65. Waldeyer, *Lebenserinnerungen*, p. 250.

66. *DN*, pp. 48 and 147. Some of Virchow's popular addresses (e.g., *Vier Reden*) are veritable sermons of this science religion.

67. Sigerist, *Great Doctors*, p. 335.

68. *BKW*, XXX (1893), 1127.

69. *A*, VI (1854), 6; XVI (1859), 384. *Briefe*, p. 112.

70. See the Virchow-Schliemann letters published in Ludwig, *Schliemann: The Story of a Gold-Seeker*, especially p. 214.

71. Semon, *op. cit.*, p. 801.

72. *Briefe*, pp. 38, 46.

73. As quoted by Kroeber in "Franz Boas: The Man," p. 22 of *Franz Boas*. Also see Boas in *Science*, N.S., XVI (1902), 443, on Virchow and his "cold enthusiasm for truth."

74. Martius in Grote (ed.), *op. cit.*, I, 7.

75. As quoted by Lubarsch in *BKW*, LVIII (1921), 1346.

76. Virchow in *BKW*, XIX (1882), 720.

77. Waldeyer, *Lebenserinnerungen*, p. 247.

78. Schleich, *op. cit.*, p. 186.

79. *GA*, pp. 472, 675, 867; *BKW*, XXXI (1894), 727.
80. *CP*, p. vii.
81. Waldeyer, *Lebenserinnerungen*, p. 247.
82. For a description of a typical examination see his admirer Semon, *op. cit.*, p. 800.
83. See the stenographic notes of his 1855/56 lectures published as *Die Vorlesungen Rudolf Virchows ueber allgemeine pathologische Anatomie aus dem Wintersomester 1855/56 in Wuerzburg.*
84. See Osler as quoted in Cush-
ing, *The Life of Sir William Osler*, I, 213; Meyer in his *Autobiography*, p. 38; Bartlett in "A Sketch of Virchow's Life and Time," p. 470 of *Lectures on the History of Medicine; a Series of Lectures at the Mayo Foundation.*
85. Insofar as it interfered "with woman's true destiny: to be the center [!] of the family," see *Ueber die Erzie hung des Weibes fuer seinen Beruf*, pp. 10, 17.
86. *OM*, I, iv.
87. Myres in *Man*, III (1903), 3.

GENERAL IDEAS

1. *A*, LXX (1877), 3.
2. *GA*, p. 56.
3. As reprinted in *OM*, I, 78.
4. *Ibid.*, p. 9.
5. *BM*, p. 99.
6. *Ibid.*, p. 108.
7. *Ibid.*, especially Chapter IV.
8. *A*, II (1849), 6.
9. *A*, I (1847), 216.
10. *Ibid.*
11. *A*, VI (1854), 27.
12. *A*, II (1849), 15.
13. *A*, V (1853), 7.
14. *A*, XXI (1861), 2.
15. Munich address of 1879 in *DN*, p. 191.
16. *DN*, p. 203.
17. For an interesting analysis of Virchow's theory of the cellular state as a metaphor, see Temkin, "Metaphors of Human Biology," in *Science and Civilization* (ed. Stauffer), pp. 169–94.
18. *A*, VIII (1855), 26. In *A*, IX (1856), 36, he quotes Lotze for the same concept.
19. *DN*, pp. 62 and 36.
20. *A*, XVIII (1860), 5.
21. *A*, IX (1856), 48.
22. *A*, XVIII (1860), 5.
23. *CP*, p. 21; *GA*, p. 51.
24. *OM*, I, 58.
25. *GA*, p. 31.
26. *OM*, I, 34. This was originally a formulation of Salomon Neumann, as Virchow himself makes clear in *A*, II (1849), 36.
27. *OM*, I, 4. It is an odd coincidence that during the great English revolution an English doctor, Chamberlen, published a pamphlet entitled *The Poor Man's Advocate.*
28. For a modern revival of the older concept, see Kershaw, *An Approach to Social Medicine.*
29. I have dealt in more detail with this problem in my articles "Hygiene in France," *Bull. Hist. Med.*, XXII (1948), 141–43, and "Medizin als Sozialwissenschaft," *Colloquium*, VI (1947), 22–24. Typical of Virchow's attitude is his classifica-

tion in 1865 of political economy as "applied natural science" (*DN*, p. 48).

30. E.g., *DN*, pp. 48, 52, and 130 ff.

31. *Ibid.*, pp. 19, 51, 109, 189; *OM*, I, 55 (reprint of 1848 article).

32. *A*, VII (1854), 28. See also *GA*, p. 7; *OM*, I, 30; *A*, V (1853), 11.

33. *GA*, p. 7.

34. *OM*, I, 15 and 28.

35. Karsner in *Bulletin of the New York Academy of Medicine*, XXII (1946), 384.

36. E.g., *DN*, pp. 34, 49, 183 ff.

37. *A*, V (1853), 10.

38. Virchow, *Vier Reden Ueber Leben und Kranksein*, p. 20.

39. *DN*, p. 118.

40. E.g., *A*, VI (1854), 5.

41. *A*, VIII (1855), 4.

42. *A*, I (1847), 9.

43. Ackerknecht in *Bull. Hist. Med.*, XXIV (1950), 45–60.

44. *A*, VI (1854), 4.

45. Rokitansky, "Der selbststaendige Wert des Wissens" in *Almanach der kaiserlichen Akademie zu Wien*, XVII (1867), 103 ff.

46. *A*, II (1849), 9; *GA*, p. 5; *DN*, p. 143.

47. Lotze in Wagner's *Handwoerterbuch der Physiologie mit Ruecksicht auf physiologische Pathologie*, I, ix ff.; Schleiden in *Grundzuege der wissenschaftlichen Botanik*, I, 57 ff.; Du Bois–Reymond, *Untersuchungen ueber tierische Elektrizitaet*, I, xxxvi ff. See also Temkin in *Bull. Hist. Med.*, XX (1946), 322 ff.

48. *DN*, p. 261.

49. Report of 1846 published in *A*, CLIX (1900), 24; also see *A*, VI (1854), 33.

50. Aschoff, *Rudolf Virchow*, p. 76. In Burnett's 1851 prize essay on the cell (*Transactions of the American Medical Association*, VII [1951], 643–832) that gives a fair survey of all outstanding cell researchers of the period, Virchow's name appears only once in a footnote (p. 807) on occasion of the myosarcoma.

51. *GA*, p. 43.

52. *A*, CI (1885), 12.

53. *A*, I (1847), 217.

54. *A*, II (1849), 10.

55. *A*, I (1847), 233.

56. *A*, I (1847), 24, and IX (1856), 31; *H*, I, 3; Virchow, *Die Vorlesungen Rudolf Virchows ueber allgemeine pathologische Anatomie aus dem Wintersomester 1855/56 in Wuerzburg*, p. 29.

57. *A*, IX (1856), 27; Virchow, *100 Jahre allgemeiner Pathologie*, p. 32.

58. Virchow, *100 Jahre allgemeiner Pathologie*, p. 35.

59. *A*, I (1847), 212, and II (1849), 27; *GA*, p. 31.

60. *A*, VI (1854), 7.

61. *A*, XIV (1858), 9.

62. Virchow, *100 Jahre allgemeiner Pathologie*, pp. 35 and 23.

63. *GA*, p. 38; Virchow, *Die Vorlesungen Rudolf Virchows ueber allgemeine pathologische Anatomie aus dem Wintersomester 1855/56 in Wuerzburg*, p. 12. In 1885 he all of a sudden attributes, with a somewhat embarrassing *sans gêne*, to "our late colleague Henle" this "misunderstanding" (*DN*, p. 221).

64. Speech at *Naturforscherversammlung* in Innsbruck, 1869; printed in *DN*, p. 91.

65. *GA*, p. 33.

66. *Ibid.*, p. 3. See also *A*, I (1847), 217, and II (1849), 9.

67. *DN*, p. 33. See also Schleich, *Besonnte Vergangenheit*, p. 190.

68. *A*, V (1853), 5.

69. *GA*, p. 14; *A*, VII (1854), 12 and 27; *DN*, p. 37.

70. *DN*, p. 38. Only in 1848 he called himself occasionally a materialist (e.g., *OM*, I, 15 and 124).

71. A forceful claim as to the basic identity of physiology and pathology can also be found in Georget, *De la Physiologie du système nerveux, et spéciale-ment du cerveau*, p. 1.

72. Report of 1846. See also *A*, I (1847), 10; *A*, VI (1854), 13; and *DN*, p. 66.

73. *A*, VI (1854), 33.

74. *A*, I (1847), 8, and CLIX (1900), 31.

75. Faber, *Nosography*, pp. 59 ff.

76. Ackerknecht in *Bull. Hist. Med.*, XXIV (1950), 58.

77. This idea to develop branches of medicine out of themselves can be found also in Cabanis or Bartlett; see Ackerknecht, *ibid.*, pp. 43 ff.

78. *A*, XVIII (1860), 6.

79. *GA*, p. 50.

80. *A*, LXX (1877), 2; *DN*, pp. 67 and 71.

81. Also see Wunderlich, *Geschichte der Medizin*, p. 350.

82. *A*, I (1847), 240, and VIII (1855), 7.

83. *A*, I (1847), 255.

84. See Temkin in *Bull. Hist. Med.*, XXIV (1950), 313.

85. See W. Pagel, "Julius Leopold Pagel" in *Victor Robinson Memorial Volume*, pp. 273–97.

86. W. Pagel, *Virchow und die Grundlagen der Medizin des 19. Jahrhunderts* and "The Speculative Basis of Modern Pathology: Jahn, Virchow, and the Philosophy of Pathology," *Bull. Hist. Med.*, XVIII (1945), 1 ff.

87. Diepgen in *Deutsche medizinische Wochenschrift*, LVIII (1932), 1256 ff.

88. Speiss in *A*, VIII (1855), 303.

89. Wunderlich in *Archiv fuer physiologische Heilkunde*, N.S., III (1859), 304.

90. *A*, VI (1854), 23–24.

91. *Ibid.*, p. 24.

92. *GA*, p. 35.

93. *GA*, p. 45.

94. *A*, I (1847), 218.

95. Virchow, *Die Vorlesungen Rudolf Virchows ueber allgemeine pathologische Anatomie aus dem Wintersomester 1855/56 in Wuerzburg*, p. 34.

96. *GA*, pp. 33 and 34.

97. *A*, VI (1854), 24.

98. *Ibid.*, p. 33.

99. Injection of syphilitic or septic material into cancers, *H*, I, 354; "Syphilization," *GA*, p. 52.

100. *A*, VI (1854), 28. He also advocated, therefore, "treating the whole person" in *Die Heilkraefte des Organismus*, p. 15.

101. *OM*, I, 41.

102. *A*, XI (1857) 6. For the relation between therapeutic nihilism and hygienic interests, see my "Hygiene in France," *Bull. Hist. Med.*, XXII (1948), p. 144.

PATHOLOGICAL PHYSIOLOGY

1. See the excellent historical study by Berg, "Die Lehre von der Faser," *A*, CCCIX (1942), 333 ff.
2. *GA*, p. 94.
3. See Henle in *Zeitschrift fuer rationelle Medicin*, 3d ser., XXXVI (1869), 279; Griesinger in *Archiv fuer physiologische Heilkunde*, 2d ser., III (1859), 289. For data on the development of blood chemistry, see Lieben, *Geschichte der physiologischen Chemie*, pp. 263 ff.
4. For the early history (especially seventeenth-century) of embolism and embolism experimentation, see the splendid study by Buess, "Zur Geschichte des Emboliebegriffs bis auf Virchow," *Acta Societatis Helveticae Scientiarum Naturalium*, CXXV (1945), 231 ff. (abstract in *Schweizer Medizinisches Jahrbuch*, 1946, pp. lvii ff.).
5. *GA*, p. 186.
6. *GA*, p. 173.
7. *WV*, II (1852), 51 ff.
8. Académie des Sciences, 1853; *A*, VI (1854), 135.
9. Virchow, *Johannes Mueller*, p. 43, for a discussion Virchow had with his teacher on the subject in 1846.
10. *A*, VI (1854), 268, 416, and XII (1857), 101.
11. *A*, VIII (1855), 140, 364; XI (1857), 222; XIV (1858), 187.
12. Lieben, *op. cit.*, pp. 406, 471.
13. *A*, VI (1854), 562 ff.
14. *A*, VI (1854), 572, and VIII (1855), 355.
15. *A*, XII (1857), 481 ff.
16. *A*, I (1847), 438, 440.
17. *Ibid.*, p. 445. In *WV*, I (1851), 303, Virchow adds some observations on haematoidin and discusses the interpretations of his discovery by others.
18. Lieben, *op. cit.*, p. 313.
19. *A*, I (1847), 464.
20. For an extensive discussion of Virchow's opinions on anthracosis and "miners' lung," see Rosen, *The History of Miners' Diseases*, pp. 318 ff.
21. He later devoted a special article to this subject (*A*, IV [1852], 515 ff.).
22. *A*, I (1847), 484.

ON THE ROAD TO *CELLULAR PATHOLOGY*

1. Cohen, *Science, Servant of Man*, p. 213.
2. Schwann, *Microscopical Researches into the Accordance of Structure and Growth of Animals and Plants*, p. 165. The 1847 edition also contains Schleiden's treatise on phytogenesis.
3. *Ibid.*, pp. 219 ff.
4. Rich in *Bulletin of the Johns Hopkins Hospital*, XXXIX (1926), 360.
5. *A*, I (1847), 94 ff.
6. See p. 69 of this book for Virchow's earlier work on pulmonary epithelia.
7. He later recognized that this had probably been old gummata (*A*, CXI [1888], 22).
8. *A*, III (1851), 197 ff.
9. *Ibid.*, p. 224.

10. *A*, V (1853), 216 ff.
11. *Ibid.*, p. 239.
12. *WV*, I (1851), 106 ff.
13. In *Die medizinische Reform*, No. 51.
14. *WV*, I (1851), 134 ff.
15. *Ibid.*, p. 135.
16. *A*, VIII (1855), 371.
17. *Ibid.*, p. 414.
18. *Ibid.*, p. 415.
19. *WV*, I (1851), 189 ff.
20. *A*, XI (1857), 381 ff.; XII (1857), 114 ff.; XIII (1858), 256 ff.
21. *WV*, I (1851), 193 ff.
22. *Ibid.*, and II (1852), 150 ff.
23. *A*, V (1853), 431.
24. *WV*, II (1852), 156.
25. *GA*, p. 839.
26. See, besides *Cellular Pathology*, the article "The Connective Tissue Problem," *A*, XVI (1859), 1 ff. Blainville had exhibited a similar predilection for what he still called the "cellular tissue."
27. Remak in *Archiv fuer Anatomie, Physiologie, und wissenschaftliche Medicin*, 1852, pp. 63 ff.
28. *A*, XI (1857), 91.
29. *WV*, II (1852), 159.
30. *Ibid.*, p. 315.
31. *A*, V (1853), 420 ff.
32. *WV*, IV (1854), 354.
33. "Tuberculosis and Its Relations with Inflammation, Scrophulosis and Typhoid," *WV*, I (1851), 81 ff.
34. For an excellent survey of tuberculosis theories of the period, see Predoehl, *Die Geschichte der Tuberkulose*.
35. *A*, I (1847), 176.
36. Virchow therefore regarded bovine tuberculosis as being closer to sarcoma than to tuberculosis (*WV*, VII [1857], 143).
37. See Virchow's and Haeckel's extensive discussion of this "relationship" in *Wiener medizinische Wochenschrift* for 1856 (Jan., Nos. 1 and 2, pp. 1 and 17; Feb., No. 8, p. 113), which has been reprinted in *OM*, I, 418 ff. and 429 ff.
38. "On the History of the Doctrine of Tuberculosis," *WV*, II (1852), 70 ff. Flick's *Development of Our Knowledge of Tuberculosis* contains lengthy translated quotations from the early papers of Virchow on tuberculosis.
39. "Differences between Phthisis and Tuberculosis," *WV*, III (1853), 98 ff.
40. Niemeyer, *Clinical Lectures on Pulmonary Consumption*, p. 11.
41. In *WV*, II (1852), 24 ff.
42. *A*, III (1851), 427 ff.
43. See also Virchow's detailed discussion of cavernous tumors in *A*, VI (1854), 524 ff.
44. Another of Virchow's important papers on muscle inflammation is his "On the Inflammation and Rupture of the Musculus Rectus Abdominis," *WV*, VII (1857), 213 ff.
45. Cartilage, synovia, and the walls of vessels are mentioned by Bichat (*Anatomie générale, appliquée à la physiologie et à la médecine*, I, xciv) as being unknown in their inflammatory reactions.
46. *A*, IV (1852), 324.
47. *Ibid.*, p. 377.
48. *Ibid.*, p. 396.
49. *H*, I, 3.
50. *A*, VIII (1855), 23. Later Virchow sometimes used the better-known version, *Omnis cellula e cellula*.
51. *Ibid.*, p. 21.
52. *Ibid.*, p. 22.

53. *Ibid.*, p. 25. Virchow found this notion of the organism as a community of smaller units already in Goethe (*Vier Reden ueber Leben und Kranksein,* p. 59).
54. John Goodsir and H. D. S. Goodsir, *Anatomical and Pathological Observations,* p. 2.
55. Remak in Archiv fuer *Anatomie, Physiologie, und wissenschaftliche Medicin,* 1852, pp. 49 and 57. E. Bouchut (*Histoire de la Médecine,* p. 367) and others claim that Remak said in this article, *Omnis cellula in cellula.* I have been unable to detect this sentence in this or other articles of Remak, whose position anyhow is sufficiently clear without it.
56. E.g., *A,* XIV (1858), 39; *H,* I, 329.
57. *A,* V (1853), 323.
58. *Ibid.*, pp. 362 ff.
59. *A,* XV (1858), 217–336.
60. *A,* VIII (1855), 113.
61. *WV,* VII (1857), 135 ff.
62. *GA,* pp. 385 and 890. See also *A,* VI (1854), 138.

SYNTHESIS

1. *H,* I, 21.
2. *Ibid.*, p. 339.
3. *Ibid.*, p. 312.
4. *Ibid.*, p. 329.
5. By F. Chance (London, 1860).
6. *CP,* p. 39.
7. *Ibid.*, p. 370.
8. *Ibid.*, p. 262.
9. *Ibid.*, p. 331.
10. *Ibid.*, p. 333. See also *GA,* pp. 14 and 15; *A,* VII (1854), 18.
11. Bouchut, *Histoire de la médecine et des doctrines médicales,* II, 211, 224, 226, 381.
12. *CP,* p. 399.
13. The Huxley lecture in *BKW,* XXXV (1898), 928.
14. *CP,* p. 485.

TUMORS

1. *KG,* I, 3.
2. See p. 76 of this book and Wolff, *Die Lehre von der Krebskrankheit von den aeltesten Zeiten bis zur Gegenwart* (a most comprehensive history of cancer theories), I, 309.
3. Sigerist has always emphasized the primary role of localism in the rise of modern surgery. See, e.g., his *Great Doctors,* p. 375.
4. Operations performed by Virchow are mentioned, for example, in *KG,* I, 332 and 425; II, 226; III, 327. Earlier operations are mentioned in *Briefe,* p. 130.
5. *A,* CXI (1888), 19–20.
6. *KG,* I, 62.
7. John Simon, W. Mueller, and Virchow's pupils Klebs, Von Hansemann, C. L. Schleich, etc. See Wolff, *op. cit.,* pp. 431 ff.
8. *KG,* I, 86.
9. *Ibid.*, p. 126. See also p. 91 of this book.
10. *A,* CLXII (1900), 178.
11. *KG,* I, 81 ff.

12. *Ibid.*, pp. 113–14.
13. *Ibid.*, p. 92.
14. *Ibid.*, p. 97.
15. Wolff, *op. cit.*, p. 195.
16. *KG*, II, 175.
17. *Ibid.*, p. 206.
18. *Ibid.*, p. 257.
19. *Ibid.*, p. 472.
20. *Ibid.*, p. 491.
21. A, CXI (1888), 5.
22. *Ibid.*, p. 18. See also *BKW*, XXX (1893), 5.

23. A, XCVII (1884), 430; CLXII (1900), 544.
24. A, VIII (1855), 371.
25. A, XCVII (1884), 410 ff.
26. Wolff, *op. cit.*, pp. 237 ff.
27. A, CLXII (1900), 544.
28. A, XCVII (1884), 427.
29. A, LXXIX (1880), 195.
30. A, CXI (1888), 18.
31. *Ibid.*, p. 11; Wolff, *op. cit.*, p. 205.
32. A, CXI (1888), 23.

PARASITES AND BACTERIA

1. For a short history of anti-contagionism, see my F. H. Garrison lecture in *Bull. Hist. Med.*, XXII (1948), 562–93.
2. *Ibid.*
3. See *BM*, p. 153; my Garrison lecture cited above, p. 592; and the chapter of this book entitled "Epidemiology and Public Health."
4. *OM*, I, 24.
5. See Orth in *Deutsche medizinische Wochenschrift*, XXXVI (1910), 1938 ff.; Virchow in *BKW*, XXI (1884), 477 ff., and XXII (1885), 605 ff.
6. A, II (1849), 263.
7. *OM*, I, 449 and 495.
8. A, LXXIX (1880), 206.
9. *WV*, V (1855), 102 ff.
10. A, IX (1856), 557 ff.
11. *WV*, VI (1856), 84 ff.
12. A, XI (1857), 79 ff., and XVIII (1860), 330 ff.
13. Gould, *Trichinosis*, pp. 57 ff.
14. A, XXXII (1865), 332 ff.; XXXV (1866), 201; XXXVII (1866), 255 ff., XCV (1884), 534 ff. The first of these articles also establishes his priority claims against Leuckart beyond any doubt. The last states

with a laudable objectivity that imported American pigs, though infected, had not produced any outbreaks of trichinosis.
15. *BKW*, XXXV (1898), 930.
16. A, LXV (1875), 196.
17. *OM*, II, 60.
18. *Ibid.*, p. 176.
19. *Ibid.*, p. 190. This is, of course, only a reaffirmation of Virchow's earlier conviction concerning the limitations of morphology (*ibid.*, p. 52). Also see A, VI (1854), 14 ff.
20. See Temkin in *Bull. Hist. Med.*, XXIV (1950), 316.
21. Virchow in A, LXXIX (1880), 10. This was really the central point of the discussion. See also Virchow, *100 Jahre allgemeiner Pathologie*, p. 22.
22. A, LXXIX (1880), 13.
23. Virchow stressed this point already in his discussions with Wunderlich. See A, XVIII (1860), 126 ff.
24. Virchow expressed this idea as early as 1854. See A, VI (1854), 24.
25. A, LXXIX (1880), 195.
26. *Ibid.*, p. 217.

27. *Ibid.*, p. 223.
28. "The Present State of Cellular Pathology," *A*, CXXVI (1891), 1. In 1900 ("The New Century," *A*, CLIX [1900], 1 ff.) he again emphasized that immunity in the last instance must reside in solid tissues, not the temporary tissue blood.
29. *OM*, I, 103–5.
30. *BKW*, XXXI (1894), 1013. Even his Third Reich biographers H. Zeiss and R. Bieling (*Behring, Gestalt und Werk*, pp. 119 and 143) feel somewhat uneasy concerning Behring's demagogic methods.
31. *BKW*, XXXI (1894), 1196.
32. *DN*, p. 195.
33. *A*, LXXIX (1880), 218, and CI (1885), 7.
34. *DN*, p. 224.
35. *A*, CLXII (1900), 174.
36. Orth, *op. cit.*, p. 1939.
37. Heymann, *Robert Koch*, p. 262. This valuable biography of Koch has unfortunately remained a torso due to the persecution of its author, a noted bacteriologist, and his eventual assassination in the Third Reich.
38. *BKW*, XXVIII (1891), 49.
39. *A*, XXXIV (1865), 11.

40. *A*, LXXXIX (1882), 183.
41. *A*, LXXXII (1880), 550.
42. *A*, CI (1885), 9.
43. *BKW*, XXVIII (1891), 83, and XXXVIII (1901), 819.
44. *OM*, I, 138; *A*, I (1847), 253. Restatements of this point of view are in *H*, *I*, 292 ff., and *OM*, I, 496 ff.
45. *BKW*, XXXI (1894), 1196.
46. Translated in *Medical Classics* (ed. E. C. Kelly), V, 712 ff.
47. Kleine in *Archiv fuer Gynaekologie*, CXLII (1930), 324.
48. *OM*, II, 88 and 126.
49. *OM*, II, 88.
50. *H*, I, 300. Another *Handbook* passage overlooked by Kleine is an objective mention of Semmelweis' theory on p. 284. Also in 1848 Virchow admitted the contagiosity of puerperal fever (*OM*, I, 296).
51. *A*, CXIII (1888), 362 and 369.
52. *A*, CL (1897), 10.
53. *BKW*, XXXV (1898), 932. For similar eulogies of Pasteur, see, for example, *A*, CL (1897), 13, and CLXII (1900), 176.
54. In Ebstein, *Deutsche Aerztereden aus dem 19. Jahrhundert*, pp. 173 ff.
55. *A*, CLXIII (1901), 183.
56. *Ibid.*, p. 174.

ANTICLIMAX

1. *A*, XVIII (1860), 1.
2. *A*, XIII (1858), 481.
3. *A*, XV (1858), 393; XVI (1859), 372; XVIII (1860), 126.
4. *A*, XLIV (1868), 145 ff.
5. Long, *A History of Pathology*, pp. 205 ff., 215 ff., 260 ff.
6. In *A*, CCXXXV (1921), 186 ff.
7. *A*, CXLIX (1897), 403.
8. *A*, CLIX (1900), 14.

9. Heischkel-Artelt, "Rudolf Virchow als Publizist," *Medizinische Rundschau*, 1947.
10. *A*, XXIII (1862), 415; *GA*, pp. 702 and 826.
11. *BKW*, XII (1875), 1; XXI (1884), 1; XXIII (1886), 489; XXV (1888), 1.
12. *Ibid.*, XXVI (1889), 8; XXXII (1895), 1102.

13. *Ibid.,* XXIV (1887), 12.
14. *A,* CLIX (1900), 5.
15. Jores, "Die Entwicklung der Lehre von der Arteriosklerose seit Virchow," *A,* CCXXXV (1921), 262 ff.
16. Aschoff, "Virchows Lehre von den Degenerationen und ihre Weiterentwicklung," *A,* CCXXXV (1921), 152 ff.

17. Lubarsch, "Virchow's Doctrine of Inflammation and Its Development," *A,* CCXXXV (1921), 186 ff.
18. Long, *op. cit.,* p. 200.
19. Ernst, "Virchows Cellularpathologie einst und jetzt," *A,* CCXXXV (1921), 134.

EPIDEMIOLOGY AND PUBLIC HEALTH

1. See Ackerknecht in *Bull. Hist. Med.,* XXII (1948), 119.
2. *OM,* II, 171.
3. *Ibid.,* I, 284.
4. *Ibid.,* p. 288.
5. *Ibid.,* p. 294.
6. *Ibid.,* p. 295.
7. *Ibid.,* pp. 304, 311.
8. On the three nineteenth-century schools of epidemiology, see Ackerknecht in *Bull. Hist. Med.,* XXII (1948), 592.
9. *OM,* I, 324.
10. *Ibid.,* pp. 25, 121.
11. *Ibid.,* p. 147.
12. *Ibid.,* pp. 135, 149.
13. *GA,* p. 506; *WV,* III (1853), 104; *KG,* II, 725; *H,* I, 344; *OM,* I, 202.
14. *OM,* I, 22.
15. *Ibid.,* pp. 121–22.
16. *Ibid.,* p. 126.
17. For the same idea developed independently by Sigerist in the 1920's, see *Kyklos,* I (1928), 60.
18. *GA,* p. 55.
19. *Ibid.* This point is repeated concerning tuberculosis in 1860 (*OM,* II, 5).
20. *OM,* I, 121–22. On the eradication of tuberculosis, see also *ibid.,* pp. 127–28.
21. Temkin in *Kyklos,* II (1929), 94–95.

22. *OM,* I, 21.
23. Cabanis, *Coup d'oeil sur les révolutions et sur la réforme de la médecine,* p. 421. I have studied this development in more detail in *Bull. Hist. Med.,* XXII (1948), 117 ff. and 562 ff.
24. *OM,* I, 461, 323.
25. *GA,* p. 895.
26. *Ibid.,* p. 927.
27. *OM,* I, 416.
28. In *A,* II (1849), 16, he remarked, "Statistics are only a method, not a science." Also see *OM,* II, 57.
29. Virchow in *Die medizinische Reform,* p. 182; *OM,* I, 285 (originally published in 1848). *OM,* II, 6, indicates that Virchow's attitude was unchanged by the 1860's.
30. *OM,* I, 535 ff.
31. *Ibid.,* pp. 521 ff.
32. *OM,* II, 271 ff.
33. *BKW,* XXI (1884), 477 ff., and XXII (1885), 605 ff.
34. *BKW,* XXIX (1892), 958.
35. *OM,* I, 447 and 494–95.
36. *Ibid.,* pp. 461–62.
37. *Ibid.,* pp. 445 and 453.
38. *Ibid.,* II, 258 and 462.
39. *Ibid.,* I, 447.
40. *Ibid.,* pp. 493 and 495.
41. *Ibid.,* p. 467.
42. *Ibid.,* II, 454–56.

43. *BKW*, XXX (1893), 153, and XXXII (1895), 1104.
44. *OM*, I, 565, and II, 334.
45. *Ibid.*, II, 184.
46. *Ibid.*, p. 15.
47. Hueppe in *BKW*, XXX (1893), 1045.
48. *OM*, I, 16.
49. *Ibid.*, II, 27.
50. *Ibid.*, I, 424.
51. *Ibid.*, pp. 119 and 21.
52. *Ibid.*, p. 19.
53. *Ibid.*, p. 21.
54. *Ibid.*
55. *OM*, II, 5.
56. *Ibid.*, I, 18, 28, 29.
57. *Ibid.*, p. 21.
58. *Ibid.*, II, 231.
59. *Ibid.*, I, 99; *DN*, p. 62.
60. *OM*, I, 563, and II, 253, 293.
61. *Ibid.*, I, 229.
62. *Ibid.*, pp. 32, 121, and II, 206, 229, 461.
63. *OM*, II, 214 and 216.
64. *Ibid.*, pp. 232 and 436.
65. *Ibid.*, pp. 205 and 208.
66. *Ibid.*, p. 253.
67. *Ibid.*, p. 340.
68. *Ibid.*, p. 369.
69. *BKW*, XXX (1893), 153.
70. *OM*, I, 29.
71. *Ibid.*, II, 106.
72. *Ibid.*, pp. 17, 20, 72, 107, 147, 172.
73. *Ibid.*, p. 6. For sanitaria, see also *A*, LXXXIX (1882), 182.
74. *OM*, II, 143 ff.
75. See *BM*, p. 109.
76. *OM*, II, 18.
77. *Ibid.*, p. 51.
78. *Ibid.*, p. 114.
79. See Virchow in *Vierteljahresschrift fuer gerichtliche und oeffentliche Medizin*, 3 ser., XV (1898), 347.
80. *OM*, II, 473 ff.
81. See Virchow in *Vierteljahresschrift fuer gerichtliche und oeffentliche Medizin*, 2 ser., XL (1884), 357, and 3 ser., II (1891), 109.
82. See my "History of Legal Medicine," *Ciba Symposia*, XI (1951), 1286–1316.
83. *OM*, II, 533 ff.
84. *Ibid.*, I, 12.
85. *Ibid.*, II, 548.

MEDICAL REFORM

1. *OM*, II, 3 and 4.
2. For Jules Guerin in 1848, see Galdston's "Social Medicine and the Epidemic Constitution," *Bull. Hist. Med.*, XXV (1951), 8 ff.
3. *BM*, p. 90.
4. *Ibid.*, p. 95.
5. For Virchow against the guild spirit, see *OM*, I, 15.
6. *Ibid.*, p. 4.
7. Virchow in *Die medizinische Reform*, p. 72.
8. *Ibid.*, p. 118.
9. *BM*, p. 100.
10. *Die medizinische Reform*, p. 14; *OM*, I, II.
11. Posner in *BKW*, XXX (1893), 1231. See also *Die medizinische Reform*, p. 63.
12. *BM*, p. 121.
13. *Ibid.*, p. 120.
14. *Die medizinische Reform*, pp. 57 and 62.
15. *BM*, p. 125.
16. *OM*, I, 9.
17. *Ibid.*, pp. 11, 34.
18. *Ibid.*, p. 13.
19. *BM*, p. 102.
20. *Ibid.*, p. 103; *OM*, I, 70.

21. *OM*, I, 70.
22. *BM*, pp. 127 ff.; *OM*, I, 60 ff. Although Virchow here declares himself for the voluntary association, his plan actually makes it obligatory.
23. *BM*, pp. 122 ff.
24. *Ibid.*, p. 124.
25. *OM*, I, 50.
26. *Ibid.*, p. 53.
27. *Ibid.*, p. 149.
28. Posner, *Rudolf Virchow*, p. 59.
29. *BM*, pp. 130 ff.
30. *Die medizinische Reform*, p. 71.
31. *Ibid.*, p. 79.

32. *OM*, I, 72.
33. *Die medizinische Reform*, p. 86.
34. *Ibid.*, pp. 77 and 54. See also pp. 136 and 149 of this book.
35. *BM*, pp. 138 ff.
36. Posner in *BKW*, XXX (1893), 1271.
37. *OM*, I, 37.
38. *Ibid.*, p. 40.
39. *Ibid.*, p. 45.
40. *Ibid.*, p. 46.
41. *Ibid.*, II, 516.
42. *Ibid.*, p. 219.
43. *Ibid.*, I, 83 and 114.
44. *BKW*, XXX (1893), 1127.

MEDICAL HISTORY

1. *A*, II (1849), 8.
2. *GA*, p. 30 (written in 1849).
3. *WV*, II (1852), 72.
4. *OM*, I, 434 (written in 1868).
5. *A*, L (1870), 7, 10.
6. *A*, LII (1871), 3. See also *OM*, I, 466.
7. *A*, LXX (1877), 3.
8. On this and Virchow's friendly relations with Hirsch in general, see Virchow's necrology of Hirsch in *BKW*, XXXI (1894), 129 ff.
9. See *Die Vorlesungen Rudolf Virchows ueber allgemeine pathologische Anatomie aus dem Wintersomester 1855/56 in Wuerzburg.*
10. Bartlett, "A Sketch of Virchow's Life and Time," *Lectures on the History of Medicine; a Series of Lectures at the Mayo Foundation*, p. 470.
11. Walsh, *Makers of Modern Medicine*, p. v.
12. *H*, I, xi; *CP*, p. vii.
13. *A*, V (1853), 409 ff.
14. *Ibid.*, pp. 281 ff.

15. *A*, XIII (1858), 344 ff.
16. *A*, XV (1858), 217 ff.
17. *A*, XXXIV (1865), 11 ff.
18. *H*, II, Part I, 205 ff.
19. *H*, I, 263 ff.
20. *A*, XXXII (1865), 139 and 547.
21. *A*, XXVIII (1863), 426.
22. *OM*, I, 434 ff.
23. *BKW*, XXIX (1892), 624. For a note on the age of syphilis in East Asia, see *A*, LIII (1871), 137.
24. *A*, XLVII (1869), 298.
25. *BKW*, XXXV (1898), 897.
26. *A*, XVIII (1860), 138 ff., 43 ff., and XX (1861), 166 ff., 459 ff.
27. *A*, XXII (1861), 190, and XXIII (1862), 194.
28. *OM*, II, 14; *A*, LXXXIX (1882), 181.
29. *OM*, II, 23 ff.
30. *DN*, p. 19.
31. Virchow, "Morgagni and the Anatomic Concept" (trans. R. E. Schluter and J. Auer), *Bull. Hist. Med.*, VII (1939), 180; *A*, LXXXIX (1882), 181.

32. *A*, XXXIV (1865), 5; *DN*, pp. 43 ff.

33. They are all quoted verbatim in *BM*, pp. 158 ff., where I have discussed in more detail these aspects of Virchow's historical work.

34. See, for example, *OM*, I, 24.

35. See, for example, *A*, IX (1856), 4; and Virchow, *Johannes Mueller*, p. 25.

36. *DN*, pp. 47–48.

37. Charcot, *Leçons cliniques sur les maladies des vieillards*, p. xxxii.

38. *DN*, p. 79.

39. Virchow, *Johannes Mueller*, p. 42.

40. *DN*, pp. 42, 43, 46, and 47.

41. Some of the most nationalistic statements of the internationalist Marx fell into this same period (see Collinet's *La Tragédie du Marxisme*, pp. 204 ff.).

42. *A*, LI (1870), 2.

43. *DN*, p. 101.

44. *Ibid.*, p. 138 (written in 1873).

45. *A*, LIII (1871), 18, 21, and 22.

46. *OM*, II, 170 (written in 1874).

47. *DN*, p. 204 (written in 1879).

48. *A*, LXX (1877), 8.

49. *A*, XCI (1883), 4.

50. *A*, I (1847), 4.

51. *A*, XXXIII (1865), 4, and *H*, I, x. See also Sigerist, *Great Doctors*, p. 346.

52. *A*, XIV (1858), 1; the Croonian lecture in *BKW*, XXX (1893), 321; and the Huxley lecture in *BKW*, XXXV (1898), 897.

53. Virchow in *Bull. Hist. Med.*, VII (1939), 975 ff. This study of Morgagni is a translation of Virchow's address presented at the Eleventh International Medical Congress at Rome in 1894.

54. *CP*, p. 2, and p. 980 of the Morgagni study cited above. What Virchow called here the anatomical concept, Charcot before him had called "la pensée anatomique."

55. For additional Schoenlein material, see *A*, XXXIII (1865), 170 ff.

56. See Temkin in *Bull. Hist. Med.*, XXIV (1950), 232 ff.

57. *A*, II (1849), 15.

58. E.g., *A*, XXXIV (1865), 11; *A*, CLIX (1900), 18; *KG*, II, 609; and especially *Vier Reden ueber Leben und Kranksein*, pp. 35 ff. and 105 ff.

59. E.g., "Epithelium" in *A*, XI (1857), 465, and "Rachitis" in *A*, CII (1885), 593.

60. *BKW*, XXXVII (1900), 1 ff., and *A*, XCI (1883), 1 ff.

61. Ackerknecht in *Bull. Hist. Med.*, XXIV (1950), 50.

62. Temkin in *Bull. Hist. Med.*, XXIV (1950), 237.

63. Virchow, *Goethe als Naturforscher und in besonderer Beziehung auf Schiller*, pp. vi and 40.

REVOLUTIONARY BEGINNINGS

1. *Briefe*, p. 38.

2. *Ibid.*, pp. 49 and 85.

3. *Ibid.*, pp. 65 and 70.

4. *Ibid.*, p. 94.

5. *Ibid.*, pp. 95 and 117.

6. *Ibid.*, p. 122.

7. For social tendencies in the 1848 movement, see Valentin, *Geschichte der deutschen Revolution 1848–49*, I, 279, and

II, 55, 96, 317; *K-H*, I, 171 ff.
8. *Briefe*, p. 140.
9. For the 1848 movement in Eastern Pomerania, see Petersdorff, *Hans von Kleist-Retzow*, pp. 102 ff.
10. *Briefe*, pp. 144 and 151.
11. *Ibid.*, p. 151. See also the report on Upper Silesia.
12. *Briefe*, pp. 149 and 151; *OM*, I, 4 and 31.
13. *Briefe*, p. 149.
14. *Ibid.*, p. 143.
15. *Ibid.*, p. 154.
16. *Ibid.*, p. 184.
17. *OM*, I, 50.
18. *Briefe*, pp. 144, 156, and 162; *OM*, I, 11, 15, and 43.
19. *OM*, I, 33.
20. *Ibid.*, p. 25.
21. *Ibid.*, p. 58.
22. *Briefe*, p. 147.
23. *OM*, I, 27.
24. *Briefe*, pp. 138 and 200.
25. *Ibid.*, p. 179.
26. *OM*, I, 125.
27. *Briefe*, p. 160.
28. *Ibid.*, pp. 159 and 163.
29. *OM*, I, 18.
30. *Ibid.*, pp. 305 and 39.
31. *Ibid.*, pp. 14, 18, and 122.
32. *Briefe*, p. 158; *OM*, I, 33.
33. Fenz, *Julius Froebel, seine politische Entwicklung bis 1849*, pp. 89 ff.
34. Struve, *Weltgeschichte*, IX, 870, 887, 14, 886.
35. *OM*, I, 54.
36. Ruge, *Aus frueherer Zeit*, IV, 72.

THE CONSTITUTIONAL CONFLICT

1. Eyck, *Bismarck*, II, 335.
2. *OM*, I, 76.
3. *K-H*, I, 23.
4. Loewenthal, *Der preussische Verfassungsstreit, 1862–66*, p. 62.
5. Reprinted in Federici's *Der deutsche Liberalismus*, p. 290. See also the anonymous publication, *Vorwaerts, mein Preussenvolk*.
6. Fenz, *Julius Froebel, seine politische Entwicklung bis 1849*, p. 147.
7. Loewenthal, *op. cit.*, p. 101; and Eyck, *op. cit.*, I, 410.
8. *K-H*, I, 246.
9. Eyck, *op. cit.*, I, 373.
10. *K-H*, I, 254.
11. *Ibid.*, p. 256.
12. Eyck, *op. cit.*, I, 461.
13. Virchow, *Stenographischer Bericht des preussischen Abgeordneten Hauses*, pp. 255–65.
14. *K-H*, I, 265.
15. *Ibid.*
16. Eyck, *op. cit.*, I, 596.
17. *Ibid.*, II, 59.
18. Loewenthal, *op. cit.*, pp. 246 ff.
19. *K-H*, I, 278.
20. Loewenthal, *op. cit.*, p. 246.
21. In Federici, *op. cit.*, p. 280.
22. *K-H*, I, 290.
23. Eyck, *op. cit.*, II, 302.
24. In Petersdorff, *Hans von Kleist-Retzow*, p. 347.
25. Wiermann, *Der deutsche Reichstag*, I, 238.
26. Kautsky in *Der Monat*, II (1950), 29 ff.

IN THE NEW REICH

1. *K-H*, I, 301 and 321.
2. Eyck, *Bismarck*, II, 376.
3. *DN*, p. 96.
4. *K-H*, I, 394.
5. *A*, LI (1870), 5, and LII (1871), 3.
6. *A*, LIII (1871), 2.
7. *DN*, p. 101.
8. *A*, CXX (1890), 1 ff. and 188 ff.
9. Virchow, "Einige internationale Gedanken," *Die Nation*, IX (1891–92), 760 ff.
10. Virchow, *Krieg und Frieden*, pp. 11–12.
11. Virchow in *Die Nation*, V (1887–88), 628.
12. *A*, CLXVII (1902), 1 ff.
13. *K-H*, II, 23.
14. Petersdorff, *Hans von Kleist-Retzow*, p. 487.
15. *DN*, pp. 116 ff.
16. Ackerknecht in *Bull. Hist.* *Med.*, Supp., III (1944), 16–31.
17. *K-H*, II, 382.
18. *Ibid.*, I, 377.
19. *Ibid.*, II, 91, 94, and 112.
20. Virchow, *Ueber die Beschraenkung der Redefreiheit im deutschen Reichstag*, p. 16.
21. *Ibid.*, pp. 6 and 21.
22. Wiermann, *Der deutsche Reichstag*, I, 200; Virchow, *Die Gruendung der Berliner Universitaet und der Uebergang aus dem Philosophischen in das naturwissenschaftliche Zeitalter*, p. 30.
23. Eyck, *op. cit.*, III, 361.
24. *K-H*, I, 336.
25. Laski, "Warum schrieb Mommsen nicht weiter?" *Der Monat*, II (1950), 62 ff.
26. *KG*, I, v.
27. *A*, CLXVII (1902), 1 ff.

DYNAMICS OF SKULL GROWTH

1. *GA*, pp. 891 ff.
2. *Ibid.*, p. 925.
3. *Ibid.*, pp. 969 ff.
4. Virchow, *Untersuchungen ueber die Entwicklung des Schaedelgrundes im gesunden und krankhaften Zustande und ueber den Einfluss derselben auf Schaedelform, Gesichtsbildung und Gehirnbau*, p. 115.
5. *Ibid.*, p. 116.
6. *A*, XIII (1858), 323 ff.
7. *Ibid.*, p. 326.

THE ORIGIN OF MAN

1. *A*, LXX (1877), 5.
2. Virchow, *Vier Reden ueber Leben und Kranksein*, p. 31.
3. *A*, IX (1856), 25.
4. *BKW*, XXX (1893), 2.
5. *DN*, p. 280.
6. Virchow's "Rassenbildung und Erblichkeit," trans. E. W. Count in *This Is Race*, p. 188; original in *Festschrift fuer Adolf Bastian* (Berlin, 1896), p. 21.
7. Virchow, *Menschen- und Affenschaedel*, p. 38.

8. *DN*, p. 290.
9. Walsh, *Makers of Modern Medicine*, p. 410.
10. *DN*, p. 207 (written in 1877).
11. *Ibid.*, p. 262 (written in 1886).
12. *Korrbl*, 1894, p. 86.
13. *Ibid.*, pp. 183 ff.
14. Virchow, *Menschen- und Affenschaedel*, p. 34.
15. *DN*, p. 298. Italics mine.
16. *BG*, 1872, pp. 157 ff., and *Korrbl*, 1873, p. 49.
17. *Korrbl*, 1892, p. 90; for polemic against G. Schwalbe, see *ibid.*, 1901, p. 83.
18. *BG*, 1882, p. 277, and 1886, p. 344.
19. *Korrbl*, 1896, pp. 81 ff.; *BG*, 1895, pp. 81 ff., 336 ff., 435 ff., 648 ff., 723 ff., and 787 ff.
20. *BG*, 1895, p. 749.
21. *DN*, p. 172.
22. For Virchow's reappraisal of of this memoir, see *ZE*, XII (1880), 1 ff.
23. Virchow, "Anthropology in the Last Twenty Years," *Annual Report of the Smithsonian Institution*, 1889, p. 565 (trans. from *Korrbl*, 1889, pp. 89 ff.).
24. *Korrbl*, 1892, pp. 89 ff.
25. *A*, LXXII (1878), 129, and LXXIX (1880), 176; *BKW*, XXI (1884), 745; *BG*, 1899, p. 647.
26. *A*, CIII (1886), 206.
27. *Ibid.*, p. 413.
28. *Ibid.*, p. 422.
29. See, for example, *DN*, p. 25, or Count's translation of "Rassenbildung," *op. cit.*, p. 192.
30. *BKW*, XXX (1893), 1.
31. Yes in *A*, CIII (1886), 11; no in *BG*, 1872, p. 163.
32. Virchow's "Rassenbildung," in *Festschrift*, p. 43.
33. *Korrbl*, 1899, p. 81.
34. Virchow's "Rassenbildung," in *Festschrift*, p. 21; Count's translation, p. 187.
35. *A*, CL (1897), 14.
36. Virchow's "Rassenbildung," in *Festschrift*, p. 30.
37. *DN*, p. 286.
38. *BKW*, XXXV (1898), 929.
39. *A*, CIII (1886), 2.
40. *Korrbl*, 1889, p. 89.

RACES, ESPECIALLY IN GERMANY

1. *Briefe*, p. 47.
2. Walsh, *Makers of Modern Medicine*, p. 361.
3. *Korrbl*, 1880, p. 3.
4. Muehlmann, *Geschichte der Anthropologie*, p. 22.
5. See Virchow's extensive paper, "Die altnordischen Schaedel in Kopenhagen," *Archiv fuer Anthropologie*, IV (1870), 55 ff.
6. *ZE*, IV (1872), 300 ff.
7. *Archiv fuer Anthropologie*, XVI (1886), 275–476.
8. E.g., in *BG*, 1872, 74 ff. Translation of Virchow and answer of De Quatrefages in *La Revue Scientifique*, 2d ser., XIV (1872), 313–18 and 318–20.
9. In *Die Nation*, IX (1891–92), 258.
10. *BG*, 1872, 74 ff.
11. *BG*, 1874, pp. 185 ff.
12. *Ibid.*, 1875, pp. 32 ff.
13. *Ibid.*, p. 229.
14. *BG*, 1873, p. 165, and 1891, p. 767.
15. Virchow, *Die Urbevoelkerung Europas*, p. 35.
16. *Korrbl*, 1896, p. 78.
17. *ZE*, IV (1872), 282; *Korrbl*, 1873, p. 44.
18. *Korrbl*, 1898, p. 75.

19. *Ibid.*, 1893, p. 117.
20. *Ibid.*, 1874, p. 11.
21. Virchow, "Beitraege zur physichen Anthropologie der Deutschen mit besonderer Beruecksichtigung der Friesen," *Abhandlungen der koeniglichen Akademie der Wissenschaften aus dem Jahre 1876*, pp. 361 and 370. See also *BG*, 1881, p. 71.
22. Published with maps in *Archiv fuer Anthropologie*, XVI (1886), 275–476; Academy paper of 1885.
23. *Archiv fuer Anthropologie*, XVI (1886), 293.
24. *Korrbl*, 1892, p. 101; *BG*, 1881, p. 69.
25. Count (trans.), Virchow's "Rassenbildung und Erblichkeit" in *This Is Race*, pp. 188 and 191.
26. Tylor in Haddon's *History of Anthropology*, p. 28.
27. For a survey of the same argument on the basis of recent material, see Lowie, *The German People*, pp. 13–20.
28. *Korrbl*, 1873, p. 52.
29. Virchow, "Anthropology in the Last Twenty Years," *Annual Report of the Smithsonian Institution*, 1889, p. 557.
30. *BG*, 1881, p. 68.
31. *Archiv fuer Anthropologie*, VI (1873), 85.
32. *BG*, 1884, p. 168.
33. Count's translation of "Rassenbildung," p. 185.
34. *BG*, 1881, p. 71.
35. *DN*, pp. 139 and 172.
36. Virchow, in *Annual Report of the Smithsonian Institution*, 1889, p. 563.
37. *Ibid.*, p. 562.
38. Count's translation of "Rassenbildung," p. 184.
39. *ZE*, IV (1872), 317.
40. *OM*, II, 488.
41. *Ibid.*, I, 20.
42. *DN*, pp. 221 ff.; see also Count's translation of "Rassenbildung," p. 182.
43. *BG*, 1887, p. 66.
44. *GA*, p. 20.
45. *Korrbl*, 1896, pp. 157 ff.
46. For a short history and most recent survey of paleopathology, see Sigerist's *A History of Medicine*, I, 38 ff. and 532 ff.
47. *BG*, 1870, p. 365; *Korrbl*, 1873, p. 49; *BG*, 1895, p. 706.
48. Virchow, "Beitraege zur Geschichte der Lues," *Dermatologische Zeitschrift*, III (1896), 1–9.
49. *Ibid.*
50. *BG*, 1895, 365 ff. and 454 ff.; *Mittheilungen und Verhandlungen der internationalen wissenschaftlichen Lepra Konferenz*, II, 79 ff.; *BG*, 1897, pp. 474 ff., 1898, pp. 489 ff., and 1899, pp. 216 ff.
51. *GA*, p. 902.
52. E.g., in *Archiv fuer Anthropologie*, IV (1870), 55 ff.
53. *A*, CLIX (1900), 288 ff.
54. *Korrbl*, 1878, p. 148.
55. *Ibid.*, 1892, p. 121. See also the paper of L. I. Angel on Virchow and anthropometry given on March 20, 1951, at the meeting of the American Association of Physical Anthropologists at Ann Arbor, Michigan.

GERMANIC AND SLAVONIC ANTIQUITIES

1. *BG*, 1894, p. 497.
2. Already in 1865 Virchow published a pamphlet, *Burial Mounds and Pile Dwellings*, as the first number of Virchow-Holtzendorff's popular lectures. For a more technical analysis of the same material, see *ZE*, I (1869), 401 ff., and *Korrbl*, 1877, pp. 77 ff.
3. *ZE*, I (1869), 411.
4. *BG*, 1874, pp. 114 ff., and 1876, pp. 165 ff.
5. *Korrbl*, 1901, p. 12.
6. *BG*, 1879, p. 257, 1871, p. 107, 1872, p. 226; *ZE*, XII (1880), 222 ff., etc.
7. *BG*, 1875, p. 100.
8. In *BG*, 1876, p. 105.
9. *ZE*, XII (1880), 228.
10. *BG*, 1872, p. 38; *Korrbl*, 1873, p. 31.
11. *BG*, 1873, p. 198.
12. *Ibid.*, 1884, p. 208.
13. *Ibid.*, 1871, pp. 31 ff., and 1873, pp. 166 ff.
14. *ZE*, II (1870), 73; *BG*, 1874, p. 114.
15. *BG*, 1883, p. 317; see also his extensive Academy paper (1883). Virchow returned to the study of face urns after his house studies. See, for example, *BG*, 1892, p. 561.
16. *BG*, 1878, pp. 206 ff.
17. *Korrbl*, 1897, p. 67.
18. *BG*, 1888, pp. 508 ff.
19. *Ibid.*, 1887, pp. 568 ff., 1888, pp. 297 ff., and 1899, pp. 553 ff.
20. *Ibid.*, 1893, p. 122.
21. *Ibid.*, 1876, pp. 40 ff.
22. *Ibid.*, 1885, p. 263.

ARCHEOLOGY IN THE NEAR EAST

1. Virchow, "Anthropology in the Last Twenty Years," *Annual Report of the Smithsonian Institution*, 1889, p. 560.
2. Ludwig, *Schliemann: The Story of a Gold-Seeker* (trans. Tait), p. 201.
3. *BG*, 1894, p. 117.
4. Virchow in Schliemann's *Ilios*, p. ix.
5. See *BG*, 1879, pp. 204 ff., and Virchow's contributions in Schliemann's *Ilios*.
6. For geology and geography, see his Academy paper, "Zur Landeskunde der Troas" (Berlin, 1880). For his studies on botany, zoology, and craniology, see his translated contributions to Schliemann's *Ilios*.
7. Article in *A*, LXXVII (1879), 174; translated in Schliemann's *Ilios*, pp. 721 ff.
8. Virchow in Schliemann's *Ilios*, pp. 724 and 725.
9. Virchow in *BG*, 1890, pp. 331 ff.
10. *ZE*, XXIII (1891), 41 ff.
11. *BG*, 1881, pp. 411 ff.; *ZE*, XIV (1882), 107 ff.; and *Das Graeberfeld von Koban im Lande der Osseten*.
12. "Die kulturgeschichtliche Stellung des Kaukasus," Berlin Academy paper, 1895.
13. *BG*, 1888, pp. 344 ff. and 399 ff.; *Korrbl*, 1888, pp. 105 ff.
14. Berlin Academy paper, 1888.

15. Virchow in *Annual Report of the Smithsonian Institution,* 1889, p. 567.
16. *BG,* 1888, pp. 340 ff., 417 ff., and 1889, pp. 44 ff.
17. *Ibid.,* 1889, pp. 459 ff.
18. *Ibid.,* 1891, pp. 23 ff.
19. For the work of Virchow and Berthelot on Antimon bronze, see *Korrbl,* 1875, pp. 5 ff., and *BG,* 1887, pp. 334 ff.
20. Paper delivered at the International Americanist Congress in Berlin, 1888.
21. *BG,* 1896, pp. 505 ff.
22. *Ibid.,* 1898, pp. 281 ff.

THE ORGANIZER OF GERMAN ANTHROPOLOGY

1. Virchow, *Gedaechtnisrede auf Carl Mayer,* p. 24.
2. *H,* I, 371.
3. Virchow, *Vier Reden ueber Leben und Kranksein,* p. 115.
4. See also *Korrbl,* 1871, p. 41.
5. Virchow, *Ueber Nahrungs- und Genussmittel,* p. 50.
6. *A,* VII (1854), 552.
7. Virchow, *Beitraege zur Landeskunde der Troas,* p. 67.
8. Virchow, *Die Heilkrafte des Organismus,* p. 6.
9. *A,* CXIII (1888), 375 (after his trip to Egypt).
10. Virchow, *Huenengraeber und Pfahlbauten,* p. 33; see also *DN,* p. 146, and *Korrbl,* 1875, p. 10.
11. Daniel, *A Hundred Years of Archeology,* p. 181.
12. *Korrbl,* 1877, p. 86.
13. *BG,* 1876, p. 77.
14. *Korrbl,* 1871, p. 42.
15. Walsh, *Makers of Modern Medicine,* p. 410; P. Honigsheim in *Festschrift fuer Pater W. Schmidt,* p. 851.
16. Ackerknecht, "On the Collecting of Data concerning Primitive Medicine," *American Anthropologist,* XLVII (1945), 427.
17. *BG,* 1896, p. 386.
18. See Virchow's necrology of De Mortillet in *BG,* 1898, p. 409.
19. *Korrbl,* 1899, p. 80.
20. *Ibid.,* 1880, p. 23.
21. *DN,* p. 171.
22. See Boas' paper on the physical anthropology of Northwest Coast Indians in *BG,* 1891, pp. 158 ff.
23. *BG,* 1895, p. 304.
24. See Virchow on Northwest Coast art in *BG,* 1887, p. 73.

EPICRISIS

1. Neuburger in *Wiener medizinische Wochenschrift,* LXXXIV (1934), 374.
2. *BKW,* XXX (1893), 2.
3. *BG,* 1875, p. 136.

Biographical Glossary

Bibliography

Index

Biographical Glossary

ADDISON, WILLIAM. 1802–1881. English medical practitioner and early microscopist.

ALISON, WILLIAM PULTENEY. 1790–1859. Professor of medicine in Edinburgh. Social reformer.

ANDRAL, GABRIEL. 1797–1876. Outstanding member of Paris Clinical School. Original primary interests semiotics and pathological anatomy, later blood chemistry (see *Essay in Pathological Hematology*, with Gavarret, 1843).

ASCHOFF, LUDWIG. 1866–1942. Prominent German pathological anatomist. Described reticulo-endothelial system.

AUERBACH, BERTHOLD. 1812–1882. Jewish-German novelist and story writer.

BACCELLI, GUIDO. 1832–1916. Pathologist and clinician in Rome. Deputy and minister. Reformer of public education.

BAER, KARL ERNST VON. 1792–1876. German-Russian embryologist and anthropologist. Discoverer of mammalian ovum. Professor in Koenigsberg and St. Petersburg (Leningrad).

BAERENSPRUNG, FRIEDRICH WILHELM FELIX VON. 1822–1863. Gifted pathologist and clinician who eventually specialized in dermatology and syphilology. Professor in Halle.

BAMBERGER, LUDWIG. 1823–1899. 1848 radical; banker in Paris exile; National Liberal after return in 1866; leader of so-called secessionists (1880); confidant of Empress Victoria, wife of Frederick III.

BARDELEBEN, HEINRICH ADOLF. 1819–1895. Prominent German anatomist and surgeon. Professor of surgery in Berlin from 1868.

BAREZ, STEPHAN FRIEDRICH. 1790–1856. Practitioner, associate professor of pediatrics, and councilor in the Education Ministry in Berlin.

BARRY, MARTIN. 1802–1855. Very active English physiologist and embryologist. Worked with Johannes Mueller, Valentin, and other German and French scientists.

BASTIAN, ADOLF. 1826–1905. German naval surgeon who turned anthropologist. Traveled in every continent, 1851–1905. Died on trip in Trinidad. Professor and Director of Ethnological Museum in Berlin.

BEALE, LIONEL SMITH. 1828–1906. Professor of medicine in London. Very active in histopathological research. Bioplasm theory.

BEBEL, AUGUST. 1840–1913. Prominent German Social Democrat leader and writer.

BECKMANN, OTTO KARL HERMANN. 1832–1860. Friend of Haeckel, pupil of Virchow. Professor of pathological anatomy in Goettingen. Died from pulmonary tuberculosis.

BEDDOE, JOHN. 1826–1911. Bristol pediatrician and anthropologist.

BEHRING, EMIL. 1854–1912. Professor of hygiene in Marburg. One of the creators of serumtherapy.

BENNETT, JOHN HUGHES. 1812–1875. Professor of medicine in Edinburgh. Able clinician and histopathologist.

BEREND, HEIMANN WOLFF. 1809–1873. Pioneer Berlin orthopedic surgeon.

BERNARD, CLAUDE. 1813–1878. Outstanding French experimental physiologist. Pupil of Magendie. Work on pancreatic digestion, glycogen formation, vasomotor system, theory of "experimental medicine."

BERNHEIM, HIPPOLYTE MARIE. 1840–1919. Originally specialist in infectious diseases. Pupil of Kuess in Strassburg. Later Professor of Medicine in Nancy. Through his work on suggestion, one of founders of modern psychotherapy.

BERT, PAUL. 1830–1886. Pupil of Claude Bernard. Founder of aviation physiology. Statesman. Died as governor of Indochina.

BICHAT, MARIE FRANÇOIS XAVIER. 1771–1802. Precursor of Paris Clinical School. Anatomist and physiologist (vitalist). Founder of histology, that is, science of tissues which compose organs. Died before able to apply his new science more fully to pathological anatomy.

BILLROTH, CHRISTIAN ALBERT THEODOR. 1829–1894. Professor of surgery in Berlin, Zurich, and Vienna. Great abdominal surgeon. Also did work in pathological microscopy and bacteriology. Friend of Johannes Brahms.

BISCHOFF, THEODOR LUDWIG WILHELM. 1807–1882. Prominent anatomist, embryologist, and physiologist in Heidelberg, Giessen, and Munich. Friend of Liebig.

BLUMENBACH, JOHANN FRIEDRICH. 1752–1840. Professor of medicine in Goettingen. Zoologist. Prominent early anthropologist.

BOAS, FRANZ. 1858–1942. German-born North American anthropologist.

BOERNER, PAUL. 1829–1885. Participant in 1848 Revolution. Later practitioner and versatile medical writer. Editor of *Deutsche medizinische Wochenschrift*.

BOUCHUT, EUGEN. 1818–1891. Able clinician, pathologist, pediatrician, hygienist, and medical historian at Paris.

BRAUELL, FRIEDRICH. 1803–1882. Professor of veterinary medicine in Dorpat and Leipzig. One of the discoverers of anthrax bacillus.

BRESCHET, GILBERT. 1784–1845. Professor of anatomy in Paris. Embryologist.

BRETONNEAU, PIERRE. 1778–1862. Practitioner in Tours. Famous for his pioneer work on typhoid fever, diphtheria, disease specificity and contagiosity.

BROCA, PAUL. 1824–1880. Pupil of Lebert. Outstanding surgeon and anthropologist. Described Broca's speech center. Founder of Société and École d'Anthropologie at Paris.

BROUSSAIS, FRANÇOIS JOSEPH VICTOR. 1772–1838. First military surgeon, then clinician at Val-de-Grâce, Paris. One of the early promoters of pathological-anatomical approach; became founder of a very influential system of "physiological medicine" (1816).

BUECHER, LOTHAR. 1817–1892. Radical in 1848–49. Became Bismarck's close collaborator after return from exile in 1864.

BUHL, LUDWIG. 1816–1880. Clinician, pathologist, and hygienist at Munich who had studied there, in Paris, and in Vienna. One of the originators of *Grundwassertheorie*.

BUNGE, GUSTAV VON. 1844–1920. Born in Dorpat, professor of physiology in Basle. From his department came first experiments with diets producing deficiency diseases.

BUSK, GEORGE. 1807–1886. English naval surgeon, naturalist, and anthropologist.

CARUS, KARL GUSTAV. 1779–1868. Court physician at Dresden. Romantic. Remarkable contributions to comparative anatomy, psychology, craniology.

CASPER, JOHANN LUDWIG. 1796–1864. Outstanding teacher and reformer of legal medicine in Berlin.

CHARCOT, JEAN MARTIN. 1825–1893. First professor of pathology, later professor of neurology at Salpetrière, where he trained numerous French and foreign pupils.

CHAUFFARD, PAUL-EMILE. 1823–1879. Paris clinician and reorganizer of medical education after 1871. Vitalist.

COHNHEIM, JULIUS. 1839–1884. Experimental pathologist. Most gifted of Virchow's pupils. Professor of pathology in Kiel, Breslau, Leipzig.

CORNIL, ANDRÉ-VICTOR. 1837–1908. French histopathologist and clinician. Collaborated with Ranvier. Postgraduate studies in Berlin.

CORRIGAN, SIR DOMINIC JOHN. 1802–1880. Famous Dublin clinician ("Corrigan's puls"), hygienist, and statesman.

CORVIN-WIERSBITZKI, OTTO VON. 1812–1886. German writer and radical politician.

CRUVEILHIER, JEAN. 1791–1874. Pupil of Dupuytren. Famous practitioner and pathological anatomist. First incumbent of Paris chair of pathological anatomy in 1836.

DAREMBERG, CHARLES VICTOR. 1817–1872. Outstanding French medical historian.

DAVAINE, CASIMIR JOSEPH. 1811–1882. Early French parasitologist. One of discoverers of anthrax bacillus.

DAVIS, JOSEPH BERNARD. 1801–1881. English physician and anthropologist.

DELBRUECK, RUDOLF VON. 1817–1903. Prussian statesman. President of chancery of North German Confederation and imperial chancery (1867–76).

DÉSOR, EDOUARD. 1811–1882. French geologist and prehistorian.

DIEFFENBACH, JOHANN FRIEDRICH. 1792–1847. French-trained German plastic and orthopedic surgeon, interested in blood transfusion. Professor in Berlin from 1832.

DONDERS, FRANS CORNELIS. 1818–1889. Famous Dutch microscopist, physiologist, ophthalmologist, and hygienist.

DONNÉ, ALFRED. 1801–1878. French pioneer microscopist and hygienist. Discoverer of trichomonas vaginalis, etc.

DUBOIS, MARIE EUGÈNE FRANÇOIS THOMAS. 1858–1941. Dutch anatomist and paleontologist. Discoverer of Pithecanthropus.

DU BOIS–REYMOND, EMIL. 1818–1896. Professor of physiology in Berlin after 1858 as successor of his teacher Johannes Mueller. Permanent secretary of Berlin Academy of Sciences.

DUNCKER, FRANZ. 1822–1888. German publisher and progressive politician.

DUTROCHET, RENÉ JOACHIM HENRI. 1776–1874. French physician and microscopist. Coined notion of endosmosis and exosmosis.

ECKER, ALEXANDER. 1816–1887. Professor of anatomy in Freiburg im Breisgau. Microscopist and anthropologist.

EHRENREICH, PAUL. 1855–1914. German physician and ethnographer (expeditions in South America).

EHRLICH, PAUL. 1854–1915. One of the greatest medical scientists of all times. Developed side-chain theory and specific therapy out of staining experiments. Became father of modern chemotherapy with discovery of arsphenamine. Work in hematology, immunology, oncology. Director of Speyer House in Frankfurt am Main.

EIJKMAN, CHRISTIAN. 1858–1930. Dutch physiologist. Produced beriberi-like disease through experimental work with shelled rice on fowl in East Indies and opened therewith scientific understanding of deficiency diseases.

EISENMANN, GOTTFRIED. 1795–1867. German political martyr (17 years in prison) and prolific medical writer.

ENGEL, JOSEPH. 1816–1899. Austrian anatomist and pathologist. Professor in Zurich, Prague, and Vienna.

FICK, FRANZ LUDWIG. 1813–1858. Professor of anatomy in Marburg. Experimental work on bone formation.

FINSCH, OTTO. 1839–1917. German traveler, ethnologist and ornithologist.

FITZ, REGINALD HEBER. 1843–1913. Boston pathologist. Pupil of Virchow. First to describe appendicitis and acute pancreatitis.

FOERSTER, AUGUST. 1822–1865. German histopathologist. Successor of Virchow in Wuerzburg. Died from "pleuresy."

FORCKENBECK, MAX VON. 1821–1892. Prussian liberal politician. Mayor of Breslau, 1873–78. Mayor of Berlin, 1878–92.

FOX, WILSON. 1831–1887. English professor of medicine and physician of Queen Victoria.

FRANTZIUS, ALEXANDER VON. 1821–1877. German physician, zoologist, and anthropologist. Lived in France and Central America, 1853–68.

FRERICHS, FRIEDRICH THEODOR. 1819–1885. German clinician in Kiel and Breslau. Successor of Schoenlein in Berlin, 1859. Famous for work on diseases of the liver.

FRIEDREICH, NIKOLAUS. 1825–1882. Son and grandson of professors of medicine in Wuerzburg. Professor of medicine in Heidelberg. Best known for his discoveries in neurology.

FROEBEL, JULIUS. 1805–1893. German political writer. Nephew of the famous educator. Radical in 1848. Newspaperman in North and Central America, 1849–57. Austrian propagandist, 1862–66. Imperial German consul general at Smyrna and Algiers, 1873–89.

FRORIEP, ROBERT. 1804–1861. German anatomist and medical writer. Prosector at Charité, 1833–46.

GALL, FRANZ JOSEPH. 1758–1828. Inventor of "phrenology." Greatest brain anatomist of his time. Left Vienna for Paris in 1805, as he was forbidden to lecture on account of his "materialism."

GENDRIN, AUGUSTIN-NICOLAS. 1796–1890. Paris clinician and physiologist. Did research on inflammation.

GLUGE, GOTTLIEB. 1812–1898. Outstanding histopathologist. German born and trained; professor in Bruxelles from 1838.

GOERCKE, JOHANN. 1750–1822. Able Prussian military surgeon and medical administrator. Founded *Pépinière* in 1795.

GOLDSTUECKER, THEODOR. 1821–1872. German-born Sanskrit scholar. From 1850 in England.

GOODSIR, JOHN. 1814–1867. Outstanding Scottish comparative anatomist and microscopist. Professor at Edinburgh from 1844.

GRAEFE, ALBRECHT VON. 1828–1870. The great Berlin ophthalmologist. Son of the famous surgeon Carl Ferdinand von Graefe. Died from tuberculosis.

GRIESINGER, WILHELM. 1817–1868. Connected with Wunderlich and Roser since high school days in Stuttgart. Professor of medicine in Tuebingen, Kiel, Cairo, Zurich. Professor of neuropsychiatry in Berlin after 1865. Though most important as psychiatrist, he made also valuable contributions in the field of infectious diseases (especially when working in Egypt with his pupil Bilharz, 1850–52).

GROHÉ, FRIEDRICH. 1830–1886. German pathological anatomist. Professor in Greifswald from 1858.

GUENSBURG, FRIEDRICH. 1820–1859. Histopathologist in Breslau.

GUETERBOCK, LUDWIG. 1814–1895. Berlin physician. Pupil of Schoenlein. Work on pus.

GUILLOT, NATALIS. 1804–1866. Early Paris histopathologist and comparative anatomist, working especially in the field of pulmonary diseases (miners' lung). Became professor of internal pathology in 1855.

GURLT, ERNST FRIEDRICH. 1794–1882. German anatomist and microscopist, originally pharmacist; connected with Berlin Veterinary Academy from 1819.

HAECKEL, ERNST HEINRICH. 1834–1919. German biologist and philosopher. Professor in Jena from 1862. Protagonist of Darwinism in Germany.

HAMY, JULES THEODORE ERNEST. 1842–1908. French anthropologist and ethnographer. Professor at Museum of Natural History (successor of De Quatrefages) and founder of Ethnological Museum in the Trocadero.

HANSEMANN, DAVID VON. 1859–1920. Outstanding German histopathologist. Grandson of the 1848 politician and banker. Professor in Berlin from 1890.

HANSEN, GERHARD HENRIK ARMAUER. 1841–1912. Norwegian pathologist. Discoverer of leprosy bacillus.

HARTMANN, ROBERT. 1831–1893. Berlin anatomist and anthropologist. 1860–61 Africa expedition.

HASSALL, ARTHUR HILL. 1817–1894. English physician, active microscopist, and hygienist (fight against food adulteration).

HECKER, JUSTUS FRIEDRICH KARL. 1795–1850. Berlin medical historian and epidemiologist.

HEINROTH, JOHANN CHRISTIAN AUGUST. 1773–1843. Psychiatrist at Leipzig. Protagonist of an ethico-religious theory of mental disease.

HELMHOLTZ, HERMANN LUDWIG FERDINAND. 1821–1894. Famous German physiologist and physicist (law of conservation of energy, 1847; sense-physiology; invention of ophthalmoscope, 1851; thermodynamics).

HENLE, FRIEDRICH GUSTAV JACOB. 1809–1885. Famous German histologist. Professor in Zurich, Heidelberg, and from 1852 in Goettingen. Contagionist and teacher of Robert Koch.

HESCHL, RICHARD LADISLAUS. 1824–1881. Austrian pathological anatomist. Successor of Rokitansky.

HEUSINGER, KARL FRIEDRICH. 1792–1883. Professor of medicine in Marburg, 1829–67. Early histologist. Made Bichat known in Germany. Comparative pathologist and medical geographer.

HIRSCH, AUGUST. 1817–1894. Famous epidemiologist, medical geographer, and historian. Medical practitioner till 1863; afterwards professor in Berlin.

HIS, WILHELM, SR. 1831–1904. Swiss-born embryologist. From 1872 in Leipzig.

HODGKIN, THOMAS. 1798–1866. English Quaker physician, pathological anatomist, and philanthropist. Pupil of Laennec. Described "Hodgkin's disease."

HOLLAND, SIR HENRY. 1788–1873. English court physician who traveled extensively.

HOLTZENDORFF, FRANZ VON. 1829–1889. German authority on criminal and international law.

HOPPE-SEYLER, ERNST FELIX IMMANUEL. 1825–1885. Professor of physiological chemistry in Strasbourg. Promotor of biochemistry in Germany (haemoglobin, protein, fermentation, etc.).

HOVERBECK, LEOPOLD VON. 1822–1875. Progressive leader in Prussia.

HUETER, KARL. 1838–1882. Son of the obstetrician Karl Christoph Hueter. Professor of surgery in Rostock and Greifswald.

HYRTL, JOSEPH. 1811–1894. Professor of anatomy in Vienna from 1845. Important teacher and researcher.

ISRAEL, OSKAR. 1854–1907. Berlin pathological anatomist.

JACOBI, ABRAHAM. 1830–1919. German born. Emigrated to U.S. after political imprisonment, 1851–53. Became promoter of pediatrics in U.S. and great ethical influence in profession.

JACOBY, JOHANN. 1805–1877. Koenigsberg physician and famous radical politician, especially under Frederick William IV.

KALTENBRUNNER, GEORG. 1804–1833. Munich-born experimental pathologist (inflammation). Pupil of Doellinger.

KARTULIS, STEPHAN. 1852–1920. German-trained Greek surgeon and bacteriologist in Alexandria. Important work, especially on amoebic dysentery.

KEBER, GOTTHARD AUGUST FERDINAND. 1816–1871. Prussian government physician; prominent comparative anatomist.

KEY, ERNST AXEL HENRIK. 1832–1901. Prominent Swedish pathological anatomist and politician.

KIWISCH RITTER VON ROTTERAU, FRANZ. 1814–1852. Professor of gynecology and obstetrician in Wuerzburg and Prague. Anti-romantic. Died from tuberculosis.

KLEBS, EDWIN. 1834–1913. German pathologist and bacteriologist. Erratic genius. Professor at Berne, Wuerzburg, Prague, Zurich; after 1893 active in Karlsruhe, Strasbourg, Asheville, N. C., Chicago, Hannover, Berlin, Lausanne, and Berne.

KLEIST-RETZOW, HANS VON. 1814–1892. Prussian reactionary politician and bigot. Close friend of Bismarck.

KLENCKE, PHILIPP FRIEDRICH HERMANN. 1813–1881. Gifted and extremely productive medical writer in Hannover.

KOCH, ROBERT. 1843–1910. Great German bacteriologist; discovered the bacilli causing tuberculosis, cholera, etc.

KOELLIKER, RUDOLF ALBERT. 1817–1905. Great Swiss histologist. Professor in Wuerzburg from 1847.

KOLLMANN, JULIUS. 1834–1918. German anatomist and anthropologist. Professor in Basel from 1878.

KRUSE, WALTER. 1864–1943. German bacteriologist and anthropologist. Professor at Leipzig.

KUBARY, JOHANNES STANISLAS. 1846–1896. Polish ethnographer (Micronesia).

KUEHNE, WILHELM. 1837–1900. Pupil of Virchow and Claude Bernard. Professor of physiology in Amsterdam and Heidelberg.

KUESS, EMILE. 1815–1871. French physician and physiologist. Last French mayor of Strasbourg, 1871.

LAENNEC, RENÉ THÉOPHILE HYACINTHE. 1781–1826. Great French clinician and pathologist. Inventor of the stethoscope. Most eminent member of the so-called Paris Clinical School.

LANGENBECK, BERNHARD RUDOLPH KONRAD. 1810–1887. Famous professor of surgery in Goettingen, Kiel, and Berlin.

LANGERHANS, PAUL, SR. 1820–1909. Berlin physician and progressive politician.

LANGERHANS, PAUL, JR. 1847–1888. German histologist ("Islets") and anthropologist. Died from tuberculosis.

LANGERHANS, ROBERT (brother of Paul Langerhans, Jr.). 1859–1904. Pathological anatomist in Berlin.

LASKER, EDUARD. 1829–1884. German liberal publicist and parliamentarian. Instrumental in codification of new German law between 1867 and 1877.

LASSALLE, FERDINAND. 1825–1864. German socialist and lawyer. Founded Allgemeiner Deutscher Arbeiterverein, the embryo of the German Social Democratic Party, in 1863.

LEBERT, HERMANN (name originally Lewy). 1813–1878. German-born histopathologist and clinician. Active in Switzerland, France, and Germany. Pupil of Schoenlein, P. Louis, Dupuytren, and Prévost. Teacher of Robin, Broca, etc. Professor of medicine in Zurich and Breslau.

LEIDY, JOSEPH. 1823–1891. Outstanding Philadelphia anatomist and paleontologist.

LEREBOULLET, DOMINIQUE-AUGUSTE. 1804–1865. French comparative anatomist, microscopist, and embryologist. Professor in Strasbourg.

LEUBUSCHER, RUDOLF. 1821–1861. German psychiatrist; friend of B. Reinhardt and Virchow. Active in Halle, Jena, and Berlin.

LEUCKART, KARL GEORG FRIEDRICH RUDOLPH. 1823–1898. Outstanding German zoologist and parasitologist. Professor in Goettingen, Giessen, and Leipzig.

LEUPOLDT, JOHANN MICHAEL. 1794–1874. Last defender of romantic medicine. Professor in Erlangen.

LEWIN, LOUIS. 1850–1929. Famous German toxicologist.

LEYDEN, ERNST VON. 1832–1910. Professor of medicine in Koenigsberg, Strasbourg, and Berlin. Pupil and successor of Traube.

LIEBIG, JUSTUS VON. 1803–1873. Famous German chemist. Paris trained; active in Giessen and Munich.

LIEBREICH, MATTHIAS EUGEN OSKAR. 1839–1908. Outstanding Berlin pharmacologist and biochemist.

LINDENSCHMIT, LUDWIG. 1809–1893. German archeologist.

LISSAUER, ABRAHAM. 1832–1908. German physician, hygienist, and anthropologist.

LISTER, LORD JOSEPH. 1827–1912. Famous British surgeon; inventor of antisepsis.

LOBSTEIN, JOHANN GEORG CHRISTIAN FRIEDRICH MARTIN. 1777–1835. German-born French clinician and pathological anatomist. Held first chair in pathological anatomy in France (Strasbourg, 1819).

LOEFFLER, FRIEDRICH AUGUST JOHANN (son of Gottfried Loeffler). 1852–1915. Famous German bacteriologist and hygienist. Professor in Greifswald. Discoverer of "Loeffler's bacillus"; exposed healthy carrier, etc.

LOEFFLER, GOTTFRIED FRIEDRICH FRANZ. 1815–1874. Outstanding Prussian reformer of military medical structure.

LOMBROSO, CESARE. 1836–1909. Very popular Italian psychiatrist and anthropologist. Connected crime with atavism and degeneration.

LOTZE, RUDOLPH HERMANN. 1817–1881. German physician and philosopher. Professor of philosophy in Leipzig, Goettingen, and Berlin.

LOUIS, PIERRE CHARLES ALEXANDRE. 1787–1872. Famous French clinician and medical statistician.

LUBARSCH, OTTO. 1860–1933. German pathological anatomist. Professor in Rostock, Posen, Kiel, and Berlin.

LUCAE, JOHANN CHRISTIAN GUSTAV. 1814–1885. Anatomist and anthropologist in Frankfurt am Main.

MAGENDIE, FRANÇOIS. 1783–1855. Influential French clinician, experimental physiologist, and pharmacologist.

MANDL, LOUIS. 1812–1881. Hungarian-born, Vienna-trained, French microscopist.

MANTEUFFEL, EDWIN VON. 1809–1895. Prussian general and politician.

MARTIUS, FRIEDRICH. 1850–1923. Professor of medicine in Rostock. Primarily interested in constitutional pathology.

MAYER, CARL. 1795–1868. Progressive German gynecologist. Father-in-law of Rudolf Virchow.

MAYER, ROSE. 1832–1913. Daughter of Carl Mayer; wife of Rudolf Virchow.

MECKEL, JOHANN FRIEDRICH, II (grandson of J. H. Meckel). 1781–1833. Most famous member of a dynasty of German anatomists. Professor in Halle. Outstanding as comparative anatomist ("the German Cuvier") and pathologist (teratologist).

MECKEL VON HEMSBACH, HEINRICH (nephew of J. F. Meckel, II). Last prominent member of the dynasty. Comparative and pathological anatomist. Died from tuberculosis.

MENDEL, GREGOR. 1822–1884. Austrian monk. Found rules of inheritance called after him.

MENDELSOHN, ARNOLD. 1817–(?). Promising German researcher. Involved in burglary of documents by Lasalle. Disappeared after leaving prison.

METCHNIKOFF, ELIE. 1845–1916. Russian-born associate of Institut Pasteur. Discoverer of phagocytosis. Nobel Prize, 1908.

MICHEL, EUGÈNE. 1819–1883. Anatomist and surgeon in Strasbourg and after 1871 in Nancy.

MOHL, HUGO VON. 1805–1872. Outstanding German botanist. Professor at Tuebingen.

MOHL, ROBERT VON (brother of Hugo von Mohl). 1799–1875. German jurist and statesman.

MOLTKE, COUNT HELMUTH VON. 1800–1891. Danish, Turkish, later Prussian officer. Successful strategist in 1864, 1866, 1870–71.

MOMMSEN, THEODOR. 1817–1903. German classical scholar, historian, and liberal. Professor at Leipzig, Zurich, Breslau, and Berlin. Nobel Prize, 1902.

MOREL, BENEDICTE-AUGUSTE. 1809–1873. French psychiatrist and anthropologist. Friend of Claude Bernard, but also of radical Catholics like Lamennais and Buchez. Inaugurated wave of "degeneration" theories in psychiatry and elsewhere through his 1857 treatise.

MORTILLET, GABRIEL DE. 1821–1898. French archeologist. Founded Ecole d'Anthropologie with Broca.

MUELLER, JOHANNES. 1801–1858. Great German physiologist, histologist, comparative anatomist, pathologist, and embryologist. Professor in Bonn and Berlin.

NACHTIGAL, GUSTAV. 1834–1885. German physician, traveler, and diplomat, active mostly in Africa.

NAEGELI, KARL WILHELM VON. 1817–1891. Famous Swiss-born botanist. Professor at Zurich, Freiburg, and Munich.

NEUMANN, SALOMON. 1819–1908. Berlin practitioner and hygienist.

NIEMEYER, FELIX VON. 1820–1871. Son of Magdeburg professor of medicine. Professor of medicine in Greifswald and Tuebingen.

OBERMEIER, OTTO. 1843–1873. German practitioner. Discoverer of spirilla causing relapsing fever. Died from cholera acquired during research.

OKEN, LORENZ. 1779–1851. Famous German romantic biologist. Professor in Jena. Founded the *Naturforscherversammlungen* in 1822.

ORTH, JOHANNES. 1847–1923. German pathological anatomist. Successor of Virchow in Berlin.

OSLER, SIR WILLIAM. 1849–1919. Famous Canadian-born clinician. Active in U.S. and England.

PAGEL, JULIUS LEOPOLD. 1851–1912. Berlin practitioner and eminent medical historian. Professor from 1898.

PAGENSTECHER, ALEXANDER. 1799–1869. Physician in Elberfeld and Heidelberg. Active as *Burschenschaftler*. Member of 1848 *Nationalversammlung* and later Badenian parliament.

PAGENSTECHER, CARL (son of Alexander Pagenstecher). 1824–1865. Very active ophthalmologist in Elberfeld. Friend of Virchow.

PAGET, SIR JAMES. 1814–1899. Great English surgeon and microscopist.

PANUM, PETER LUDWIG. 1820–1885. Outstanding Danish physiologist and epidemiologist. Worked in Berlin and Paris. Professor at Kiel and Copenhagen.

PETTENKOFER, MAX VON. 1818–1901. Outstanding German physiological chemist and hygienist. Originally pharmacist and actor. Professor in Munich from 1847. Committed suicide.

PFEUFER, KARL VON. 1806–1869. German clinician and medical reformer. Friend of Henle and the poet Platen. Professor in Zurich, Heidelberg, and Munich.

PITT-RIVERS, AUGUSTUS HENRY LANE FOX. 1827–1900. English army officer and archeologist. Best known for his collections of weapons and other instruments, and his excavations.

PIUS IX (Giovanni Maria Mastai-Ferretti). 1792–1878. Pope, 1846–1878. After liberal beginnings very reactionary.

POLLENDER, ALOYS. 1800–1879. German practitioner and microscopist. Observed first anthrax bacillus (in 1849).

PORTAL, BARON ANTOINE. 1742–1832. Famous French anatomist, pathologist, and surgeon. Court physician under changing dynasties from 1788 to his death.

POSNER, CARL. 1854–1928. Berlin urologist and medical writer.

PRUNER-BEY, FRANZ. 1808–1882. German-born physician, epidemiologist, and anthropologist. In Egypt, 1830–60. Lived later in Paris and Pisa.

PURKINJE, JOHANNES EVANGELISTA. 1787–1869. Famous physiologist. Professor in Breslau and Prague.

QUATREFAGES DE BRÉAU, JEAN LOUIS ARMAND DE. 1810–1892. French physician, zoologist, and anthropologist. Professor in Toulouse and at Paris Natural History Museum.

RADEMACHER, JOHANN GOTTFRIED. 1772–1850. German country practitioner (in Goch, Rhineland). Invented empiricist system of therapeutics, *Erfahrungsheillehre,* derived from Paracelsus.

RAMON Y CAJAL, SANTIAGO. 1852–1934. Famous Spanish neuroanatomist. Professor in Valencia, Barcelona, and Madrid.

RANKE, JOHANNES. 1836–1916. Physiologist and anthropologist. First professor of anthropology in Munich, 1886.

RANKE, LEOPOLD VON. 1795–1886. Leading German historian. Professor in Berlin, 1825–71.

RASPAIL, FRANÇOIS VINCENT. 1794–1878. French scientist and liberal. Originally a theologian. Repeatedly in prison and parliament. Inventor of a special therapeutic system.

RECKLINGHAUSEN, FRIEDRICH DANIEL VON. 1833–1910. Eminent German pathologist. Professor in Koenigsberg, Wuerzburg, and Strasbourg.

REICHERT, KARL BOGISLAUS. 1811–1883. German histologist and embryologist. Pupil of K. E. von Baer and Johannes Mueller. Professor in Dorpat, Breslau and Berlin.

REINACH, SALOMON. 1858–1932. French archeologist. Excavations near Smyrna, on Lesbos, Thasos, at Carthage, Corsica, etc. Keeper at the Museum at St. Germain and lecturer at the Ecole du Louvre.

REINHARDT, BENNO. 1819–1852. German pathologist. Friend and successor of Virchow in Berlin. Died from tuberculosis.

REMAK, ROBERT. 1815–1865. Outstanding German embryologist and neurologist.

RETZIUS, ANDERS ADOLF. 1796–1860. Swedish zoologist, anatomist, and anthropologist. Introduced his racial classification on the basis of dolicho-, respectively brachycephaly in 1842.

RICHTER, ADOLF LEOPOLD. 1798–1876. Prussian military surgeon. His ideas concerning a reform of army medicine were realized in Prussian and German regulations of 1868 and 1873.

RICHTER, EUGEN (son of Adolf Richter). 1838–1906. German progressive politician. Journalist after being dismissed from government service. In parliament from 1867.

RICORD, PHILIPPE. 1800–1889. American-born, outstanding French syphilologist.

RIECKE, KARL FRIEDRICH. 1802–(?). German military surgeon, practitioner (in Nordhausen), epidemiologist, and prehistorian.

RINDFLEISCH, GEORG EDUARD. 1836–1908. Professor of pathology in Zurich, Bonn, and Wuerzburg. Neovitalist.

RINECKER, FRANZ VON. 1811–1883. Versatile, able clinician in Wuerzburg.

RINGSEIS, JOHANN NEPOMUK VON. 1785–1880. Romantic physician. Regarded diseases as consequence of sin. Professor and official in Ministry of Interior in Munich.

ROBIN, CHARLES PHILIPPE. 1821–1885. Well-known French biologist and pioneer histologist. Anticlerical politician. Professor in Paris.

ROHLFS, GERHARD. 1831–1896. German physician and explorer. Made numerous expeditions to Africa.

ROKITANSKY, KARL. 1804–1878. Great Vienna pathological anatomist. Professor from 1834. Friend of Skoda and Semmelweis. Furthered the careers of Billroth, Ed. Klebs, Meynert, Stricker.

ROON, COUNT ALBRECHT VON. 1803–1879. Prussian general and politician. Reorganizer of army as War Minister, 1859–72.

ROSENKRANZ, JOHANN KARL FRIEDRICH. 1805–1879. German Hegelian philosopher. Professor in Koenigsberg.

ROUX, PIERRE PAUL EMILE. 1853–1933. Pupil and successor of Pasteur. Worked with Yersin in 1889 on diphtheria toxine, and with Metschnikoff on inoculation of syphilis in monkeys.

RUGE, ARNOLD. 1803–1880. German neo-Hegelian philosopher. In prison, 1825–30. Published with Marx *Deutschfranzoesische Jahrbuecher*, Paris, 1843. On extreme left in Frankfurt Parliament, 1848. From 1850 in England.

RUGE, LOUIS. 1812–1897. Berlin practitioner. Brother of Arnold Ruge, brother-in-law of Virchow.

SALKOWSKI, ERNST LEOPOLD. 1844–1923. Eminent Berlin biochemist.

SCHAAFFHAUSEN, HERMANN. 1816–1893. Anatomist and anthropologist. Professor in Bonn.

SCHERER, JOHANN JOSEPH. 1814–1869. Pioneer German biochemist. Professor in Wuerzburg.

SCHLEICH, CARL LUDWIG. 1859–1922. Berlin surgeon and writer.

SCHLEIDEN, MATTHIAS JACOB. 1804–1881. Famous German botanist. Somewhat erratic. Professor in Jena, Dresden, Dorpat. Resided later in Frankfurt, Darmstadt, Wiesbaden.

SCHLIEMANN, HEINRICH. 1822–1890. In business till 1863; then archeologist. Excavated ruins of Troy, Mycenae, Orchomenos, and Tiryns.

SCHLOSSBERGER, JULIUS EUGEN. 1819–1860. Widely traveled biochemist. Professor in Tuebingen.

SCHMIDT, ALEXANDER. 1831–1894. Famous German-Russian physiologist. Professor in Dorpat.

SCHMIDT, JOSEPH HERMANN. 1804–1852. Prussian obstetrician and able medical administrator; supported by Von Vincke. Died from tuberculosis.

SCHOENLEIN, JOHANN LUCAS. 1793–1864. Famous German clinician. Professor in Wuerzburg, Zurich, and Berlin.

SCHOMBURGK, SIR ROBERT HERMANN. 1804–1865. SCHOMBURGK, MORITZ RICHARD. 1811–1890. Brothers. German-born travelers. Expeditions mostly to Central America.

SCHUETZ, WILHELM MORITZ STEPHAN LUDWIG. 1808–1857. Prominent Berlin physician.

SCHULTZ-SCHULTZENSTEIN, KARL HEINRICH. 1798–1871. Able physiologist and botanist. Professor in Berlin. Romantic systematist.

SCHULZE-DELITZSCH, HERMANN. 1808–1883. German progressive politician and economist. Organizer of co-operative societies.

SCHWANN, THEODOR. 1810–1882. Eminent German physiologist and microscopist. From 1839 in Belgium.

SCHWEINFURTH, GEORG AUGUST. 1836–1925. Famous German traveler. Made numerous expeditions in East and Central Africa.

SEMMELWEIS, IGNAZ PHILIPP. 1818–1865. Hungarian obstetrician. Demonstrated etiology and prevention of puerperal fever in 1847 in Vienna.

SEMPER, KARL. 1832–1893. German naturalist and ethnologist (Philippines). Nephew of the famous architect.

SEYDEL, KARL THEODOR. 1812–1872. German civil servant. Mayor of Berlin 1863–72. Brother-in-law of Virchow.

SIMON, SIR JOHN. 1816–1904. Famous British pathologist and hygienist. First Health Officer of London.

SIMPSON, ALEXANDER RUSSELL (nephew of Sir James Young Simpson). 1835–1916. Professor of obstetrics in Edinburgh.

SKODA, JOSEPH. 1805–1881. Famous Vienna clinician. Professor from 1846.

SMITH, ANDREW HEERMANCE. 1837–1910. New York practitioner and medical writer.

SPIESS, GUSTAV ADOLF. 1802–1875. Prominent Frankfurt physician. Friend of F. Woehler. Proponent of a nerve pathology.

STEINEN, KARL VON DEN. 1855–1929. Professor of ethnology and director of ethnological museum in Berlin. Fieldwork in South America.

STOECKER, ADOLF. 1835–1909. Berlin court preacher after 1874; leader of Christian Socialist (anti-Semitic) Party.

STOKVIS, BAREND JOSEPH. 1834–1902. Prominent Dutch clinician. Professor of medicine in Amsterdam.

STRUVE, GUSTAV VON. 1805–1870. Lawyer and radical German politician in Mannheim. Organized two uprisings in 1848. Phrenologist. In U.S. 1851–63. Served in Union army.

THIERSCH, KARL. 1822–1895. Prominent German surgeon. Professor in Erlangen and Leipzig.

THOMSEN, CHRISTIAN JURGENSEN. 1788–1865. Famous Danish archeologist.

TRAUBE, LUDWIG. 1818–1876. Pupil of Skoda and Schoenlein. Founder of experimental pathology in Germany. Professor of medicine in Berlin.

TWESTEN, KARL. 1820–1870. Judge; Prussian liberal leader.

UNRUH, HANS VICTOR VON. 1806–1886. Prussian liberal politician. Engineer.

VALENTIN, GABRIEL GUSTAV. 1810–1883. Born in Breslau; pupil of Purkinje. Eminent histologist and physiologist. Professor in Berne after 1836.

VARRENTRAPP, JOHANN GEORG. 1809–1886. Prominent physician in Frankfurt am Main. Active sanitarian.

VELPEAU, ALFRED ARMAND LOUIS MARIE. 1795–1867. Famous French anatomist, obstetrician, and surgeon. Pupil of Bretonneau of Tours. Professor of surgery in Paris.

VOGEL, JULIUS. 1814–1880. Clinician and pathologist in Goettingen, Giessen, and Halle.

VOGT, CARL. 1817–1895. German zoologist and anthropologist. Early work with Agassiz. Prominent radical in 1848. Professor in Geneva after 1852. Evolutionist.

VROLICK, WILLEM. 1801–1863. Son of Amsterdam professor. Pathological anatomist and zoologist. Professor in Amsterdam after 1831.

WAGNER, RUDOLPH. 1805–1864. Physiologist and comparative anatomist. Pupil of Cuvier. Professor in Erlangen. Successor of Blumenbach in Goettingen, 1840.

WALDECK, FRANZ LEO BENEDIKT. 1802–1870. Judge; leader of Prussian left liberals, especially in 1848.

WALDEYER, WILHELM (later von Waldeyer–Hartz). 1836–1921. Pupil of Henle in Goettingen. Professor of pathological anatomy in Breslau, of anatomy in Strasbourg and Berlin. Eminent histologist and anatomist. Neuron theory, etc.

WALSH, JAMES JOSEPH. 1865–1942. American physician and Catholic writer.

WEIDENREICH, FRANZ. 1873–1948. German-born anatomist and paleoanthropologist. Professor in Strasbourg, Frankfurt, and Peking. Died in New York.

WEIGERT, CARL. 1845–1904. Outstanding German pathological anatomist. Cousin of Paul Ehrlich. Collaborator of Cohnheim. Professor in Leipzig and Frankfurt.

WEISMANN, AUGUST. 1834–1914. German biologist. Professor in Freiburg. Author of germ-plasm theory of heredity.

WELCH, WILLIAM HENRY. 1850–1934. Prominent American pathologist and bacteriologist. Professor at Johns Hopkins University.

WELCKER, HERMANN. 1822–1897. Anatomist and anthropologist. Professor in Giessen and Halle.

WINDISCHMANN, KARL JOSEPH HIERONYMUS. 1775–1839. Mystic romantic physician. Professor in Aschaffenburg and Bonn.

WUNDERLICH, CARL REINHOLD AUGUST. 1815–1877. Outstanding German clinician. Professor of medicine in Tuebingen and, from 1850, Leipzig. Famous for his systematic studies in clinical thermometry (1868). Founded in 1842 with Griesinger and Roser the *Archives for Physiological Medicine.*

ZENKER, FRIEDRICH ALBERT. 1825–1898. Able professor of pathological anatomy in Dresden and Erlangen.

ZIMMERMANN, GUSTAV HEINRICH EDUARD. 1817–1866. Prussian army surgeon and very active microscopist. Worked mostly on blood. Died from cholera during Austrian war of 1866.

Bibliography

THE ABBREVIATIONS listed as final items in some entries correspond to those used throughout the book. For alphabetical listings, refer to the Key to Abbreviations on page xv.

Ackerknecht, E. H. "Anticontagionism between 1821 and 1867," *Bulletin of the History of Medicine*, XXII (1948), 562–93.
——. *Beitraege zur Geschichte der Medizinalreform von 1848*. Leipzig, 1932. Also published in Sudhoff's *Archiv fuer Geschichte der Medizin*, XXV (1932), 61–183. ABBREV. *BM*.
——. "Elisha Bartlett and the Philosophy of the Paris Clinical School," *Bulletin of the History of Medicine*, XXIV (1950), 45–60.
——. "History of Legal Medicine," *Ciba Symposia*, XI (1951), 1286–1316.
——. "Hygiene in France, 1815–1848," *Bulletin of the History of Medicine*, XXII (1948), 117–55.
——. "Medizin als Sozialwissenschaft," *Colloquium*, VI (1947), 22–24.
——. "On the Collecting of Data Concerning Primitive Medicine," *American Anthropologist*, XLVII (1945), 427–32.
——. "Paul Bert's Triumph," *Bulletin of the History of Medicine*, Supp., III (1944), 16–31.
Angel, L. I. "Rudolph Virchow and Anthropological Standards." Paper delivered at the meeting of the American Association of Physical Anthropologists at Ann Arbor, Michigan, on March 20, 1951. Abstract in *American Journal of Physical Anthropology*, IX (1951), 245–46.
Archiv fuer Anthropologie. Ed. A. Ecker, L. Lindenschmitt, *et al.* Braunschweig, 1866——.
Archiv fuer pathologische Anatomie und Physiologie und fuer klinische Medizin. Ed. R. Virchow, B. Reinhardt, *et al.* Berlin, 1847——. Known since 1903 as *Virchows Archiv*.... ABBREV. *A*.
Aschoff, L. *Rudolf Virchow*. Hamburg, 1948. First edition, 1940, was seized and destroyed.
——. "Virchows Lehre von den Degenerationen und ihre Weiterentwicklung," *Archiv fuer pathologische Anatomie und Physiologie und fuer klinische Medizin*, CCXXXV (1921), 152–185.

Baker, J. R. "The Cell Theory," *Quarterly Journal of Microscopical Science*, LXXXIX (1948), 103 ff., XC (1949), 87 ff. and 331.

Bartlett, Willard. "A Sketch of Virchow's Life and Time," *Lectures on the History of Medicine; a Series of Lectures at the Mayo Foundation, 1926–1932*, pp. 457–89. Philadelphia, 1933.

Becher, W. *Rudolf Virchow*. Berlin, 1891.

Behring, E. A. *Gesammelte Abhandlungen zur aetiologischen Therapie von ansteckenden Krankheiten*. Leipzig, 1893.

Berg, Alexander. "Die Lehre von der Faser," *Archiv fuer pathologische Anatomie und Physiologie und fuer klinische Medizin*, CCCIX (1942), 333–460.

Berliner klinische Wochenschrift. Ed. C. Posner, L. Waldenburg, et al. Berlin, 1864–1921. ABBREV. *BKW*.

Bichat, M. F. X. *Anatomie générale, appliquée à la physiologie et à la médecine*. 4 vols. in 2. Paris, 1801.

——. *Recherches sur la vie et la mort*. Paris, 1800.

Billroth, C. A. T. *The Medical Sciences in the German Universities*. New York, 1924.

Bismarck, Otto von. *Gesammelte Werke*. 15 vols. Berlin, 1933.

Boas, Franz. "Rudolf Virchow's Anthropological Work," *Science*, N. S., XVI (1902), 441–45.

Boerner, Paul. "Rudolf Virchow bis zur Berufung nach Wuerzburg," *Nord und Sued*, XXI (1882), 105–30.

Bouchut, E. *Histoire de la médecine et des doctrines médicales*. Paris, 1873.

Broussais, F. J. V. *Examen des doctrines médicales*. 4 vols. Paris, 1829–34.

Buechner, Georg. *Georg Buechner: Werke und Briefe*. Ed. Fritz Bergemann. Leipzig, n.d.

Buess, H. "Zur Geschichte des Emboliebegriffs bis auf Virchow," *Acta Societatis Helveticae Scientiarum Naturalium*, CXXV (1945), 231 ff. Abstract in *Schweizer medizinisches Jahrbuch*, 1946, pp. lvii ff.

Burnett, W. I. "The Cell, Its Physiology, Pathology and Philosophy," *Transactions of the American Medical Association*, VI (1853), 643–832.

Cabanis, P. J. G. *Coup d'oeil sur les révolutions et sur la réforme de la médecine*. Paris, 1804.

Charcot, Jean Martin. *Lecons cliniques sur les maladies des vieillards*. Paris, 1874.

Chauffard, P.-E. Article in *Le Correspondant*, 1868, *circa* p. 205.

Cohen, I. B. *Science, Servant of Man*. Boston, 1948.

Collinet, M. *La Tragédie du Marxisme*. Paris, 1948.

Conklin, Edwin G. "Predecessors of Schleiden and Schwann," in J. Cattell, (ed.), *Biological Symposia*, I, Part I, 58–66. Lancaster, Pa., 1940.

Count, E. W. *This is Race*. New York, 1950. Translation of Virchow's "Rassenbildung und Erblichkeit," pp. 176–93.

Cushing, H. *The Life of Sir William Osler*. 2 vols. Oxford, 1925.

Daniel, J. E. *A Hundred Years of Archaeology*. London, 1950.

Diepgen, P. "Virchow und die Romantik," *Deutsche medizinische Wochenschrift*, LVIII (1932), 1256–58.

——, and Rosner, E. "Zur Ehrenrettung Virchows und der deutschen Zellforscher," *Archiv fuer pathologische Anatomie und Physiologie und fuer klinische Medicin*, CCCVII (1940–41), 457–89.

Du Bois-Reymond, E. *Untersuchungen ueber tierische Elektrizitaet*. 2 vols. Berlin, 1848.

Ebstein, Erich Hugo. *Deutsche Aerztereden aus dem 19. Jahrhundert*. Berlin, 1926.

"The Economy of Sanitary Improvements," *Liverpool Health of Towns Advocate*, No. 8, April, 1846.

Engels, Friedrich. *Lage der arbeitenden Klassen in England*. Leipzig, 1845.

Ernst, P. "Virchows Cellularpathologie einst und jetzt," A, CCXXXV (1921), 52–151.

Eyck, E. *Bismarck*. 3 vols. Zuerich, 1943.

Faber, K. *Nosography*. New York, 1923.

Federici, F. *Der deutsche Liberalismus*. Zuerich, 1946.

Fenz, Ernst. *Julius Froebel, seine politische Entwicklung bis 1849*. Bern, 1932.

Finkenrath, K. *Die Medizinalreform*. Leipzig, 1929.

Fischer, Alfons. *Geschichte des deutschen Gesundheitswesens*. 2 vols. Berlin, 1933.

Fischer, J. "Geheimpolizeiberichte ueber Wiener Aerzte, 1855–57," *Janus*, XLIII (1939), 214–31.

Flick, L. E. *Development of our Knowledge of Tuberculosis*. Philadelphia, 1925.

Froelich, P. *Rosa Luxemburg*. Hamburg, 1949.

Galdston, I. "Social Medicine and the Epidemic Constitution," *Bulletin of the History of Medicine*, XXV (1951), 8–21.

Georget, Etienne Jean. *De la Physiologie du système nerveux, et spécialement du cerveau*. 2 vols. Paris, 1821.

Gerould, John H. "The Dawn of the Cell Theory," *Scientific Monthly*, XIV (1922), 268–77.

Gerth, H. *Die sozialgeschichtliche Lage der buergerlichen Intelligenz um die Wende des 18. Jahrhunderts*. Frankfurt, 1935.

Goodsir, John, and Goodsir, H. D. S. *Anatomical and Pathological Observations.* Edinburgh, 1845.

Gould, S. E. *Trichinosis.* Springfield, Ill., 1945.

Griesinger, W. Review of R. Virchow's *Die Cellular-Pathologie, Archiv fuer physiologische Heilkunde,* 2d ser., III (1859), 289–99.

Gross, S. D. *Autobiography of Samuel D. Gross.* 2 vols. Philadelphia, 1887.

Grote, L. R. (ed.). *Die Medizin der Gegenwart in Selbstdarstellungen.* 8 vols. Leipzig, 1923–29.

Gruber, G. B. "Aus der Jugendzeit von Rudolf Virchow," *Archiv fuer pathologische Anatomie und Physiologie und fuer klinische Medizin,* CCCXXI (1952), 462–81.

Haddon, A. C. *History of Anthropology.* London, 1949.

Haeckel, Ernst H. P. A. *The Story of the Development of a Youth: Letters to His Parents, 1852–1856.* Trans. G. B. Gifford. New York, 1923.

Heischkel-Artelt, Edith. "Rudolf Virchow als Publizist," *Medizinsche Rundschau,* No. 7, 1947.

Henle, F. G. J. *General Pathology.* Philadelphia, 1853.

——. "Schlusswort," *Zeitschrift fuer rationelle Medizin,* 3d ser., XXXVI (1869), 276–79.

Heymann, Bruno. *Robert Koch, 1843–1882.* Leipzig, 1932.

Honigsheim, P. "Die geistesgeschichtliche Stellung der Anthropologie, Ethnologie, Urgeschichte und ihrer Hauptrichtungen," *Festschrift fuer Pater W. Schmidt,* ed. W. Koppers (Wien, 1928).

Hueppe, F. "Rudolf Virchow. Oeffentliche Gesundheitspflege und Seuchenlehre," *Berliner klinische Wochenschrift,* XXX (1893), 1043–45.

Jores, L. "Die Entwicklung der Lehre von der Arteriosklerose seit Virchow," *Archiv fuer pathologische Anatomie und Physiologie und fuer klinische Medizin,* CCXXXV (1921), 262–72.

Karling, John S. "Schleiden's Contribution to the Cell Theory," *Biological Symposia,* ed. J. Cattell (Lancaster, Pa., 1940), I, Part I, 37–57.

Karsner, H. T. "Pathology, Old and New," *Bulletin of the New York Academy of Medicine,* XXII (1946), 371–88.

Kautsky, B. "Bismarck und die deutsche Gegenwart," *Der Monat,* II (1950), 29 ff.

Kelly, E. C. (ed). *Medical Classics.* 5 vols. Baltimore, 1936–41.

Kershaw, John D. *An Approach to Social Medicine.* Baltimore, 1946.

Klebs, E. "Rudolf Virchow. Gedenkblaetter zu seinem 70sten Geburtstage," *Deutsche medizinische Wochenschrift,* XVII (1891), 1165–68.

Kleine, H. O. "Semmelweis und Virchow," *Archiv fuer Gynaekologie,* CXLII (1930), 324–28.

Der Kleine Virchow. Published by the Prussian Ministry of Culture. Berlin, 1901.

Klein-Hattingen, O. *Geschichte des deutschen Liberalismus*. 2 vols. Berlin, 1911. ABBREV. *KH*.

Koch, Robert. Letters to Fluegge. H. B. Jacobs collection of Johns Hopkins Institute of the History of Medicine.

Korrespondenzblatt der deutschen Gesellschaft fuer Anthropologie, Ethnologie und Urgeschichte. Braunschweig, 1870–1920. Bound with *Archiv fuer Anthropologie*. ABBREV. *Korrbl.*

Kroeber, A. L., et al. *Franz Boas*. (Memoir Series of the American Anthropological Association, No. 61.) Menasha, Wis., 1943.

Kroeger, G. *The Concept of Social Medicine in Germany, 1779–1932*. Chicago, 1937.

Krumbhaar, E. P. "The Centenary of the Cell Doctrine," *Annals of Medical History*, 3 ser., I (1939), 427–37.

Laski, M. J. "Warum schrieb Mommsen nicht weiter?" *Der Monat*, II (1950), 62 ff.

Lebert, H. *Biographische Notizen*. Berlin, 1869.

——. *Physiologie pathologique*. Paris, 1845.

Leikind, M. C. Introduction to F. Cohn's "Bacteria: The Smallest of Living Organisms," *Bulletin of the History of Medicine*, VII (1939), 49–57.

Lieben, Fritz. *Geschichte der physiologischen Chemie*. Leipzig, 1935.

Loewenthal, F. *Der preussische Verfassungsstreit, 1862–66*. Munich, 1914.

Long, E. R. *A History of Pathology*. Baltimore, 1928.

Lotze, R. H. "Leben, Lebenskraft," in R. Wagner (ed.), *Handwoerterbuch der Physiologie mit Ruecksicht auf physiologische Pathologie* (4 vols. in 5; Braunschweig, 1842–53), I, ix–lviii.

Lowie, R. H. *The German People*. New York, 1945.

Lubarsch, O. "Biographische Einleitung," *Archiv fuer pathologische Anatomie und Physiologie und fuer klinische Medizin*, CCXXXV (1921), 1–30.

——. "Rudolf Virchow und sein Werk," *Berliner klinische Wochenschrift*, LVIII (1921), 1345–49.

——. "Virchows Entzuendungslehre und ihre Weiterentwicklung bis zur Gegenwart," *Archiv fuer pathologische Anatomie und Physiologie und fuer klinische Medizin*, CCXXV (1921), 186–211.

Ludwig, Emil. *Schliemann: The Story of a Gold-Seeker*. Trans. D. F. Tait. Boston, 1931.

Martius, Friedrich. Autobiographical essay, *Die Medizin der Gegenwart in Selbstdarstellungen*, ed. L. R. Grote (Leipzig, 1923), I, 105–40.

Die medizinische Reform. Ed. R. Virchow and R. Leubuscher. Berlin, July 10, 1848–June 29, 1849 (weekly).

Mehring, F. *Karl Marx.* Berlin, 1933.

Meyer, Robert. *Autobiography of Dr. Robert Meyer.* New York, 1949.

Mommsen, Theodor. "Ich wuenschte ein Buerger zu sein," *Die Wandlung,* III (1948), 69–70.

Muehlmann, W. E. *Geschichte der Anthropologie.* Bonn, 1948.

Myres, J. L. "Rudolf Virchow," *Man,* III (1903), 1–4.

Neuburger, Max. "Rokitansky," *Wiener medizinische Wochenschrift,* LXXXIV (1934), 369–76.

Niemeyer, F. von. *Clinical Lectures on Pulmonary Consumption.* London, 1870.

Obermeier, Otto. "Vorkommen feinster, eine Eigenbewegung zeigender Faeden im Blut von Recurrenskranken," *Centralblatt fuer die medizinischen Wissenschaften,* IX (1873), 145–47.

———. "Rudolf Virchow und die Bakteriologie," *Deutsche medizinische Wochenschrift,* XXXVI (1910), 1937–39.

Orth, J. "Rudolf Virchow vor einem halben Jahrhundert," *Archiv fuer pathologische Anatomie und Physiologie und fuer klinische Medizin,* CCXXXV (1921), 31–44.

Osler, W. "Rudolf Virchow, the Man and the Student," *Boston Medical and Surgical Journal,* CXXV (1891), 425–27.

Pagel, Julius. *Rudolf Virchow.* Berlin, 1906.

Pagel, W. "Julius Leopold Pagel," *Victor Robinson Memorial Volume* (New York, 1948), pp. 273–97.

———. "The Speculative Basis of Modern Pathology: Jahn, Virchow and the Philosophy of Pathology," *Bulletin of the History of Medicine,* XVIII (1945), 1–43.

———. *Virchow und die Grundlagen der Medizin des 19. Jahrhunderts.* (Jenaer Medizinhistorische Beitraege, No. 14.) Jena, 1931.

Pansch, Carl. *Geheimrat Prof. Dr. Rud. Virchow aus Schivelbein, unser grosser Gelehrter.* (Geheimes Judentum, Nebenregierung, und Juedische Weltherrschaft, No. 2.) Leipzig, 1892. Pamphlet of a series.

Petersdorff, H. V. *Hans von Kleist-Retzow.* Stuttgart, 1907.

Pettenkofer, Max von. "The Value of Health to a City," *Bulletin of the History of Medicine,* X (1941), 473–503, 593–613.

Posner, C. *Rudolf Virchow.* Wien, 1921.

———. "Zur Geschichte des Aerztlichen Vereinswesens in Berlin," *Berliner klinische Wochenschrift,* XXX (1893), 1230–31, 1257, 1271.

Predoehl, A. *Die Geschichte der Tuberkulose.* Hamburg, 1888.

Quatrefages de Bréau, Jean Louis Armand de. "Observations de M. de Quatrefages," *La Revue Scientifique*, 2d ser., XIV (1872), 318–20.

Recklinghausen, F. von. "Nachruf auf Rudolf Virchow," *Archiv fuer pathologische Anatomie und Physiologie und fuer klinische Medizin*, CLXXI (1903), 2.

Reiss, W., and Stuebel, A. *Necropolis of Ancon.* Berlin, 1887.

Remak, R. "Ueber die Entstehung des Bindegewebes und des Knorpels," *Archiv fuer Anatomie, Physiologie, und wissenschaftliche Medizin*, 1852, pp. 63–72.

——. "Ueber extracellulaere Entstehung thierischer Zellen und ueber Vermehrung derselben durch Theilung," *Archiv fuer Anatomie, Physiologie, und wissenschaftliche Medizin*, 1852, pp. 47–57.

Rich, A. R. "The Place of Dutrochet in the Development of Cellular Theory," *Bulletin of the Johns Hopkins Hospital*, XXXIX (1926), 330–65.

Rindfleisch, G. E. von. "Rudolf Virchow. Allgemeine Pathologie und pathologische Anatomie," *Berliner klinische Wochenschrift*, XXX (1893), 1034–36.

Rokitansky, K. "Der selbstaendige Wert des Wissens," *Almanach der kaiserlichen Akademie zu Wien*, XVII (1867), 103 ff.

Rosen, George. *The History of Miners' Diseases.* New York, 1943.

——. "What is Social Medicine?," *Bulletin of the History of Medicine*, XXI (1947), 674–733.

Ruge, Arnold. *Aus frueherer Zeit.* 4 vols. Berlin, 1862–67.

Schleich, C. L. *Besonnte Vergangenheit.* Berlin, 1923.

Schleiden, M. J. *Grundzuege der wissenschaftlichen Botanik.* 2 vols. Leipzig, 1845.

Schliemann, Heinrich. *Ilios.* New York, 1881.

Schlumberger, H. G. "Origins of the Cell Concept in Pathology," *Archives of Pathology*, XXXVII (1944), 396–407.

Schwalbe, J., et al. *Virchow Bibliographie.* Berlin, 1901.

Schwann, Th. *Microscopical Researches into the Accordance of Structure and Growth of Animals and Plants.* London, 1847.

Semon, Felix. "Some Personal Reminiscences," *British Medical Journal*, II (1902), 800–2.

Sigerist, H. E. *Great Doctors.* New York, 1933.

——. *A History of Medicine.* Vol. I. New York, 1951.

——. "Kultur und Krankheit," *Kyklos*, I (1928), 60–63.

——. *Medicine and Human Welfare.* New Haven, 1941.

Simonds, J. C. "On the Sanitary Conditions of New Orleans as Illustrated by Its Mortuary Statistics," *Southern Medical Reports*, II (1850), 204–46.

Simpson, A. R. Article on Virchow in *Scottish Medical and Surgical Journal*, XI (1907).

Smith, A. H. "Reminiscences of Virchow," *Post-Graduate,* XVII (1902), 469–74.

Struve, Gustav. *Weltgeschichte.* 9 vols. New York, 1852–60.

Sudhoff, K. (ed.). *Rudolf Virchow und die deutschen Naturforscherversammlungen.* Leipzig, 1922. ABBREV. *DN.*

Temkin, Owsei. "The European Background of the Young Dr. Welch," *Bulletin of the History of Medicine,* XXIV (1950), 308–18.

——. "German Concepts of Ontology and History around 1800," *ibid.,* 232 ff.

——. "Materialism in French and German Physiology of the Early Nineteenth Century," *ibid.,* XX (1946), 322–27.

——. "Metaphors of Human Biology," *Science and Civilization,* ed. R. C. Stauffer (Madison, Wis., 1949), pp. 169–94.

———. "Studien zum 'Sinn'-Begriff in der Medizin," *Kyklos,* II (1929), 21–105.

Trendelenburg, Fr. *Aus Heiteren Jugendtagen.* Berlin, 1924.

Valentin, V. *Geschichte der deutschen Revolution 1848–49.* 2 vols. Berlin, 1930–31.

Verhandlungen der Berliner Gesellschaft fuer Anthropologie, Ethnologie und Urgeschichte. Berlin, 1869–1902. Bound with *Zeitschrift fuer Ethnologie* since 1870. ABBREV. *BG.*

Verhandlungen der physikalisch-medizinischen Gesellschaft zu Wuerzburg. Ed. A. Koelliker, J. Scherer, R. Virchow, *et al.* Erlangen, 1850——. ABBREV. *WV.*

Virchow, Rudolf. *Alttrojanische Graeber und Schaedel.* Berlin, 1882.

——. "Anthropology in the Last Twenty Years," *Annual Report of Smithsonian Institution,* 1889, pp. 550 ff. Trans. from *Korrespondenzblatt der Deutschen Gesellschaft fuer Anthropologie, Ethnologie und Urgeschichte,* 1889, pp. 89 ff.

——. *Beitraege zur Landeskunde der Troas.* Berlin, 1880.

——. *Beitraege zur physischen Anthropologie der Deutschen mit besonderer Beruecksichtigung der Friesen.* Berlin, 1877. Originally published in *Abhandlungen der koeniglichen Akademie der Wissenschaften aus dem Jahre 1876* (Berlin, 1877) pp. 1–390.

——. *Briefe an seine Eltern, 1839 bis 1864.* Ed. M. Rabl. Leipzig, 1907. ABBREV. *Briefe.*

——. *Die Cellularpathologie.* 4th ed. Berlin, 1871. ABBREV. *CP.*

——. *Cellular Pathology.* Trans. F. Chance. London, 1860.

——. *Crania Ethnica Americana.* Berlin, 1892.

——. *Drei historische Arbeiten Virchows zur Geschichte seiner Vaterstadt Schivelbein.* Berlin, 1903.

——. *Gedaechtnisrede auf Carl Mayer.* Berlin, 1869.

——. *Gesammelte Abhandlungen aus dem Gebiet der oeffentlichen Medizin und der Seuchenlehre.* 2 vols. Berlin, 1879. ABBREV. *OM.*

——. *Gesammelte Abhandlungen zur wissenschaftlichen Medizin.* Frankfurt, 1856. ABBREV. *GA.*

——. *Goethe als Naturforscher und in besonderer Beziehung auf Schiller.* Berlin, 1861.

——. *Das Graeberfeld von Koban im Lande der Osseten.* Berlin, 1883.

——. *Die Gruendung der Berliner Universitaet und der Uebergang aus dem Philosophischen in das naturwissenschaftliche Zeitalter.* Berlin, 1893.

—— (ed. and contributor). *Handbuch der speziellen Pathologie und Therapie.* 6 vols. Erlangen, 1854. ABBREV. *H.*

——. *Die Heilkraefte des Organismus.* Berlin, 1875.

——. *Huenengraeber und Pfahlbauten.* Berlin, 1866.

——. *100 Jahre allgemeiner Pathologie.* Berlin, 1895.

——. *Johannes Mueller.* Berlin, 1858.

——. *Die krankhaften Geschwuelste.* 3 vols. Berlin, 1863. ABBREV. *KG.*

——. *Krieg und Frieden.* Berlin, 1877.

———. Letters and manuscripts. Thor Jager collection, Wichita, Kansas.

——. *Menschen- und Affenschaedel.* Berlin, 1870.

——. "Rassenbildung und Erblichkeit," *Festschrift fuer Adolf Bastian* (Berlin, 1896). English translation in E. W. Count, *This Is Race* (New York, 1950), pp. 176–93.

——. *Die Sektionstechnik im Leichenhause des Charitékrankenhauses.* Berlin, 1875.

——. *Ueber den Werth des pathologischen Experiments.* Berlin, 1881.

——. *Ueber die Beschraenkung der Redefreiheit im deutschen Reichstag.* Berlin, 1879.

——. *Ueber die Chlorose und die damit zusammenhaengenden Anomalien im Gefaessapparat.* Berlin, 1872.

——. *Ueber die Erziehung des Weibes fuer seinen Beruf.* Berlin, 1865.

——. *Ueber Nahrungs- und Genussmittel.* Berlin, 1868.

——. *Untersuchungen ueber die Entwicklung des Schaedelgrundes im gesunden und krankhaften Zustande und ueber den Einfluss desselben auf Schaedelform, Gesichtsbildung und Gehirnbau.* Berlin, 1857.

——. *Die Urbevoelkerung Europas.* Berlin, 1874.

——. *Vier Reden ueber Leben und Kranksein.* Berlin, 1862.

——. *Die Vorlesungen Rudolf Virchows ueber allgemeine pathologische Anatomie aus dem Wintersemester 1855/56 in Wuerzburg.* Jena, 1930.

——. Numerous articles in the following periodicals (for individual listings, see Schwalbe's bibliography):

Abhandlungen der koeniglichen Akademie der Wissenschaften zu Berlin; Archiv fuer Anthropologie; Archiv fuer pathologische Anatomie und Physiologie und fuer klinische Medizin (ABBREV. A); *Berliner klinische Wochenschrift* (ABBREV. BKW); *Jahresbericht ueber die Leistungen und Fortschritte der gesamten Medizin; Korrespondenzblatt der Deutschen Gesellschaft fuer Anthropologie, Ethnologie und Urgeschichte* (ABBREV. Korrbl); *Die medizinische Reform; Verhandlungen der Berliner Gesellschaft fuer Anthropologie, Ethnologie, und Urgeschichte* (ABBREV. BG); *Verhandlungen der physikalisch-medizinischen Gesellschaft in Wuerzburg* (ABBREV. WV); *Zeitschrift fuer Ethnologie* (ABBREV. ZE).

Vorwaerts, mein Preussenvolk. Leipzig, 1862.

Waldeyer, Wilhelm von. "Gedaechtnisrede auf Rudolf Virchow," *Abhandlungen der koeniglich preussischen Akademie der Wissenschaften aus dem Jahre 1903* (Berlin, 1903), pp. 1–52.

——. *Lebenserinnerungen.* Bonn, 1921.

Walsh, J. J. *Makers of Modern Medicine.* New York, 1915.

Welch, W. H. "Rudolf Virchow, Pathologist," *Boston Medical and Surgical Journal,* CXXV (1891), 453–57.

Weressaiew, W. *Beichten eines praktischen Arztes.* Leipzig, 1902.

Wiermann, H. *Der deutsche Reichstag.* 2 vols. Leipzig, 1884.

Wilson, J. W. "Cellular Tissue and the Dawn of the Cell Theory," *Isis,* XXXV (1944), 168 ff.

——. "Dutrochet and the Cell Theory," *Isis,* XXXVII (1947), 14 ff.

Wolff, Jacob. *Die Lehre von der Krebskrankheit von den aeltesten Zeiten bis zur Gegenwart.* 4 vols. Jena, 1926.

Wunderlich, C. R. A. "Einige Worte fuer Herrn Prof. Virchow," *Archiv fuer physiologische Heilkunde,* N. S., III (1859), 303–04.

———. *Geschichte der Medizin.* Stuttgart, 1859.

Zeiss, Heinz, and Bieling, R. *Behring, Gestalt und Werk.* Berlin, 1941.

Zeitschrift fuer Ethnologie. Ed. A. Bastian, R. Hartmann, R. Virchow, *et al.* Berlin, 1869——. ABBREV. ZE.

Index

ADDISON, William, 65n, 267
ALISON, W. P., 128, 267
Amyloid: staining to identify, 67–68; mentioned, 95, 121
ANDRAL, Gabriel, 62, 95, 106, 119, 148n, 151, 267
ANGEL, L. I., 262n55
Anticontagionism: of Virchow, 107, 124, 125
Army reform in Prussia, 169, 172, 176–77, 178, 179
ARTELT, W., ix
ASCHOFF, L., vi, vii, 28, 43, 255n16, 267
ASHMEAD, A. S., 219
AUBERT-ROCHE, Louis-Rémy, 128
AUERBACH, Berthold, 11, 190, 267
AUFRECHT, Emanuel, 23

BACCELLI, G., 31, 267
BAER, Karl Ernst von, 153, 201, 231, 232, 235, 267
BAERENSPRUNG, F. von, 14, 267
BAEUMLER, Christian, 23
BAGINSKY, Adolf, 23
BAKER, J. R., 70n, 71
BAKUNIN, Michael Alexandrovitch, 166
BAMBERGER, Ludwig, 16, 188, 267
BARDELEBEN, H. A., 6, 13, 19, 267
BAREZ, S. F., 14, 267
BARRY, Martin, 65n, 267
BARTLETT, Willard, 147
BASTIAN, Adolf, 30, 37, 218, 230, 232, 267
BEALE, Lionel Smith, 113, 267
BEBEL, August, 183, 268
BECHER, W., viii, 245n16, 246n63

BECKMANN, O., 13, 21, 246n49, 268
BEDDOE, John, 212, 268
BEHRING, Emil: criticism of Virchow, 48, 58, 115; mentioned, 5, 106, 124, 268
BELCK, W., 221
BENIVIENI, Antonio, 235
BENNETT, John Hughes, 56, 65, 108, 268
BENSEN, H. W., 150
BEREND, Heimann Wolff, 138, 268
BERG, A., 70n
BERNARD, Claude: different from Virchow, 44; mentioned, 23, 45, 87, 91, 106, 109n, 151, 268
BERNHEIM, Hippolyte Marie, 23, 268
BERRES, Joseph, 71
BERT, Paul, 185, 268
BERTHELOT, M., 269n19
BERTRAND, A., 221
BICHAT, M. F. X.: influence on Virchow, 51, 52, 54n, 67, 104, 150, 151; mentioned, 71, 74, 122, 251n45, 268
BIERMER, Anton, 21
BILLROTH, C. A. Theodor, 38, 111, 268
BISCHOFF, Th., 19, 268
BISMARCK, Otto von: as Virchow's political adversary, 4, 25–26, 171, 181; Virchow's judgment of, 37; on Prussian electoral law, 167; takes power in 1862, 172–73; on "blood and iron," 174; on Poles, 175n; on incompetence of parliament in foreign affairs, 176; opposition to Center Party,

293

184; mentioned, 27, 151, 180n, 190, 201, 242

BLAINVILLE, Henri-Marie Ducrotay de, 251n26

BLANC, Louis, 166

Blastema theory: of Rokitansky, 11, 82; Virchow's weakening of, 61, 75–76, 78, 82–83, 96; of Schwann, 63, 72–74

BLUMENBACH, J. F., 227, 231, 232, 268

BOAS, Franz: influenced by Virchow, 235–36; mentioned, 35, 216, 268

BOERHAAVE, Herman, 3, 51, 147, 150

BOERNER, P., 4n, 268

BOETTICHER, Captain, 227

BOLK, Louis, 206

Bone: growth of, 77, 96, 198; pathology of, 78; mentioned, 120, 121, 196

BOTKIN, Sergei Petrovitch, 23

BOUCHUT, E.: on Virchow and Broussais, 93, 268

BOUILLAUD, Jean-Baptiste, 106

BRANDENBURG, Count, 18

BRAUELL, F., 110, 113, 268

BRESCHET, G., 69, 269

BRETONNEAU, Pierre, 116, 269

Bright's disease, 81

BROCA, Paul, 151, 204, 212, 234, 269

BROUSSAIS, F.: influence on Virchow, 58n, 95, 151; his irritation concept in Virchow, 93; mentioned 50, 51, 53, 79, 113n, 269

BROWN, Robert, 72

BROWNING, Robert, 28

BROWN-SEQUARD, Charles-Edouard, 87

BRUCH, Karl Wilhelm Ludwig, 74

BRUECKE, Ernst Wilhelm, 6

BUCHEZ, Philippe-Joseph-Benjamin, 46

BUECHER, Lothar, 4, 22, 269

BUECHNER, Georg, 128, 164

BUESS, Heinrich, ix, 250n4

BUHL, L., 109, 269

BUNGE, G. von, 50, 269

BUSCH, Friedrich, 23

BUSK, George, 204, 269

CABINIS, Pierre Jean Georges: on medicine as a social science, 46, 128, 132; mentioned, 49

CALMEIL, Louis-Florentin, 46

Cancer. See Carcinoma

Carcinoma: Johannes Mueller on, 74; Virchow on, 74–76, 97; epithelial origin of, 104, 119

CARSWELL, Robert, 90

CARUS, K. G., 196, 269

CASPER, J., 137, 269

Cellular pathology: predecessors of theory, 73–74, 83–84; Virchow's first formulation of theory, 81; 1855 article on, 83; 1858 book on, 89–98; and bacteriology, 107–8, 112; mentioned, 121, 122–23

Cellular theories: history of, 70–74

CHANTRE, Ernest, 227

CHARCOT, Jean Martin, 148, 151, 240, 258n54, 269

Charité Hospital: Virchow's position at, 7, 8; monopolization of by army, 141; mentioned, 10, 24, 120, 159

CHAUFFARD, Paul-Emile, 44, 269

Chlorosis, 119

Cholera: Virchow on pathology of, 107; mentioned, 17, 44, 114, 125–26, 129, 151

Cholesteatoma, 76

Cloudy swelling, 94

COHEN, I. B., 70

COHN, Ferdinand Julius, 20

COHNHEIM, Julius, 23, 24, 65, 105, 112, 113, 118, 269

COINDET, Jean François, 102

COLLINET, M., 258n41

COMTE, Auguste, 46

CONDILLAC, E. B. de, 49

CONDORCET, M. J. de: on morphology, 239–40

CONKLIN, E. G., 70n.

Connective tissue: the "third estate" of cells, 45; origin of heteroplastic neoplasms, 77; development into bone, 77; component groups of, 89; main germinative center of body, 96; mentioned, 78, 121

CONRINGIUS, H., 209

CORDULA, Saint, 241

CORNIL, A.-V., 23, 269

CORRIGAN, Sir Dominic, 128, 269

CORVIN-WIERSBITZKI, Otto von, 16, 269

CORVISART, N., 52

COUNT, E. W., ix

CRANEFIELD, Paul, ix

CRAWFORD, Helen, ix

Cretinism: Virchow's study of in 1851, 195–96; mentioned, 22, 121, 128

CRUVEILHIER, Jean, 51, 53, 59, 148n, 151, 269

CZERMAK, Johann Nepomuk, 21

DANIEL, J. E., 224n

DAREMBERG, Ch., 153, 270

DARWIN, Charles, 148, 199, 201, 206

DAVAINE, C. J., 110, 270

DAVIDSON, William, 128

DAVIS, J. B., 199, 270

DEITERS, Otto, 21

DELBRUECK, Rudolf von, 187, 270

DESCARTES, R., 46

DESGENETTES, René, 124

DÉSOR, E., 232, 270

Deutsche Fortschrittspartei: founding, 25, 170; program, 170–71; inability to attract workers, 171; split, 178; as minority party, 179; policy in the constitutional conflict, 179–80; mentioned, 183, 185, 186

Diapedesis, 65n, 118, 121

DIEFFENBACH, L., 229, 270

DIEPGEN, P., 56, 71n

Diphtheria: Virchow on, 116

DOELLINGER, Ignaz, 150, 153

DONDERS, F. C.: Virchow's priority discussion with, 78; mentioned, 14, 68, 77, 270

DONNÉ, A., 56, 65, 72, 74, 154, 270

Dropsy (hydrops): chapter on in Handbook, 87

DRYSDALE, John, 113

DUBOIS, M. E., 203, 270

DU BOIS-REYMOND, Emil: his agnosticism, 52; mentioned, 6, 30, 49, 270

DUJARDIN, Félix, 154

DUMORTIER, E., 73

DUNCKER, Franz, 25, 270

DUTROCHET, R., 65n, 72, 73, 154, 270

ECKER, Alex., 69, 211, 231, 232, 270

Egyptian archaeology, 228

EHRENREICH, Paul, 233, 270

EHRLICH, Paul: staining methods of, 65, 121; and cellular pathology, 113; mentioned, 13, 270

EIJKMAN, Chr., 120, 270

EISENMANN, G., 21, 153, 190, 270

Elections in Prussia: in 1858, 168; in 1861, 170; in 1862, 172; in 1863, 176; in 1866, 178

Embolism: Virchow's early studies of, 62–64; mentioned, 9, 8, 7, 120

Endocrinology, 120

ENGEL, Joseph, 231, 270

ENGELS, Friedrich, 128, 166

Epithelioma, 76, 103, 105

ERASISTRATUS, 60

ERNST, P., 255n19

EYCK, E., 179

FALLOPIUS, G., 60

Fatty degeneration, 75, 82, 95, 122

FERNEL, Jean, 51

FEUERBACH, Ludwig, 52

Fibrin: Virchow's experiments on, 60–61, 91

Fibrinogen, 61

FICK, F. L., 197, 198, 270
FINKENRATH, K., 138n
FINSCH, O., 233, 271
FISCHER, Alfons, 138n
FISCHER, Eugen, 231
FISCHER, Is., 139n
FITZ, Reginald Heber, 23, 271
FLAUBERT, Gustave, 46
FLUEGGE, Carl, 115n
FODÉRÉ, François Emanuel, 46
FOERSTER, August, 13, 271
FOLLIN, François, 154
FONTANA, Felice, 72
FORCKENBECK, Max von, 25, 170, 188, 271
FORSTER, Georg, 232
Fox, Wilson, 23, 28, 271
FRACASTORIUS, G., 235
FRANTZIUS, Alexander von, 12, 233, 271
FREDERICK III: role of Virchow in his last disease, 29; mentioned, 176, 184, 189
FREDERICK WILLIAM III, 4, 159, 191
FREDERICK WILLIAM IV, 159, 167, 168
FREILIGRATH, Ferdinand, 128
FRERICHS, F. T., 24, 240, 271
FREUD, Sigmund, 3
FRIEDREICH, Nikolaus, 21, 24, 240, 271
Friedrich-Wilhelms Institut: outstanding pupils of, 5: Virchow for its abolition, 5, 141; 1845 addresses at, 9–10; 1874 address at, 111; Festschrift of, 150
FROEBEL, Julius: political influence on Virchow, 166–67; identified, 271
FROELICH, P., 168n
FRORIEP, Robert, 8, 59, 196, 271
Fungi: Virchow's work on, 108

GAFFKY, Georg, 5
GALDSTON, I., 256n2
GALL, Franz Joseph, 92, 132, 218, 271

Gastric ulcer: Virchow on, 85
GAUB, Hieronymus, 51
GEGENBAUER, Karl, 21
GENDRIN, Augustin-Nicolas, 81, 271
GEORGET, Etienne Jean, 46, 249n71
GERHARDT, Carl, 21
GERLACH, Joseph: as pioneer in experimental embryology, 204; mentioned, 6
GEROULD, J. H., 71n
GERTH, H. H., ix, 245n17
Giant cells, 94
GILBERT, Judson, ix
GLADSTONE, W. E., 224
Glanders, 102, 103, 108, 148
GLISSON, Francis, 60, 152
GLUCK, Themistocles, 23
GLUGE, G., 56, 73, 75, 78, 98, 271
GOERCKE, J., 5, 271
GOETHE, Johann Wolfgang von: Virchow's book on, 7, 154–55; mentioned, 196, 200, 252n53
GOLDSTUECKER, Theodor, 17, 22, 271
GOODSIR, John: priority in cell theory, 83; mentioned, 81, 84, 271
GORGAS, William C., 124
GOULD, S. E., 253n13
GRAEFE, Albrecht von, 24, 101, 271
GRAEVELL, F., 138
GRAWITZ, Paul, 23
GREW, Nehemiah, 71
GRIESINGER, Wilhelm, 9, 19, 21, 48, 53, 147, 271–72
GROHÉ, F., 21, 272
GROSZ, George, 4
GRUBER, G., 245n19
GUENSBURG, F., 13, 74, 272
GUERIN, Jules, 256n2
GUETERBOCK, L., 56, 73, 272
GUILLOT, Natalis, 69, 154, 272
GURLT, E. F., 8, 272

HAECKEL, Ernst: as Virchow's opponent, 21, 45, 201, 236, 241;

as Virchow's student, 35n, 38; his judgment of Virchow, 37, 39; and Darwinism, 201; identified, 272

HAESER, Heinrich, 150

HALLER, Albrecht von, 60, 73, 143, 240

HAMY, J., 228, 272

HANSEMANN, David von, 24, 252n7, 272

HANSEN, G. H. Armauer, 30, 110, 272

HARMAN, John W., ix

HARTMANN, R., 231, 272

HARVEY, William, 15

HASSALL, A. H., 56, 272

HASSE, K. E., 21

HEBRA, Ferdinand, 21

HECKER, J. F. K.: on epidemiology, 127–28; mentioned, 6, 272

HEGEL, Georg Wilhelm Friedrich, 52

HEIN, A., 12

HEINROTH, Johann, 51, 272

HEISCHKEL-ARTELT, Edith, ix, 119

HELMHOLTZ, Hermann, 5, 6, 32, 272

Helminthology: Virchow's contribution to, 109

HENLE, F. G. Jacob, 6, 9, 24, 45, 78, 92, 113n, 118, 147, 154, 272

HENSEN, V., 21, 24

HERBST, E., 109

HERDER, J. G., 232

HERODOTUS, 198

HERWEGH, Georg, 153

HESCHL, R., 231, 272

Heterology: not malignancy, 90, 97, 100; mentioned, 86, 96

HEUSINGER, K. F., 71, 153, 273

HEWSON, William, 72

HEYMANN, B., 254n37

HILDEBRANDT, J. M., 233

HIPPOCRATES, 51, 79, 198

HIRSCH, August, 21, 147, 218, 257n8, 273

HIRSCHFELD, Ernst, viii

HIS, Wilhelm Sr., 6, 21, 231, 232, 273

Hodgkin's disease, 104, 273

HOFFMANN, K. E. E., 21

HOLBEIN, H., 148

HOLLAND, Sir Henry, 76, 273

HOLTZENDORFF, F. von, 26, 273

HOMER, 224, 225, 226

HONIGSHEIM, P., 264n15

HOOKE, Robert, 71

HOPPE-SEYLER, E. Felix, 23, 49, 273

Hospitals: Virchow as reformer of, 135–36; history of, 148–50

HOVERBECK, Leopold von, 25, 170, 273

HUEPPE, Ferdinand, 5, 23

HUETER, K., 23, 24, 273

HUNTER, John, 59, 60, 147, 148, 150

HUXLEY, Thomas Henry, 148

Hydrops. See Dropsy

Hyperthyroidism, 102

Hypochondria: Virchow on, 85

HYRTL, J., 231, 273

ICTERUS catharralis, 69n

Inflammation: not necessarily dilatation of vessels, 80, 87, 91; parenchymatous, 80–81; degenerative nature of, 81, 95; Handbook chapter on, 87; stages of, 94–95; possible without nerves or vessels, 94; exudative, 96; Cohnheim's vascular theory of, 118; Weigert's necrotic theory of, 118; Virchow's last inflammation theory, 119; mentioned, 121, 122

Inflammation cells: shown to be degenerating cells by Virchow, 63, 78; Virchow's work with Reinhardt on, 75

Irritation: relation to inflammation, 87, 95; Virchow on nature of, 92–96; in tumor formation, 101; mentioned, 121, 205

ISRAEL, Oskar, 24, 273

JACOBI, Abraham, 30, 273
JACOBY, Johann, 141, 177, 273
JAGER, Thor: manuscript collection
    of, ix, 35n, 38, 120, 246n56
JORES, L., 255n15

KALTENBRUNNER, G., 13, 273
KANT, Immanuel, 52, 232
KARLING, J. S., 70n
KARSNER, H. T., 248n35
KARTULIS, S., 117, 273
KEBER, G., 110, 115, 273
KEITH, Sir Arthur, 206
KEY, Axel, 23, 273
KINKEL, G., 16
KIWISCH, Franz, 20, 273
KLEBS, Edwin: as Virchow's op-
    ponent, 48, 106, 201; philoso-
    phy of, 52; 1878 attack on Vir-
    chow, 112–14; mentioned, 21,
    23, 38, 115, 120, 241, 252n7,
    273
KLEINE, H. O., 117
KLEIST-RETZOW, H. von, 185, 274
KLENCKE, H., 52, 56, 74, 274
KOCH, Robert: cholera discoveries
    of, 107, 117, 129; relation with
    Metchnikoff, 115n; tuberculosis
    discoveries of, 116, 117; 1875
    excavations with Virchow, 221;
    mentioned, 118, 274
KOELLIKER, R.: priority in cell
    theory, 83; mentioned, 6, 20, 23,
    38, 57, 69, 77, 154, 274
KOERTE, F., 11
KOLLMANN, Julius, 232, 274
KROEGER, G., 138n
KRUMBHAAR, E. P., 71n
KRUSE, W., 24, 274
KUBARY, J., 233, 274
KUEHNE, W., 23, 274
KUESS, Emile, 23, 81, 151, 274
KUESTER, E., 150
KUESTNER, Otto, 23
Kulturkampf: Bismarck's inaugura-
    tion of, 184–85; Virchow's sup-
    port of, 185–86, 213, 241

KUPFER, Karl Wilhelm, 6
KUSSMAUL, Adolf, 21

LACHMANN, Karl Friedrich Jo-
    hannes, 21
LAENNEC, R., 51, 53, 79, 90, 148n,
    274
LAMARCK, J. B., 71n
LANGENBECK, Bernhard, 24, 101,
    274
LANGERHANS, Paul, Sr., 11, 25, 274
LANGERHANS, Paul, Jr., 23, 274
LANGERHANS, Robert, 24, 274
LARREY, D. J., 198
LASKER, E., 188, 274
LASSALLE, F.: and liberals, 168,
    170, 188; alliance with Bismarck,
    171, 176; identified, 274
LAUTNER, G., 65
LA VALLETTE ST. GEORGE, Adolf
    von, 6
LAVERAN, Alphonse, 66, 124
LEBERT, Hermann: influence on
    Virchow, 53, 54n; mentioned, 8,
    13, 21, 24, 38, 56, 74, 78, 79,
    90, 274
LEEUWENHOEK, Anton von, 71
Legal medicine, 137
LEHMANN-HAUPT, F., 227
LEIDY, Joseph, 109, 274
LEIKIND, M., 20n
LÉPINE, Raph., 23
Leprosy: Virchow's study of in
    Spain and Portugal, 27; Vir-
    chow's study of in Norway, 104,
    110, 148–49; in the Middle
    Ages, 126; non-hereditary na-
    ture of, 206; pre-Columbian,
    219, 228
LEREBOULLET, D. A., 154, 274
LEUBUSCHER, Rudolf, 12, 13, 17,
    46, 126, 138, 142, 275
LEUCKART, K. G. F. Rudolph, 109,
    275
Leukemia, 65–66
LEUPOLDT, J., 51, 275
LEWIN, Louis, 13, 275
LEYDEN, Ernst von, 5, 23, 275

LIEBIG, Justus von, 53, 275
LIEBEN, F., 250
LIEBERKUEHN, Nathaniel, 6
LIEBREICH, M. E. O., 23, 275
LINDENSCHMIDT, L., 211, 215, 232, 275
LISSAUER, A., 211, 275
LISTER, Lord Joseph, 28, 30, 275
Listerism, 117
LOBSTEIN, J. G., 76, 90, 275
LOCKE, John, 49
LOEFFLER, Friedrich, 5, 111, 124, 275
LOEFFLER, Gottfried, 142, 275
LOESCH, F., 110
LOMBROSO, C., 218, 275
LONG, E. R., 122, 254n5
LOTZE, R. H., 49, 247n18, 275
LOUIS, Pierre, 53, 148n, 275
LOWIE, Robert H., ix, 262n27
LUBARSCH, O., 24, 119, 123, 255n 17, 275
LUCAE, J. C. G., 232, 275
LUDWIG II, 182
LUDWIG, Emil, 225

MAGENDIE, F., 48, 51, 52, 106, 150, 275
MALACARNE, M., 196
MALGAIGNE, J.-F., 198
MALPIGHI, Marcello, 71, 73, 150
MANDL, L., 74, 275
MANTEUFFEL, E. von, 26n, 275
MARC, Charles Chrétien Henri, 46
MARCHAND, Felix, 5, 23
MARCUS, A. F., 153
MARTIUS, F., 5, 23, 36, 276
MARX, K. F. H., 148
MARX, Karl, 20, 44, 45, 52, 55, 162, 167, 258n41
MAYER, Carl: as liberal leader, 11, 17, 138; ethnographic interests, 229; mentioned, 101, 166
MAYER, Rose (wife of Rud. Virchow), 19, 20, 276
MECKEL, Johann Friedrich II, 51, 71, 150, 232, 276

MECKEL VON HEMSBACH, Heinrich, 6, 13, 22, 66, 68, 245n19, 276
MEHRING, Franz, 4
MÉLIER, François, 128
MENDEL, Gregor, 206, 276
MENDELSOHN, Arnold, 8, 12, 276
Metaplasia: Virchow's definition of, 97, 104; as origin of sarcoma, 103; and transformism, 200; mentioned, 20, 122
Metastasis: and calcium, 85, 91; in tumors, 85, 101, 103, 105; compared to embolism, 91
METCHNIKOFF, Elie, 114, 115n, 276
METTERNICH, Prince Clemens von, 4
MEYEN, Franz Julius Ferdinand, 5, 71
MICHEL, Eugène, 104, 276
MIDDLETON, W. S., ix
MIESCHER, Johann Friedrich, 6
MILNE-EDWARDS, Henri, 72, 109
MIRBEL, Charles François Brisseau de, 71, 73
MOHL, Hugo von: priority in cell theory, 83; mentioned, 71, 73, 276
MOHL, Robert von, 179, 276
MOLTKE, H. von, 227, 276
MOMMSEN, Theodor: testament of, 33n; mentioned, 25, 190, 276
MOREL, Benedicte-Auguste, 205, 276
MORGAGNI, Giovanni Battista, 47, 74, 122, 150, 152
MORTILLET, Gabriel de, 232, 264n 18, 276
MUEHLMANN, W. E., 234
MUELLER, August, 6
MUELLER, Johannes: pupils of, 6; influence in Virchow's Wuerzburg appointment, 22; and method of natural sciences, 48; and method of staining tissues, 67n; description of cells, 72, 73; on cancer, 74; on tumors, 76, 99; Virchow's biography of, 153;

mentioned, 7, 13, 16, 56, 78, 84, 98, 147, 150, 151, 276
MUELLER, Wilhelm, 242n7
Myelin, 68
Myoma, 97, 104
Myosarcoma, 77
MYRES, J. L., 274n87

NACHTIGAL, G., 232, 276
NAEGELI, K. W. von, 76, 276
NAPOLEON III, 173, 181
National Liberals: their attack on Virchow, 149n; founding and purpose of, 178–79, 180n; economic policy of, 182; and Anti-Socialist Law, 187; 1880 split, 188; and budget control, 189; mentioned, 181, 185, 186
Naturforscherversammlung. See Versammlung deutscher Naturforscher und Aerzte
NEUBURGER, Max, 240
NEUMANN, Salomon: on natural and artificial diseases, 127; mentioned, 4, 13, 17, 25, 46, 138, 247n26, 277
Neuroglia, 86
Neuroma, 77, 104
NIEMEYER, F. von, 79, 277
NIGHTINGALE, Florence, 136
NOTHNAGEL, Hermann, 5, 23

OBERMEIER, O., 24, 110, 113, 277
Ochronosis, 119
OKEN, Lorenz, 71, 72, 196, 277
OPPOLZER, Johann, 19
ORTH, J., 23, 37n, 38, 116, 277
OSLER, Sir William, 5, 23, 28n, 30, 240, 277

PACHYMENINGITIS hemorrhagica, 86
PAGEL, Julius, 4n, 56, 277
PAGEL, Walter, ix, 56, 249n85
PAGENSTECHER, A., 140, 277
PAGENSTECHER, C., 12, 24, 277

PAGET, Sir James, 28, 109, 277
PANDER, H. C. von, 153
PANSCH, C., 189n, 214
PANUM, P., 12, 13, 277
PARACELSUS, (Aureolus Philippus Theophrastus Bombastus von Hohenheim), 3, 28, 50, 150
Parametritis, 119
PASTEUR, Louis, 28, 106, 117, 118, 201, 254n53
Pathological physiology, 52–54, 59, 60, 88
Pépinière. See Friedrich-Wilhelms Institut
PETTENKOFER, Max von: discussions with Virchow on ground-water theory, 129; mentioned, 130, 132n, 133, 277
PETTY, Sir William, 46
PFEUFER, K. von, 8, 9, 24, 53, 277
PFLUEGER, E., 6
Phlebitis: Virchow's early research on, 59–60, 120; his experiments on pulmonary artery, 62–64
Pigments: pathological, 68–70, 120
PINEL, Philippe, 50
PITT-RIVERS, A. H. L. F., 228, 277
PIUS IX, 184, 187, 277
PLAUT, Alfred, ix
Polish question, 15, 163, 174
POLLENDER, A., 110, 277
PONFICK, Emil, 23
PORTAL, Ant., 52, 277
POSNER, Carl, viii, 21, 139n, 277
PRINGLE, Sir John, 124
PROCHASKA, Georg, 71
Progressive Party. See Deutsche Fortschrittspartei
PROUDHON, Joseph, 166
PRUNER-BEY, Franz, 204, 277
PRUTZ, Robert, 4
PURKINJE, J., 67, 72, 73, 93n, 278
PUTTKAMMER, R. V. von, 188
PYE-SMITH, Philip Henry, 28

QUACKERY, 142–43
QUATREFAGES DE BREAU, Jean Louis Armand de: and Darwin-

ism, 201; his *Race prussienne*, 209; Virchow's refutation of, 209–10, 212, 214, 234; mentioned, 202, 215, 233, 278

QUESNAY, François, 46

RABL, Carl, 233

Races: not permanent, 200, 205, 210, 213; no lower races, 203, 215; origin of, 205; of ancient Germans, 208–9, 210, 211, 212; of ancient Scandinavians, 209; of Finns, 209–10; of Lapps, 210; of ancient Slavs, 211, 212; of German schoolchildren (1876 survey), 212–14; and nationalities, 215–16; of American aborigines, 216; of Philippines, 217

RADEMACHER, J. G., 45, 58, 278

RAMON Y CAJAL, Santiago, 27, 278

RANKE, Johannes, 232, 235, 278

RANKE, Leopold von, 180, 278

RASPAIL, François: priority in cell theory, 83; mentioned, 72, 73, 154, 278

RAYER, Pierre, 148n

RECKLINGHAUSEN, Friedrich von: his respect for Virchow, 28; mentioned, 20, 23, 24, 38, 118, 278

REED, Walter, 124

REESE, H. H., ix

REICHERT, K., 5, 6, 24, 278

REIMER, Georg, 12

REINACH, Salomon, 221, 278

REINHARDT, B., 6, 8, 12, 13, 17, 75, 79, 95, 126, 278

REISS, W., 216

REMAK, Robert: promoted to *Privatdozent*, 13; and cell theory, 74, 83–84; and epithelial origin of cancroids, 76, 104; priority discussion with Virchow, 78; mentioned, 6, 8, 19, 57, 69, 73, 88, 108, 138, 278

RETZIUS, Anders, 196, 215, 278

REUTER, Fritz, 190

REVEILLÉ-PARISE, Joseph-Henri, 46

RICH, A., 70, 72, 250n4

RICHTER, Adolf Leopold, 186, 278

RICHTER, Eugen, 26, 186, 188, 278

RICKER, Gustav, 123

RICORD, Philippe, 85, 107, 278

RIECKE, K., 124, 278

RINDFLEISCH, G. E., 21, 24, 50, 279

RINECKER, F. von, 20, 279

RINGSEIS, Joseph Nepomuk von, 20, 51, 153, 279

ROBIN, Charles, 74, 118, 154, 279

ROESCHLAUB, A, 153

ROHLFS, G., 232, 279

ROKITANSKY, Karl: theory of dyscrasias, 11, 55, 80; Virchow's criticism of, 45, 51, 60, 63, 69, 83, 99; philosophy of, 52; as a pathological anatomist, 53; and localism, 58, and blood chemistry, 61, 62; and blastema hypothesis, 82; mentioned, 24, 48, 73, 77, 79, 119, 147, 150, 240, 279

ROMBERG, M., 85

ROON, A. von: his army reform, 169, 279

ROSEN, George, ix, 138n, 250n20

ROSENKRANZ, J., 17, 279

Ross, Sir Ronald, 124

ROSTAN, Léon, 46

ROTH, Moritz, 23

ROUX, P. P. Emile, 111, 279

ROUX, Wilhelm, 23

ROYER-COLLARD, Hippolyte, 72

RUGE, Arnold, 4, 11, 16, 166, 167, 190, 279

RUGE, Louis, 166, 279

SAINT-PIERRE, C. I. de, 132

SAINT-SIMON, Claude Henri de, 46

SALKOWSKI, E., 23, 279

Sarcoma, 103

SCHAAFFHAUSEN, H., 232, 279

SCHERER, J., 20, 21, 279

SCHIFF, Moritz, 87

SCHILLER, Johann Christoph Friedrich, 7

SCHLEICH, C. L.: his memoirs quoted, 15; mentioned, 28n, 37, 252n7, 279

SCHLEIDEN, Matthias Jacob, 49, 70, 72, 279

SCHLIEMANN, Heinrich: excavations at Hissarlik, 30, 225–27; excavations in Egypt, 30, 227; friendship with Virchow, 30, 224, 225–27; mentioned, 35, 218, 279

SCHLOSSBERGER, J., 66, 279

SCHLUMBERGER, H. G., 70n

SCHMIDT, Alexander, 23, 279

SCHMIDT, Joseph Herman: support of Virchow, 12; pamphlet against Virchow, 16; identified, 280

SCHOENLEIN, J. L.: Virchow's biography of, 153; mentioned, 6, 8, 79, 150, 258n55, 280

SCHOMBURGK, M. R., 229, 280

SCHOMBURGK, R. H., 229, 280

SCHOPENHAUER, Arthur, 52

SCHUETZ, Wilhelm, 138, 280

SCHULTZE, Max, 6

SCHULZE-DELITZSCH, Hermann, 25, 170, 280

SCHULTZ-SCHULTZENSTEIN, K. H., 5, 72, 280

SCHURZ, Carl, 162

SCHWALBE, Gustav, viii, 261n17

SCHWALBE, Julius, vii–viii

SCHWANN, Theodor, influence of his cell theory, 56–57, 73–74, 75–76, 82; Virchow's criticism of his cell theory, 63, 70, 83; his blastema theory of cells, 72–74; mentioned, 6, 71, 77, 280

SCHWEINFURTH, Georg August, 30, 280

Sedimentation rate, 61

SEMMELWEIS, I.: Virchow on, 117; mentioned, 19, 280

SEMON, Sir Felix, 247n82

SEMPER, Karl, 232, 280

SERVETUS, Miguel, 51

Sewage disposal: improvement of

in Berlin, 132–35; mentioned, 130

SEYDEL, K. T., 25, 280

SIGEL, Franz, 162

SIGERIST, Henry E., viii, 153, 246n67, 252n3, 255n17, 258n51, 262n46

SIMON, Sir John, 86, 106, 252n7, 280

SIMONDS, J. C., 132n

SIMONSEN, V., 223

SIMPSON, A. R., 23, 280

SKODA, J., 24, 280

SMITH, A. H., 23, 97n, 119, 280

Socialism: Virchow on, 166, 183; antisocialist laws, 187–88; mentioned, 162, 167, 179

SOEMMERING, Samuel Thomas, 196, 231, 232

SPERANSKY, A. D., 123

SPIESS, G. A., 57, 92, 118, 280

STAHL, G. E., 45

STANNIUS, F. H., 6

STEINEN, K. von den, 233, 280

STEVENS, Vaughan, 204, 233

STOECKER, Adolf, 188, 280

STOKVIS, B. J., 30, 280

STRUVE, G. von, 15, 166, 167, 280

STUEBEL, A., 216

SUDHOFF, Karl, 14, 150

SYDENHAM, Thomas, 50, 115

SYLVIUS (de la Boë), Franz, 235

Syphilis: Virchow on, 85, 103; antiquity of, 218–19, 257n23; mentioned, 112, 114, 148, 249n99

TEMKIN, Owsei, viii, 127, 247n17, 249n84, 253n20, 258n56

THIERSCH, K., 104, 281

THOMSEN, Ch. J., 223, 281

Thrombosis: Virchow's study of, 62–63; main forms of, 64; mentioned, 87

TIEDEMANN, Friedrich, 153

TISSOT, Simon, 143

TOMMASI-CRUDELI, Corrado, 23

Toxines: bacterial, 111, 112, 114

TRAUBE, Ludwig: on Virchow's political career, 189; Virchow on, 245n12; mentioned, 8, 12, 19, 24, 48, 138, 281

TREVIRANUS, G. R., 71

Trichinosis: Virchow's work on, 109–10, 253n14; mentioned, 151

Tuberculosis: first work of Virchow on, 78–80; his later errors, 116; epidemiology of, 126, 127; mentioned, 97, 104, 134, 148, 206

TUCHOLSKY, Kurt, 4

Tumors: 1863 book on, 98–105; definition of, 99; local cause and beginning, 100; origin in connective tissue, 102; two subgroups (cystical and pseudoplasms), 102; mentioned, 121

TURPIN, P. J. F., 73

TWESTEN, Karl, 26n, 281

Typhoid fever: epidemiology of, 130; mentioned, 22, 124, 134

Typhus: in Upper Silesia, 14–15, 124–25; in Spessart, 22; epidemiology of, 107, 127, 129–30; distinguished from typhoid, 124; mentioned, 148

UNITED STATES: military hygiene of, 26; Virchow's friends in, 30; mortality rate in cities, 130; as a political model for Germany, 162, 167; need for racial study in, 217; trichinosis in, 253n14

UNRUH, H. V., von, 170, 281

UNZER, Johann August, 143

Uric acid infarction of kidney, 66–67

VALENTIN, G., 6, 72, 73, 93, 281

VALENTIN, V., 258n7

VARRENTRAPP, J. G., 145, 281

Veddahs, 230

VEIT, A. C. G., 21

VELPEAU, A., 105, 151, 281

Versammlung deutscher Naturfor-scher und Aerzte: of 1847 in Aachen, 14; of 1861 in Hannover, 26; of 1865 in Hannover, 26, 151; of 1871 in Rostock, 183, 185; of 1858 in Karlsruhe, 199–200; of 1888 in Cologne, 207; of 1885 in Strassburg, 218; of 1876 in Hamburg, 229; mentioned, 27, 152, 233

VESALIUS, Andreas, 150

VICTORIA, Queen, 29

VILLEMIN, Jean Antoine, 124

VILLERMÉ, Louis-René, 46, 128

VIRCHOW, Adele (daughter of Rudolf), 233

VIRCHOW, Carl (son of Rudolf), 233

VIRCHOW, Carl Christian Siegfried (father of Rudolf), 3, 16, 19, 35

VIRCHOW, Hans (son of Rudolf), 36, 217, 233

VIRCHOW, Johanna Marie née Hesse (mother of Rudolf), 3

VIRCHOW, Marie (daughter of Rudolf), 233

VIRCHOW, Rudolf: attacked by Nazi and Russian governments, vi; childhood, 1–5; student days, 5–7; doctor's thesis, 7; first historical publications, 7, 159; self-confidence, 10, 33–34; participants in first courses, 12; pupils in Wuerzburg, 21, 38; pupils in Berlin, 23–24; as a linguist, 27; his "testament," 31–32; negative traits, 37–39; agnosticism, 51; as a philologist, 153–54; on Goethe, 154–55; distrust of own authority, 234

—Doctor: first medical publications, 8; mechanistic approach, 9, 49; 1848 trip to Upper Silesia, 14–15, 31, 124–25; Die medizinische Reform, 17, 138; as a clinician, 24, 37; on democracy of cells, 45; on medicine as a social science, 46; on method of natural sciences, 47–48; chemical bias, 49, 61, 107; on new

vitalism, 50; romantic element, 56; on localism, 57–58, 86, 100; on therapeutics, 58–59; against humoralists and solidists, 92; interest in surgery, 100, 113, 252; against embryological tumor theory, 105, 113; on infectious diseases, 110–11; on bacteriology, 111–14, 117–18; technique of dissection, 119; 1860 summary of his work, 120; sociological theory of epidemics, 125–28; on statistics, 129, 130; anti-French episode, 151; on internationalism in science, 152. See Versammlung deutscher Naturforscher und Aerzte for meetings at which Virchow participated
—*Statesman*: activity in 1848 revolution, 15–16; *Die medizinische Reform*, 17, 138; on economic problems of revolution, 162, 164–67; on Schleswig-Holstein, 175; duel affair with Bismarck, 177; against 1871 constitution, 182; 1869 plea for disarmament, 183; for peace and reconciliation in 1870, 183; for international arbitration, 184; against colonialism, 184; Kulturkampf mistake, 185–86; on administrative reform, 186; combatting anti-Semitism, 188
—*Anthropologist*: on Darwinism, 199–202; on Neanderthaler, 202; on Pithecanthropus, 203; on atavism, 204; on heredity, 206; on paleopathology, 218; excavations of pile dwellings and walled mounds, 220–21; on house types, 223; in Caucasus, 227; on social evolution, 230
VIREY, Julien-Joseph, 46, 128
VOGEL, Julius, 13, 21, 56, 66, 72, 74, 281

VOGT, Carl, 143, 199, 232, 281
VOSS, A., 232
VROLICK, W., 232, 281

WAGNER, Rudolph, 232, 281
WALDECK, F. L. B., 166, 170, 281
WALDEYER, Wilhelm: his memoirs quoted, 28; mentioned, 33, 38, 104, 119, 231, 232, 233, 281
WALLER, Augustus, 65n
WALSH, J., 147, 207, 281
WALTHER, Philipp Franz von, 153
WEGSCHEIDER, E., 11, 19
WEIDENREICH, F., 198n, 203, 231, 281
WEIGERT, C., 23, 112, 118, 281
WEISMANN, August, 206, 281
WEITLING, Wilhelm, 166
WELCH, W., 147n, 240, 282
WELCKER, H., 231, 232, 282
Welfenfund, 182
WENZEL, J., 71, 196
WENZEL, K., 71, 196
WERESSAIEW, W., 145n
WIEBE (Geheime Oberbaurat), 133
WILLIAM I, 25, 29, 168, 187
WILLIAM II, 29, 190
WILLICH, August, 162
WILSON, J. W., 70n
WINDISCHMANN, K., 51, 282
WOLFF, Caspar Friedrich, 73, 150
WUNDERLICH, C.: doubts about cellular pathology, 57; mentioned, 9, 48, 53, 118, 147, 282

YERSIN, Alexandre-John-Emile, 111

ZENKER, F., 109, 282
ZIEMSSEN, Hugo Wilhelm von, 21
ZIMMERMANN, G., 65n, 282
ZIMMERMANN, Johann Georg, 143

212 – Survey of school children